The
HUMAN RESOURCE PRACTITIONER'S
Guide to
HEALTH, SAFETY and CORPORATE RISK

JOHN HUCKSTEPP

BLANK
CANVAS LTD

Published in the UK by A Blank Canvas Ltd., 55 Hoghton Street, Southport, PR9 0PG

A Human Resource Practitioner's Guide to Health, Safety and Corporate Risk

1st Edition,

Copyright © A Blank Canvas Ltd, 2015

The Human Resource Practitioner's duties in organisation design (workplaces, equipment), resourcing, recruitment (knowledge, skills experience and other factors), capability, competence (information, instruction, training), performance and reward, considering UK health, safety, equality, data protection and employment law, working conditions data, and statistics on deaths, illnesses and injuries at work.

Printed and bound in Great Britain by:

Clays Ltd, St Ives Plc.

British Library cataloguing in Publication data.

ISBN 978-0-9935141-0-4

FOREWORD

We live in a world full of uncertainty.

Wars in Iraq, Afghanistan, Libya and Syria, uprisings across parts of Africa and the expansion of the self-proclaimed Islamic State have triggered a mass exodus of migrants into Europe and increased fears of acts of terrorism closer to home.

The economic crisis in China is affecting western economies because of the high level of inter-dependence and the scale of the potential fallout.

Mark Carney, Chairman of the Bank of England, recently spoke at Lloyd's of London on the economic risks of global climate change that have not been paralleled for millennia.

The growth of technology which has brought so many benefits has opened new opportunities for criminals to engage in data theft and cyber-terrorism, fraud on an unprecedented scale and deaths attributed to the release of information.

Globalisation has significantly reduced costs but has been linked to the use of child, forced or poverty labour by major brands. Incidents like the Rana Plaza collapse in Bangladesh, the reported Adidas and Nike child labour allegations, and high incidence of suicide amongst employees at manufacturers of Apple products have shaken those organisations into action.

The size and buying power of some organisations has provided opportunities for abuse with at least one supermarket admitting to supplier mistreatment, contrary to the grocery sector's code of practice.

Rogue employees working across the banking sector have caused the collapse of major financial organisations which have profoundly affected the global economy, whilst systemic failures have caused significant and unexpected harm to organisations like BP and Volkswagen.

HR Practitioners that understand these challenges can create organisations, recruit personnel and deliver training that reduces risks and ensure that when unexpected events occur, teams have the skills and resilience to face them in an organisation that can flex with changing circumstances.

Friendly Fire

Whilst the big news stories command organisations to take stock and put plans and systems in place, un-reported and under-reported news stories have wider implications for organisations, particularly when the harm caused by physical, psychosocial and other exposures affects employees to such a significant extent.

It is hard to conceive that over the 12 month period to April 2015[1]:

- 2 million workers suffered from medical conditions or illnesses that were caused by or exacerbated by work,
- 13,000 people died in the UK as a consequence of work,
- 1 in 46 employees suffered an accident at work,
- 1 in 200 workers suffered an injury so serious that they needed to take a week or more off work,
- 23.3 million working days were lost due to work related ill-health,
- 4.1 million working days were lost due to workplace injuries

> *2 million workers suffer from conditions or illnesses caused by or exacerbated by work*

> *27 million working days lost to work related injury or ill-health.*

Collectively, these events represent an estimated cost to the UK of £14.3 billion.

Employees are absent due to sickness[2] for an average of almost 7 days a year (3%) at an estimated cost of £554 per employee. This figure has increased on the same period last year, despite a belief from three quarters of organisations that it is possible to reduce sickness absence, and has occurred at the same time that many employees are frightened of absence for fear of its effect on redundancy calculations.

The extent to which musculoskeletal injuries, back pain and mental ill health contribute to these figures is substantial.

HR at the Zeitgeist

HR has an important role to play in building an organisation that can deliver its goals, and meet the needs of its employees and the wider society in which it operates. There are many critics that do not seem to believe that is the case. In the summer of this year, the Harvard Business Review[3] (HBR) ran a front page that said:

It's time to blow up HR and build something new.

Adi Ignatius, Editor of the HBR, claimed many of the initiatives HR see as best practices are damaging organisations because of their negative effect on employee motivation and manager autonomy. It would be easy to put that headline down as nothing more than sensational journalism, but HR received a strong wake-up call from an the Institute of Employment Studies (IES) survey[4] that found two thirds of managers and three quarters of non-managers not satisfied with HR services.

Managers specifically criticised a focus on strategy over proactivity; a lack of expertise, reliability and innovation; and the inaccessibility of the HR function (its remoteness and responsiveness). The IES published a call for HR to become:

- More engaged in finding out what customers wanted;
- Accessible and responsive to provide help and support when that support was needed at all levels of the organisation;
- An independent function, balancing organisation and employee needs;
- A business led approach to strategy that puts strategically important business problem solving at the top of the agenda;
- A proactive function that spots problems ahead of time and works with managers to address them before the impact is felt by the organisation.

The IES survey found that line managers did not want business partners, but people partners, providing expert, reliable, well-informed and responsive support, understanding employee needs.

People Partners – expert, reliable, well-informed, responsive

We know that in some of the most basic areas, HR data is not always effectively captured and measured. Where metrics are captured, HR and Health and Safety data is seldom analysed in terms of the wider impact to the organisation[5]. Calculating the impact is often seen as too complex, or too time consuming, for an organisation focussed with limited time and resources, despite the impact that information might have on organisational decision making[6]. Calculations seldom factor in re-organisation, recruitment, induction, administration and investigation costs[7] let alone lost output, lost orders, etc.

Research by Armstrong[8] links successful business, profitability, productivity, operational performance, and lower hospital mortality rates to a variety of HR activities. HR practitioners have the ability to shape and influence organisations through a variety of tools and techniques.

It is surprising how few organisations have a clearly defined vision to help employees understand what they are working to achieve, or support managers in their decision-making role. Even fewer organisations have defined values to inform managers and other employees as to how they should achieve the vision.

Where the values are clearly defined, there are too many organisations allowing the noise around performance to swamp the noise around safety[9].

Your mission should get your employees up in the morning and your values should help them to sleep.

The HR Profession Map requires that '*Great HR professionals work from a deep business, contextual and organisational understanding to develop actionable insight, and prioritise HR strategies that make the most difference at any given time… prioritised and tailored… identifying opportunities and risks and acting on them.*'[10]

The Benefits

For organisations seeking a competitive advantage, a clever focus on health, safety and employee well-being can bring significant wider benefits to the business. Research into the impact of investment into safety[11] identified benefits which included:

- Improvements in staff morale leading to improved employee retention and applicant quality, which in turn can lead to increased productivity and performance.
- Reduced absence cuts costs and provides improvements in productivity, efficiency and quality of service.
- Reduced insurance claims lead to lower premiums, reduced pressure from insurers, and reduced legal exposure.
- Meeting stakeholder targets can help to support investment decisions.
- Avoiding poor media is part of the corporate image value. Positive coverage can influence reputation in both product and labour markets[a].

References

[1] Health and Safety Statistics Annual Report for Great Britain 2014/15, ONS

[2] Simply Health/CIPD Absence Management Report, CIPD, 2015

[3] Harvard Business Review, July-August 2015

[4] What Customers Want From HR, Report 453, Institute for Employment Studies, August 2008

[5] Perceptions of the cost implications of health and safety failures, Haefeli, Haslam & Haslam, HSE, 2005

[6] The cost of non-injury accidents, Health & Safety Laboratory, HSE, 2007

[7] Costs to Britain of workplace fatalities and self-reported injuries and ill health, 2012/13, HSE

[8] Handbook of Human Resource Management Practice, Michael Armstrong, Kogan Page, 2014

[9] Paraphrased from Lord Cullen's Inquiry into the Ladbroke Grove Incident.

[10] http://www.cipd.co.uk/cipd-hr-profession/profession-map/

[11] Perceptions of the cost implications of health and safety failures, Haefeli, Haslam & Haslam, HSE, 2005

[a] As an example, RateMyEmployer.co.uk has over 8,000 employers and almost 40,000 ratings from employees as at September 2015.

TABLE OF CONTENTS

THE LEGAL CONTEXT

Human Resource and Health & Safety practitioners are not new to the law. Both have had exposure to the legal process, either in the form of an employment tribunal, or through involvement in civil insurance claims. The fundamental basis for that work is the legislation, principally in the form of the Equality Act 2010, Employment Rights Act 1996, Data Protection Act 1984, Health and Safety at Work etc. Act 1974.

These particular pieces of legislation provide the basis upon which employers, employees, and society interact. They protect employees and others from discrimination, harassment and victimisation; enable employees to engage in activities without fear of sanction, protect the health, safety and welfare of employees and others, and ensure that data held about individuals is used in a proper manner.

The Equality Act

The Equality Act was passed in 2010 to combine previous Acts of Parliament and incorporate the requirements of the European Equal Treatment Directive. The new law establishes rights for persons with 'protected characteristics' not to suffer detriment or other unacceptable treatment.

The Equality Act sets out the following nine 'Protected Characteristics':

- **Age**;
- **Sex** (male or female);
- **Sexual orientation** (towards persons of the same sex, the opposite sex, or either sex).
- **Gender reassignment** (a person who is proposing to undergo, is undergoing or has undergone a process, or part of a process);
- **Disability** – a physical or mental impairment, that has a substantial and long-term adverse effect on a person's ability to carry out normal day-to-day activities, or a progressive condition (HIV infection, cancer or multiple sclerosis)
- **Race** (includes colour, nationality, ethnic or national origins);
- **Religion** (includes lack of religion) or belief (includes a philosophical belief);
- **Marriage/Civil Partnership** and
- **Pregnancy and Maternity.**

Discrimination claims can be made on the grounds of a single protected characteristic, or more than one unrelated characteristic.

Unacceptable Behaviours

Employers cannot discriminate, directly or indirectly, harass, or victimise persons with, associated with, or perceived to hold protected characteristics. In this context, people include those applying for work; working for an employer; wishing to join a pension fund or works related social club; those being considered for promotion, training, redundancy; or any other work related activity. Similarly, employers, or their employees (acting vicariously) cannot harass or victimise persons with protected characteristics.

Employers will also be acting unreasonably if they fail to make reasonable adjustments, or ensure that their employees are aware of their duties and responsibilities under the Act.

Direct and Indirect Discrimination

Direct discrimination occurs where someone is treated 'less-favourably' because they possess, someone they are associated with possesses, or they are perceived to possess, a protected characteristic.

Indirect discrimination occurs when a person applies a provision, criterion or practice which applies to others, but puts those people that do share a protected characteristic at a particular disadvantage when compared to others, and it cannot be shown to be a proportionate means of achieving a legitimate aim.

Harassment

Harassment occurs when:

- A person engages in unwanted conduct because of a protected characteristic;
- A person engages in unwanted sexual conduct; or
- A person engages in unwanted conduct (related to sex or gender reassignment) and because of rejection or submission, they are treated less favourably…

…and that conduct has the purpose or effect of violating the other's dignity, or creating an intimidating, hostile, degrading, humiliating or offensive environment.

Where a third party harasses a person in the course of employment, the employer must take reasonably practicable steps to prevent the third party from doing so.

> *The employer must be aware that the person has been harassed in the course of employment on at least two occasions by a third party. It does not matter whether the third party is the same or a different person on each occasion.*

Victimisation

Victimisation occurs when one person subjects another to a detriment because he has or may (or there is a perception that he has or may):

- Bring proceedings under the Act;
- Give evidence or information in connection with proceedings under the Act;
- Doing 'any other thing' for the purposes or in connection with this Act; or
- Make an allegation that a person has contravened this Act (unless the allegation is made in bad faith).

Reasonable Adjustments

Employers must make reasonable adjustments where provisions, criteria or practices; physical features; or the lack of an auxiliary aid puts a disabled person at a substantial disadvantage in relation to a relevant matter in comparison with persons who are not disabled.

The Employment Tribunal

Cases brought under the Equality Act in relation to work are normally heard by the Employment Tribunal. The trend for average compensation awards by the tribunals has increased in recent years.

Sex Discrimination	2011/12	2012/13	2013/14	2014/15
Maximum award (£GBP)	89,700	318,630	168,957	557,039
Median award (£GBP)	6,746	5,900	8,039	13,500
Mean award (£GBP)	9,940	10,552	14,336	23,478

Disability Discrimination	2011/12	2012/13	2013/14	2014/15
Maximum award (£GBP)	390,871	387,472	236,922	239,913
Median award (£GBP)	8,928	7,536	7,518	8,646
Mean award (£GBP)	22,183	16,320	14,502	17,319

Race Discrimination	2011/12	2012/13	2013/14	2014/15
Maximum award (£GBP)	4,445,023	65,172	162,593	209,188
Median award (£GBP)	5,256	4,831	5,513	11,203
Mean award (£GBP)	102,259	8,945	11,203	17,040

Other Discrimination (Median)	2011/12	2012/13	2013/14	2014/15
Religion (£GBP)	4,267	4,759	3,191	1,080
Sexual Orientation (£GBP)	13,505	6,319	6,824	6,000
Age (£GBP)	6,065	4,499	6,000	7,500

The following table shows the number of claims[12] brought under the Equality Act…

Type of Discrimination	2011/12	2012/13	2013/14	2014/15
Sex	10,783	18,814	13,722	4,471
Disability	7,676	7,492	5,196	3,106
Race	4,843	4,818	3,064	1,858
Age	3,715	2,818	1,994	1,087
Pregnancy	1,861	1,589	1,248	790
Religion/Belief	939	979	584	339
Sexual Orientation	613	639	361	189

Although there is a significant reduction in the number of tribunal applications, latest results show that awards for Sex, Race, and Age discrimination are up on previous years. Disability discrimination awards have increased compared to last year. In simple terms, whilst the likelihood of a case being brought has diminished (perhaps temporarily), the level of potential award has generally increased.

Recent evidence shows an increase in employment tribunal applications. This is explained in more detail in the next section.

The Employment Rights Act

The Employment Rights Act (ERA96) sets out the principal duties and rights of employers and employees. These include a right to a statement of employment particulars which sets out rights from commencement of employment through to rights to notice on termination.

It provides for terms in relation to the location of work, remuneration including itemised pay statements, guarantee payments, unlawful deductions, and how any subsequent changes to terms and conditions of employment will be managed. It also sets out special arrangements to be applied in relation to medical suspension and termination of Employment, including rights on redundancy.

Protecting Employees

A large proportion of the ERA protects particular groups of workers that engage in activities which unscrupulous employers may perceive as being contrary to the interests of the organisation. It does this through the provision of rights for employees to participate in activities without fear of poor treatment, or other detriment, including dismissal by virtue of them.

The list has been extended through subsequent legislation and now includes:

- Time off for public duties, including jury service;
- Time off to act as Occupational Pension Fund Trustees or Employee Representatives;
- Leave for ante-natal care, dependants, family or domestic reasons,
- Shop and betting workers in relation to Sunday working;
- National minimum wage, tax credit, or pension enrolment related rights;
- Employees involved in health and safety cases;
- Employees working within the working time limits; or
- Exercising their right to time off for study or training.

The Flexible/Part Time Working Regulations

The Flexible Working Regulations, the Part-Time Workers (Prevention of Less Favourable Treatment) Regulations and the Fixed-Term Employees (Prevention of Less Favourable Treatment) Regulations set down the details of the rights of employees requesting flexible working, working part time, or on a fixed term contract from suffering a detriment.

Maternity and Paternity Rights

A series of rights relating to Maternity Leave, Adoption Leave, Parental Leave, and Paternity Leave have been established through such legislation as the Maternity and Parental Leave, etc. Regulations 1999, the Paternity and Adoption Leave Regulations 2002, and the Additional Paternity Leave Regulations 2010. These regulations provide rights to time off and rights to pay and other benefits following the birth or adoption of a child, and set down specific duties over and beyond the Equality Act.

The Public Interest Disclosure Act

The Public Interest Disclosure Act 1998 safeguards those making protected disclosures – sometimes referred to as 'whistle-blowing' or 'raising concerns', i.e. the right not to suffer detriment, including protection from dismissal.

This was updated by the Enterprise and Regulatory Reform Act 2013 which:

- Requires disclosures to be in the public interest to receive 'protection';

- Changes the way disclosures not made in good faith are handled by tribunals,
- Protects whistle-blowers from co-worker bullying or harassment, and
- Widened the definition of workers[13].

In 2015 the Department for Business Innovation and Skills (BIS) published their Guidance and Code of Practice[14]. The Code identifies the importance of the following factors as being key to the success of an effective whistleblowing policy in work:

- Recognising workers are valuable ears and eyes
- Getting the right culture
- Providing training and support
- Responding to concerns
- Controlling through effective systems to capture and address concerns
- Resolving the wrongdoing quickly

Information and Consultation of Employees Regulations

The Information and Consultation of Employees Regulations 2004 requires organisations with over 50 employees (since 2008) to inform and consult with employee representatives on:

- The recent and probable development of their activities and economic situation;
- The situation, structure and probable development of employment within the undertaking and on any anticipatory measures envisaged, in particular, where there is a threat to employment within the undertaking; and
- Decisions likely to lead to substantial changes in work organisation or in contractual relations, including redundancies and matters relating to a Transfer of Undertakings.

Other Employment Legislation

Older legislation in the form of the Trade Union and Labour Relations (Consolidation) Act 1992 continues to regulate trade unions, employer's associations, collective bargaining, collective redundancies, industrial action, and the role of ACAS.

The Employment Relations Acts 1999 and 2004 set down rights relating to trade union recognition, leave for family and domestic reasons, disciplinary and grievance hearings, and the minimum wage. They also paved the way for legislation on Information and Consultation.

The Employment Tribunal

Like the Equality Act, cases brought under the Employment Rights Act are normally heard by an Employment Tribunal. According to the British Chambers of Commerce[15], the average cost for an employer to defend itself at an Employment Tribunal was £8,500 in 2011. This cost is incurred before any consideration of the Award and it remains unusual for a Tribunal Chairperson to award costs to an employer.

The Employment Tribunal can hear a variety of cases linked to employment matters which are described below. Taking Unfair Dismissal as a specific example, the table below shows the maximum, mean and median awards for the last four years.

Unfair Dismissal	2011/12	2012/13	2013/14	2014/15
Maximum Award (£GBP)	173,408	236,147	3,402,245	238,216
Mean Award (£GBP)	4,560	4,832	5,016	6,955
Median Award (£GBP)	9,133	10,127	11,813	12,362

Although the maximum award produces the biggest headline, and a single settlement of £3,402,245 warrants that, the steady increase in mean and median awards amount to an increase of 50% and 35% respectively over the last four years. The table below shows total Tribunals cases heard each year and the split between single and multiple claims.

	2011/12	2012/13	2013/14	2014/15
Total claims accepted	186,331	191,541	105,803	61,308
Single claims	59,247	54,704	34,219	16,420
Multiple claim cases	5,662	6,278	3,126	1,921
Multiple claims	127,084	136,837	71,584	44,888
Mean no. claims per case	22.4	21.8	22.9	23.4

The substantial reduction in tribunal cases

It is clear to see that there has been a substantial reduction in tribunal claims in the year 2013/14 which was maintained in 2014/15 following the introduction of application and hearing fees for employment tribunals. At present it costs £390 to bring a claim for simple cases (e.g. wage related) and £1,200 for more significant cases such as unfair dismissal, discrimination, or whistleblowing[16].

The cost to bring a claim has clearly had an impact on the number of tribunal applications, but there are other factors that have similarly reduced the number of claims being heard. These include:

- The introduction of the 2 year service requirement for claims,
- The cap of one year's salary as a limit on unfair dismissal payments,
- The ACAS early conciliation process.

Unions are working hard currently to overturn the legislation that led to the introduction of fees and would like to see a judicial review. The government has adopted a considered approach. One outcome may be a reduction in the costs of the hearing but few predict that the cost for 'justice' will be removed altogether. Details of the numbers of claims can be seen by subject matter on the following table.

	2011/12	2012/13	2013/14	2014/15
Breach of Contract	32,075	29,820	16,762	8,250
Equal pay	28,801	23,638	17,202	9,621
National Minimum Wage	511	500	259	161
Part Time Worker	774	823	1,163	304
Redundancy Pay	14,661	12,748	6,663	2,939
TUPE: fail to Inform/Consult	2,594	1,591	1,219	568
Redundancy – Fail to I/C	7,984	11,075	3,604	2,307
Unauthorised Deductions	51,185	53,581	27,385	28,701
Unfair Dismissal	46,326	49,036	28,528	12,652
Working Time	94,697	99,627	49,087	31,451
Written Statement: Pay	1,287	1,363	940	282
Written Statement: Dismiss	962	808	433	209
Written Statement: Terms	3,630	4,199	2,226	925
Others[b]	5,919	6,901	12,328	19,756
Total	**321,836**	**332,859**	**193,968**	**129,966**

Recent evidence is that the number of claims have started to increase as claimants are becoming more accustomed to the tribunal fees and are balancing those costs in relation to their overall claim.

There has been an increase in Employment Tribunal Applications in Quarter 1 of 2015. Applications were up almost 40% on the same period in the previous year.

Employment Tribunal applications up 40% Q1 2015 to Q1 2014

---

[b] Others include claims raised under the Public Interest Disclosure Act.

The Data Protection Act

The Data Protection Act 1984 establishes protection for individuals on whom data is processed, obtained, recorded, stored, updated, and/or shared.

Many organisations need to register in order to comply with the Act and it may be that your organisation has already done so. If the organisation is only processing personal data for staff[c] administration purposes[17], they do not have to register with the Information Commissioners Office. However, registration is only one duty under the Act.

Individual Rights

Individuals have a right to know whether personal data is being processed about them. They have a right to know the personal data held, the purposes for which it is being processed, and the recipients or classes of recipients to whom the information may be disclosed.

The Act establishes a right for individuals to receive the information provided they submit a written request and, if required, pay an amount of money (not in excess of the statutory maximum).

Individuals also have the right to prevent processing likely to cause damage or distress although this right can be forfeited:

- By their prior consent,
- Where the processing is necessary for the performance of a contract to which the individual is a party,
- In order to comply with a legal obligation, or
- Where the processing is necessary to protect the vital interests of the data subject.

Sensitive Data

Particular duties apply to organisations holding sensitive data relating to an individual's racial or ethnic origin, political opinions, religious or other beliefs, trade union membership, physical or mental health or condition, sexual life, commission or alleged commission of any offence, or proceedings for any offence committed or alleged to have been committed by him.

---

[c] The term 'staff' includes all past, existing or prospective members of staff who are employees, office holders, temporary and casual workers, and also agents and volunteers. The personal information held about them includes all personnel and work management matters, e.g. their qualifications, work experience, pay and performance.

Automated Decision Making

The Act makes specific reference to the processing by automatic means of personal data on performance, reliability or conduct in a way that constitutes, or is likely to constitute, the sole basis for a decision significantly affecting a person.

> *Processing by automatic means as the sole basis for a decision significantly affecting a person*

Under these circumstances, an individual is entitled at any time, by notice in writing, to require the data controller to ensure that no decision which significantly affects that individual is based solely on the processing by automatic means of personal data.

Employee Behaviour

Employers have a duty to protect data subjects from the acts or omissions of their employees, including risk of data loss, unintentional release, or increasingly, as a consequence of cyber-crime.

Employers have a duty to inform employees of their responsibilities, particularly regarding the need to follow security protocols in the design, specification, acquisition or use of data systems at work. The use of mobile technology such as laptop, smart-phone, unencrypted data sticks, and the protection of passwords, all increase the vulnerability of company data. It is important that employees understand how the data protection principles apply to their work.

Data Protection Principles

The Data Protection principles are described below.

1. Personal data shall be processed fairly and lawfully, and only in defined circumstances.
2. Personal data shall be obtained only for one or more specified and lawful purposes, and shall not be further processed in any manner incompatible with that/those purpose(s).
3. Personal data shall be adequate, relevant and not excessive in relation to the purpose or purposes for which they are processed.
4. Personal data shall be accurate and, where necessary, kept up to date.
5. Personal data processed for any purpose or purposes shall not be kept for longer than is necessary for that purpose or those purposes.
6. Personal data shall be processed in accordance with the rights of data subjects under this Act.
7. Appropriate technical and organisational measures shall be taken against unauthorised or unlawful processing of personal data and against accidental loss or destruction of, or damage to, personal data.

8. Personal data shall not be transferred to a country or territory outside the European Economic Area unless that country or territory ensures an adequate level of protection for the rights and freedoms of data subjects in relation to the processing of personal data.

These principles are likely to form the basis of any civil claims or criminal prosecution arising from the actions or inactions of the employer (especially point 7), or employee failings described above.

> *Cyber-crime can lead to civil and criminal prosecutions*

The Future of the Data Protection Act

Globalisation, the tendency of organisations to centralise data processing, changes to individual rights and protections, and the expansion of new technologies including the World Wide Web and the 'Internet of Things' have changed, and are continuing to change the way in which data is being and is required to be captured, stored and used.

This has led the European Commission to prioritise the re-evaluation of the Directive on which the UK Data Protection Act is based. This will almost certainly culminate in new UK legislation in the next two to five years.

The Health and Safety at Work Etc. Act 1974

Principal Duties

The principal legislation that underpins health and safety law in the UK is the Health and Safety at Work etc. Act 1974 (HASAWA)[18].

Section 2 sets out the legal duty every employer has to 'ensure, so far as is reasonably practicable, the health safety and welfare at work of all his employees'.

These include, so far as reasonably practical, duties in relation to:

> *'...to ensure, so far as is reasonably practicable, the health, safety and welfare at work of all his employees'*

- The provision and maintenance of plant and systems of work that are safe and without risks to health;
- Arrangements for ensuring safety and absence of risks to health in connection with the use, handling, storage and transport of articles and substances;
- The provision of such information, instruction, training and supervision as is necessary to ensure the health and safety at work of his employees;
- As regards any place of work under the employer's control, the maintenance of it in a condition that is safe and without risks to health and

the provision and maintenance of means of access to and egress from it that are safe and without such risks;

- The provision and maintenance of a working environment for his employees that is safe, without risks to health, and adequate as regards facilities and arrangements for their welfare at work.

HASAWA also sets out duties to persons other than employees (e.g. visitors and contractors); duties of employees, persons in control of premises and manufacturers. The Act also defines union recognition rights for purposes of safety, i.e. to appoint safety representatives, to consult and to create a safety committee.

The Act places the following duties on employees (Sections 7 and 8):

- To take reasonable care for the health and safety of themselves and of other persons who may be affected by their acts or omissions at work;
- To co-operate with employers and others, as regards any duty or requirement imposed, so far as is necessary to enable any duty or requirement under a relevant statutory provision to be performed or complied with.
- Not to intentionally or recklessly interfere with, or misuse anything provided, in the interests of health, safety or welfare under any of the relevant statutory provisions.

In all cases, there is a duty on employers not to charge employees for *'anything done or provided'* for the purpose of their safety.

Fines

In 2013/14 the HSE and others issued 13,790 enforcement notices for breaches under HASAWA and its relevant statutory provisions. The level of fines vary, but there are some indicative cases[19] below:

- Loss of two fingers in works accident – fined £10,000 plus £5,959 costs;
- Death of freight driver – fined £300,000 plus £26,000 costs;
- Hand Arm vibration injury to council worker – fined £25,000 plus £9,417 costs;
- An NHS Trust was fined £180,000 when a patient, who was also an HSE Inspector, sustained third degree burns when a warming mattress he was lying on overheated – fined £180,000 plus £14,970 costs
- A DIY Giant at which a worker was crushed by a Fork Lift Truck was fined £65,000 plus costs of £18,500.

Fines are uninsurable and do not reflect the full costs of the incident.

Health & Safety Regulations

HASAWA enables the Secretary of State to pass Regulations and over time a comprehensive series of subordinate legislation has been produced (sometimes referred to as Relevant Statutory Provisions). These include:

Confined Spaces

Construction (Design & Management)

Control of Noise at Work

Control of Vibration at Work

Control of Substances Hazardous to Health

Health & Safety Consultation with Workers

Health & Safety (Display Screen Equipment)

Health & Safety (Enforcing Authority)

Health & Safety Information for Employees

Health & Safety (Safety Signs and Signals)

Workplace (Health, Safety and Welfare)

Work at Height

Health & Safety (Training for Employment)

Health & Safety (Fees)

Management of Health and Safety at Work

Manual Handling Operations

Lifting Operations and Lifting Equipment

Personal Protective Equipment

Provision and Use of Work Equipment

Reporting Injuries, Diseases, and Dangerous Occurrences

Safety Representatives & Safety Committees

Working Time

Approved Codes of Practice

In some cases, the HSE has published 'Approved Codes of Practice' (ACOPs) which outline the preferred or recommended methods that can be used to comply with the Regulations, and Guidance on achieving compliance. ACOPs hold a unique status in law. They have been approved by the HSE with the consent of the Secretary of State. They give practical advice on how to comply with the law. If organisations follow the advice, they will be doing enough to comply with the law in respect of those specific matters on which the Code gives advice.

Organisations may use alternative methods to those set out in the Code in order to comply with the law, however, if an employer is prosecuted for a breach of health and safety law, and it is proved that they did not follow the relevant provisions of the Code, they will need to show that they complied with the law in some other way or a Court will find them at fault.

The HSE are currently reviewing the status of their ACOPs and some have been replaced with guidance but many still remain.

Specific Features of the Health & Safety at Work Act

There are some special features of the Health & Safety at Work Etc. Act 1974, such as the way that guilt is applied (including personal liability), foreseeability, the different types of duty, and the onus of proof. These are described below.

Guilt despite not committing the offence

Should an employee commit an offence due to the actions or default by another person, that other person shall be guilty of the offence, and may be charged with, and convicted of, the offence irrespective of whether or not proceedings are taken against the employee that committed the offence in the first place.

Personal Liability by consent, connivance or neglect

Where an offence under any of the relevant statutory provisions is committed by an organisation, and that offence is proven to have been committed with the consent, connivance, or neglect of a director, manager, secretary or other similar officer of the organisation (or a person who was purporting to act in such a capacity), he as well as the organisation shall be guilty of that offence and shall be liable to be proceeded against and punished accordingly.

Foreseeability

Whilst an organisation can only be found guilty if it could have foreseen the potential for harm, in statute the test is different to the common law and a defendant will not escape responsibility unless he can show the circumstances of the accident were 'unforeseeable' or 'exceptional'[20].

Absolute, Practicable and Reasonably Practicable Duties

The law sets out three types of duty: Absolute duties are those that shall or must be undertaken. Practicable duties are those actions which must be undertaken where they are physically possible. Reasonably Practicable duties are those that must be carried out unless the duty-holder can demonstrate that the effort (cost, time, effort) would be grossly disproportionate to the benefits of risk reduction that would be achieved.[21].

> *These are best described with an example. Section 20 of the Construction (Design and Management) Regulations 2015 reads 'The demolition or dismantling of a structure must be planned [**an absolute duty**] and carried out in such a manner as to prevent danger or, where it is not* **practicable** *to prevent it, to reduce danger to as low a level as is* **reasonably practicable**.'

Onus of Proof

In any proceedings for an offence consisting of a failure to comply with a requirement to do something so far as is practicable or so far as is reasonably practicable, or use the best practicable means to do something, the duty falls on the accused to prove that it was not practicable or reasonably practicable to do more than was done to satisfy the requirement, or that there was no better practicable means than was used.

Remedy

Where a person is convicted of an offence which appears to the court to be a matter which is in his power to remedy, the court may order him to take such steps as may be specified to remedy those matters within a given time period.

Corporate Manslaughter and Homicide Act

Where an organisation owes a duty of care to a person, and that person suffers death, it will fall to a jury to consider:

- Whether there was a relevant duty of care;
- Whether there was a gross breach of that duty;
- Whether there was a failure to comply with legislation; and
- How serious that failure was, and how much of a risk of death it posed.

The jury may also consider the extent to which evidence suggests poor attitudes, policies, systems or practices within the organisation were likely to have encouraged any failure, or to have produced a tolerance of them, with regard to any health and safety guidance that relates to the alleged breach or any other matters they consider relevant.

The duty of care arises from a wide variety of circumstances and legislation and for the purposes of this legislation, the definition is wide, particularly in the definition of persons to whom the legislation applies.

If the case is proven, the organisation is liable to an *unlimited* fine, a court order to remedy the breach and address any deficiencies in its policies, systems or practices, and an order to publicise its conviction which can include the fact that it was convicted, the specific particulars of the offence, the amount of the fine imposed, and any remedial order it received.

> *'Corporations have neither bodies to be punished nor souls to be condemned, Edward Thurlow, 1778'*

Gross Negligence Manslaughter

Gross Negligence Manslaughter occurs where a death is the result of a grossly negligent[22] (though otherwise lawful) act or omission on the part of the defendant.

Gross Negligence Manslaughter is likely to be found in cases involving professional workers who are appointed into roles where their actions or inactions can cause the death of another, e.g. medical personnel, gas or electrical technicians, engineers, drivers of vehicles, etc.

As above, there is a four stage test for jurors to consider when hearing gross negligence manslaughter cases. This is known as the Adomako Test:

- Was there a duty of care to the deceased;
- Was there a breach of that duty of care;
- Did the breach cause (or significantly contribute) to the death of the victim;
- Should that breach of duty be characterised as gross negligence.

Company Directors Disqualification Act

Directors may be disqualified for 5 years in the event of a summary conviction (Magistrates Court), or 15 years in the event of a conviction on indictment (Crown Court).

Civil Law

Where an organisation owes a duty of care to a person, and that duty is breached causing harm, that person can pursue a claim under civil law for losses in the form of 'damages'. These damages include out of pocket expenses such as costs of prescriptions, taxi fares, etc.; loss of earnings arising from the differences in pay received and this can include lost overtime or bonus earnings, and compensation for pain and suffering caused.

As described earlier, these claims are covered through an Employers' Liability Insurance Policy which organisations are legally obliged to have in place. The level of premium, and the ability to obtain that insurance at all, is a function of attitude to safety and previous claim history. Some examples of personal injury claims include:

- An office worker that tripped over a carpet with a hot drink - £20,000
- An electrician suffers electric shock whilst at work - £17,500

In response to the costs associated with the administering and processing these claims, a new protocol (since 2013) has been established to help reduce the costs (particularly legal costs) associated with claim handling. In many cases, claims are much lower than the levels described above and the new process concentrates on claims that are likely to be below £25,000[23].

The Modern Slavery Act

In 2015, the government passed a law targeting slavery, servitude, forced or compulsory labour, and human trafficking. This legislation contains a duty

'Transparency in Supply Chains' on commercial organisations with turnover in excess of £36 million (or belonging to a group with such turnover) to prepare a statement in each financial year regarding the steps that the organisation has taken to ensure that slavery and human trafficking is not taking place, either in its own business, or in any of its supply chains[24].

Many organisations have instigated new Supplier Qualification Questionnaires and it is entirely likely that this will manifest in a requirement for suppliers to these large organisations to undertake similar activities in order to validate the whole supply chain.

HR Policies and Procedures

As a consequence of many of the duties arising from the legislation, HR departments have introduced specific HR Policies and Procedures. These typically fall into four main categories:

Equality

These procedures typically include equal opportunities, diversity, bullying and harassment, dignity at work, sex discrimination, race discrimination, age (retirement), and in some organisations, AIDS.

Traditional HR activities

These typically include recruitment, promotion, training, redundancy, wages and salaries, benefits, and information and consultation. This group also includes discipline and grievance, sickness absence, and union relations.

The Do Not Policies

This group typically includes policies relating to drugs and alcohol, the misuse of technology (e-mails, social media, etc.).

Other Policies

This group includes policies such as dress codes, work-life balance, and whistle blowing (or raising concerns). In some cases, there may also be a health and safety policy.

These procedures have often been borne out of history and experience and provide a framework for Human Resources. Procedures are often criticised for being too wordy, too complex, and reactive, rather than improving employee engagement and performance. They do, however, create questions:

- How can there be so many separate policies for equality and HR activities when they are so closely linked?
- Why does AIDS warrant a policy in its own right, when other progressive conditions, blood borne viruses (BBVs), biological hazards, or hazards in general do not?
- How well do the separate policies (for example, sickness absence, bullying, and drugs and alcohol) work together to solve more complex problems?
- How well do the policies reflect the organisation's duties (such as the Data Protection Principles)?

Perhaps the issue is not so much the detail of the policies, but the fundamental approach and role of HR within organisations to support the wider organisational mission and vision, and to continuously and consistently uphold the principles and values in the environment the organisation operates.

References

[12] https://www.gov.uk/government/statistics/tribunals-and-gender-recognition-certificate-statistics-quarterly-april-to-june-2015

[13] http://www.pcaw.org.uk/guide-to-pida

[14] Whistleblowing: Guidance for Employers and Code of Practice, March 2015, Department for Business, Innovation and Skills, March 2015

[15] Fees for accessing employment tribunal service will boost business confidence, Adam Marshall, British Chambers of Commerce Press Release, 14/12/2011

[16] https://www.citizensadvice.org.uk/work/problems-at-work/employment-tribunals-from-29-july-2013/what-will-it-cost-to-make-a-claim-to-an-employment-tribunal/employment-tribunals-how-much-will-it-cost-to-make-a-claim/

[17] https://ico.org.uk/for-organisations/

[18] Government Legislation can be found at the Government legislation website: www.legislation.gov.uk

[19] Selection of IIRSM published reports 2013 to 2014

[20] Reasonable Foreseeability, Simon Allen, The Law Society Gazette, 4 November 2013

[21] "ALARP" at a glance, HSE Web site, captured 3rd August 2015

[22] Gross Negligence Manslaughter, Prosecution Policy and Guidance, CPS, 2015

[23] Pre-Action Protocol for Low Value Personal Injury (Employers' Liability and Public Liability) Claims

[24] Transparency in Supply Chains etc. A practical guide, Home Office, 2015

ENVIRONMENTAL CONTEXT

In recent years, there have been significant changes to the way that organisations operate. These have included:

- Changing working methods
- Changes in sectoral employment
- Changes in working time
- Increased workforce diversity
- The globalisation of markets
- Fundamental changes to the way that people work

Changing Working Methods

Technology has enabled a growth in flexible working, including dispersed teams, home working and hot-desking. This has meant that traditional theories about team working and relationships at work have had to evolve as employees have become scattered and team members have lost direct physical contact.

These roles have often lent more towards outcome based measures of performance, often requiring a high level of self-motivation, at the same time autonomy has been reduced through automation and planning systems such as the way that field service engineer work is dictated by work planning systems with integrated journey planning software.

In manufacturing and engineering industries the introduction of robotics and process data systems have changed the way that manufacturing happens, whilst new technology has fundamentally replaced the way that some jobs are performed. For example, those engaged in electricity generation are more likely to be working offshore, at height, maintaining a wind turbine than working in the control room of a coal fired power station.

In the care sector technical advances have fundamentally changed diagnosis and treatment, sometimes creating new exposures to chemical, radiological, and biological hazards for those involved in the sector.

Technology such as smart phones have enabled new ways of communicating with clients. This increase in 24 hours a day, seven days a week living has fuelled longer and wider working hours, placing greater pressures on workers to respond flexibly, and with greater levels of innovation.

Changes in Sectoral Employment

Over the last thirty years, there have been significant changes in employment[25]. Whilst some sectors (such as manufacturing) have reduced by more than half, there has been a two- and even three-fold increase in some activities.

Numbers employed in:

- Accommodation and Food Services, Information and Communications, and Education have increased significantly.
- Administration, and Human Health and Social Care have more than doubled,
- Real Estate, and Professional and Technical services have tripled.
- Construction has stayed broadly the same.
- Agriculture, mining, quarrying and electricity generation have reduced significantly.
- Manufacturing, which employed a quarter of the UK workforce, has seen a fall of 60%.

Consistent across many of these sectors is how the work activity, the use of technology, and the ways in which people work together have changed.

These changes have created a gap between demand and supply for personnel with the knowledge, skills and experience necessary to perform the role. These challenges occur most commonly in growing sectors where skills are understood but there is a lack of trained staff; and in new sectors where skills requirements are still being established and defined.

The Globalisation of Markets

Organisations have become increasingly global. Today, companies like British Petroleum ($359bn) and Samsung ($305bn) have a greater annual revenue[26] than many countries annual Gross Domestic Product[27] (Columbia $332bn, Denmark $297bn).

Recent publicity of the tax record in the UK of some global organisations, such as Starbucks, Apple, Amazon and Google, have caused consternation amongst members of the public and undermined the reputation of these organisations.

Fuelled by the development of new technology and capitalising on substantially reduced labour costs, less rigorous legislation and regulation; overseas call centres and manufacturing centres have become common place.

Globalisation has created a need to communicate with managers, teams and supply chains operating across different time zones, significantly extending working hours and widening the need for workers to be available.

Trends in Working Time

The growth of the service sector and changing production methods have led to an increase in hours of operation resulting in changes to both the volume and variety of working time. According to the latest European Working Conditions Survey[28]:

- 2 in 5 male and 1 in 3 female workers do not work the same daily hours.
- 1 in 5 workers do not work the same number of days each week.
- Workers regularly work outside of standard 'rostered' working hours.
- More than half work at least one day in the weekend.
- 20% of men say they work too many hours.

Working long or varied hours has consequences. Approximately 30% of employees working longer or more varied hours report poor work-life balance, increased risk to safety, and negative effects on health.

Between 1999 and 2009[29], the greatest increase in employees working shifts 'most of the time' across both males and females, has been in the Sales sector, although plant and machine operators in manufacturing, and those working in the personal protection industries have also seen a substantial widening of operating hours.

> *The Greatest increase in employees working shifts has occurred in the Sales sector*

The Changing Nature of Work

In 2009, when the HSE published 'Good Jobs' by The Work Foundation, they defined six quality factors[30] that contributed to full and fulfilling employment. Good jobs were presented by the authors as being good for productivity at the same time that they provided well-being, personal growth, fulfilment and self-worth to employees. The six quality factors are Security, Autonomy, Variety, Equity, Recognition and Strength of relationships (SAVERS).

Many HR practitioners will relate this with the Hackman & Oldham model[31] (1980) which identifies variety and autonomy, feedback, job significance and task identity as motivation factors in job design.

The most significant change between 1980 and 2009 has been the emergence of 'Security' as a new element. The need for organisations to be agile and responsive, combined with a realisation that technical expertise cannot be justified on a full time basis, has created 4.5 million self-employed workers[32] (15% of the total labour market) and estimates of 750,000 workers (2.5%) on zero hours contracts[33]. This provides a combined total of 5.25 million or 17.5% of the total workforce. Zero hours contracts were largely unknown before the summer of 2013[34], but by April 2015 there were believed to be 1.8 million contracts in place in the UK[35].

The further division of labour and increased automation in work is undermining autonomy[36] and reducing opportunities for variety in work, despite a statutory duty[37] on organisations to design workplaces, to choose work equipment, and working methods with a view to '*alleviating monotonous work and work at a predetermined work-rate and so reduce their effect on health*'[38].

At the same time, a multitude of events and practises have undermined perceptions of equity, recognition, and relationships at work. A survey[39] at the start of 2015 found that 37% of employees were intending to leave their job at the start of 2015. More than half of those indicated a desire to progress, earn more, or find a more interesting role, whilst a quarter felt under-appreciated.

Workforce Diversity

As well as changes to the hours of operations, there have also been substantial changes to the diversity of people employed:

Gender Balance

Between 1971 and 2013[40] the number of males in work fell from 92% to 76%, the number of females in work rose from 53% to 67%. According to the ONS, this increase is largely attributable to the expansion of the service sector: Women make up 82% of workers in caring, leisure and other services, 77% of employees in administrative and secretarial roles, and almost two thirds of sales roles.

The fall in the numbers of men in work is largely attributed to the demise of the manufacturing and engineering sectors, with females making up just 10% of workers employed in that sector.

There remains a significant variance between males and females in management roles with the latest data suggesting a ratio of men to women of 2:1.

The Increase in Ethnic Minorities

According to the 2011 census[41], over 20% of people aged 16-64 in England and Wales did not classify themselves as English, Welsh, Scottish, Northern Irish, or British (EWSNIB).

29% of non-EWSNIB people aged 16-64 in England and Wales described themselves as unemployed in the 2011 census compared to just 5% of those who classified themselves as EWSNIB, although the number of people not born in the UK and now in work is increasing.

8% of people living in Britain[42] (4.2 million) report that their main language is not English. Of these, 3% (138,000) indicated that they could not speak English at all, and a further 17% (726,000) indicated that they could not speak English very well.

This group (sometimes referred to as migrant workers) are regarded by the HSE as vulnerable workers, not only because of their language and cultural experience, but also because of the difference in competence and training across different countries. There are further concerns that migrant workers may not have received the same level of immunisation against Tuberculosis, Measles, Mumps and Rubella.

These figures highlight the importance of effective communication, induction and training processes to ensure safety and minimise risk particularly amongst contractors and temporary workers that may not be recruited by the organisation.

The Increase in Older Workers

The phasing out of the default retirement age in 2006, combined with a number of other factors has fundamentally changed attitudes to work for those over 65. This situation is continuing to develop as changes to the state pension age commence in 2016 (women) and 65 from 2019 (men).

Between July 1995 and July 2015, the proportion of over 65s in work has more than doubled[43] (from 5.1% to 10.4%) at the same time that numbers over 65 has continued to grow (from 8,743,000 to 11,266,000), resulting in an increase of people aged over 65 and in work from 445,000 to 1,166,000 (an increase of 160%).

A 160% increase in people aged over 65 and in work in 20 years.

This change can have implications for reward strategies and for employee well-being as it is likely that employees joining the workforce today may be expected to work for 50 years or more. Some correspondents are already contemplating a 4 generation workforce by 2030[44].

Society Expectations

Changes in sectoral employment that reflect societal demands, changes in working methods and technology has created an expectation that the world of work is always 'on'. There is now a 24/7 day expectation that a request made today will be settled immediately, delivered tomorrow and in a manner that reflects excellent customer service, without a recognition that a worker somewhere is going to have to do something, or risk something, in order to make that happen.

At the same time, changes to sectoral work, improvements in working methods, and better health and safety performance has created an expectation across society that its workers will return home at the end of their turn, in no worse condition than when they left. When employees are hurt at work an organisation's reputation across its product and labour market respond, causing a significant impact on the organisation.

References

[25] 2011 Census Analysis, 170 Years of Industry Release, ONS, 2013

[26] https://en.wikipedia.org/wiki/List_of_largest_companies_by_revenue

[27] http://knoema.com/nwnfkne/world-gdp-ranking-2015-data-and-charts

[28] Eurofound (2012), Fifth European Working Conditions Survey, Publications Office of the European Union, Luxembourg

[29] Changes in shift work patterns over the last ten years (1999 to 2009), Office for National Statistics, HSE, 2011

[30] http://www.hse.gov.uk/research/rrhtm/rr713.htm

[31] J.R. Hackman and G.R. Oldham. Work Redesign. Pearson Education, Inc, 1980

[32] EMP09: Employees and self-employed by occupation. ONS, 12 August 2015

[33] Contracts with No Guaranteed Hours, Employee contracts that do not guarantee a minimum number of hours: 2015 update, ONS, September 2015

[34] Various sources including the Institute of Leadership and Management (Inspire, August 2013), and The Guardian, 30 July 2013

[35] Unions press Labour to commit to ban on zero-hours contracts, Northern Echo, April 2015

[36] Presentation by Peter Cheese, Head of the CIPD, at the launch of BSI 76000

[37] Management of Health and Safety at Work Regulations 1999, Schedule 1 General Principles of Prevention, (d)

[38] Principles of Prevention, Ibid.

[39] Institute of Leadership and Management Survey, Published January 2015

[40] Full Report – Women in the Labour Market, ONS, 2013

[41] Full Report – Ethnicity and the Labour Market, 2011 Census, ONS, 2014

[42] 2011 Census: Quick Statistics for England and Wales, 2011 Census, ONS, 2013

[43] Labour Market Statistics, September 2015: A05 NSA: Employment, unemployment and economic inactivity by age group (not seasonally adjusted). ONS, 16 September 2015.

[44] The Future of Work, published by the UK Commission for Employment and Skills (UKCES), 2014

LEADERSHIP

When we consider potentially catastrophic events it is easy to assume that they happened as a consequence of operator error, poor planning or design, or a lack of basic systems and processes. Evidence suggests that there is seldom a single cause.

BP

BP had established itself as the leading petroleum brand for sustainability[45] before multiple events caused loss of life, substantial clean-up costs, litigation, and reputational damage. BP had not had a good history in the USA before the Deepwater Horizon incident because of previous events including:

- The Texas City disaster (killed 15, injured 180 workers). BP admitted safety failings and paid out over $2 billion[46].
- Subsequent pipeline leaks in Alaska led to fines and restitution charges.

The Deepwater Horizon incident claimed the job of the then CEO Tony Haywood, although some of his comments, including a statement that '*I would like my life back*' did not endear him to the families that had lost theirs. According to the Economist[47], charges associated with the spill are over $50 billion with litigation still to come.

Volkswagen

Volkswagen had established a corporate goal[48] to "*offer attractive, safe and environmentally sound vehicles which can compete in an increasingly tough market and set world standards in their respective class*".

They had published a commitment to become the "most sustainable automotive company in the world", identified '7 Core Values', introduced a "Code of Conduct", and established an oversight committee with responsibility for 'Corporate Social Responsibility and Sustainability'. Despite this, Volkswagen is currently calculating the cost of software designed to cheat emissions tests on over 11 million cars sold worldwide. Whilst Volkswagen have attributed the event to 'a couple of software engineers', the American CEO told the American Government '600,000 people worldwide have to be managed in a different way'. The VW Works Council Chief said: 'We need in future a climate in which problems … can be openly communicated to superiors… in which it's possible and permissible to argue with your superior'.

Primark, Matalan, Benetton...

Events across the supply chain can also have a profound impact on organisational performance and reputation. Fuelled by demand for cheaper clothing, many retailers had sourced clothing from around the world including Bangladesh.

Several high street stores had engaged garment manufacturers at the Savar Building in Rana Plaza to fulfil their orders, but when the Savar Building started to show cracks, work was not suspended and 1,137 people died when the building collapsed. 41 people were arrested and currently face a murder charge[49].

The murder charge was introduced when evidence came to light that staff and management had forced workers to enter the building despite their concerns about major cracks the day before.

The Herald of Free Enterprise

The investigation into the Herald of Free Enterprise[50] tragedy, in which 189 passengers and employees died, led to the conclusion that 'underlying or cardinal faults lay higher up in the company...from top to bottom the body corporate was infected with the disease of sloppiness'.

16 Major Accidents

An analysis of 16 major accidents found the following leadership failings as contributory factors:

- *Lack of safety commitment (implicated in 12/16 cases).*
- *Complacency and lack of oversight (11/16 cases).*
- *Inadequate training and competence (11/16 cases)*
- *Lack of learning from previous events (10/16 cases).*
- *Inadequacy of procedures (9/16 cases).*
- *Insufficient hazard awareness and control (9/16 cases).*
- *Inadequate safety communications (8/16 cases).*
- *Lack of clarity of roles and responsibilities (5/16 cases).*
- *Poor management of change (5/16 cases).*

It is hard to conceive that organisations or their employees set out to cause such substantial damage to themselves, their employees, or the communities in which they operate. There are indications that leadership styles, visions and goals provide mixed messages to managers and supervisors who find themselves left to balance the competing priorities of controlling risk and producing returns.

Executives and managers can face personal prosecution if a health and safety offence is committed through their consent, connivance or neglect. Directors can be disqualified and face a charge of gross negligence manslaughter if the offence leads to death.

Leading Health & Safety

When exploring root causes of incidents at work, elements like leadership often play a key role. According to Armstrong[51], managers of the business often underestimate the importance of health and safety policies.

In 2005[52], 79% of organisations indicated that health and safety was directed at board level. However, the research found the following failings:

- Significant gaps in the extent to which boards had reviewed policies.
- The frequency at which they had discussed health and safety.
- The number of boards that took no action following receipt of safety reports.
- The number of boards that discussed health and safety only when an issue arose.

The authors[53] encouraged boards to review the frequency, scope, response, and their approach to consultation on health and safety.

A survey published in 2005[54], found that 85% of large organisations had assigned health and safety responsibility to a particular role. Unfortunately, this was documented in only 80% of cases, and worse, the appointed person was only fulfilling the duties in 67% of cases.

> *1/3rd of Appointed Safety Directors not fulfilling role*

In 2007, the HSE and the Institute of Directors published joint guidance[55] on safety leadership. This was subsequently updated in 2013. The guidance established three essential principles:

Strong and active leadership from the top
Visible, active commitment from the board; Establishing effective 'downward' communication systems and management structures; Integration of good health and safety management with business decisions.
Worker involvement
Engaging the workforce in the promotion and achievement of safe and healthy conditions; Effective 'upward' communication; Providing high-quality training.
Assessment and Review
Identifying and managing health and safety risks; Accessing (and following) competent advice; Monitoring, reporting and reviewing performance.

The guidance provided by the HSE uses the Plan, Do, Check, Act approach and identifies a series of standards and measures against which leaders can assess their own performance in relation to leading safety at work.

Their checklist (below) identifies a series of questions to help executives to assess their own performance in relation to the leadership of health and safety.

PLAN	• How do you demonstrate the board's commitment to health and safety?
DO	• What have you done to ensure your organisation, at all levels including the board, receives competent health and safety advice? • How are you ensuring all staff – including the board – are sufficiently trained and competent in their health and safety responsibilities? • How confident are you that your workforce, particularly safety representatives, are consulted properly on health and safety matters, and that their concerns are reaching the appropriate level including, as necessary, the board? • What systems are in place to ensure your organisation's risks are assessed, and that sensible control measures are established and maintained?
CHECK	• How well do you know what is happening on the ground, and what audits or assessments are undertaken to inform you about what your organisation and contractors actually do? • What information does the board receive regularly about health and safety, e.g. performance data and reports on injuries and work-related ill health? • Do you compare your performance with others in your sector or beyond? • Where changes in working arrangements have significant implications for health and safety, how are these brought to the attention of the board?
ACT	• What do you do to ensure appropriate board-level review of health and safety?

During construction of the site of the London Olympic Games[56], the project achieved 22 periods of one million hours without a reportable accident in a construction industry which is traditionally linked with high numbers of incidents, injuries and illnesses (commonly serious or fatal).

The following drivers were cited as being key to the success of the project:

- A safety vision that was translated into strategic action using behavioural safety training, comprehensive processes and procedures and multiple communication channels.
- Engagement with the supply chain culminating in a collaborative, mutually responsible, challenging, and learning culture.
- Regular monitoring of performance against the vision and other key performance indicators including safety culture which was supported by regular review and audit activity.
- A clear health and safety structure that involved all levels of the hierarchy.
- Communication processes that worked horizontally and vertically across the organisation and used multiple methods.
- Formal learning activities providing structured learning alongside informal learning through site visits and shared experiences.
- The promotion of wellbeing over safety to produce a wider awareness and achieve a higher level of engagement.

FRC Guidance

In September 2014, the Financial Reporting Council published its Guidance on Risk Management, Internal Control and Related Financial and Business Reporting[57]. Their guidance stated that 'shareholders and other stakeholders should be well informed about the principal risks and prospects of the company'.

Leadership beyond Process

One of the common mistakes made by boards is that they incorporate safety as an agenda point in their regular meetings and discuss safety as a single point, often at the start of the meetings. Whilst this activity is seemingly undertaken in response to good advice, the board should consider business and environmental risks, as well as those relating to health, safety and welfare as a part of all board deliberations, and plans should establish the necessary competence, control, communication, and co-operation implications of their decisions.

Leaders have the power to determine the nature of work, the working conditions, workplace exposures, and levels of employee support.

Implications for Leaders

The leadership team are responsible for establishing strategic processes, which drive tactical arrangements, which impact on operational activities and cause risk[58]. These are illustrated in the table below.

STRATEGIC DECISIONS

Ownership/Control;
Standards;
Structures;
Targets;
Internal processes;
External processes;
Health and Safety processes

TACTICAL PLANS

Working procedures;
Equipment Selection
Management;
Supervision;
Communications;
Inspection;
Maintenance;
Work planning;
Risk assessment;
Recruitment;
Training;
Pay;
Welfare;
Event management;
Feedback;

OPERATIONAL CIRCUMSTANCES

Competence;
Motivation;
Work arrangements;
Risk perception;
Situation awareness;
Fatigue;
Physical health;
Front line comms;
Work pressure;
Compliance attitude;
HR suitability;
Work environments;
Workplace design;
Operational and safety equipment

Many of these themes are directly linked to HR metrics, highlighting the criticality of HR activities on the management of risk. The CIPD Profession has established a standard for those leading HR to fulfil their professional duty to demonstrate personal leadership and professional impact; lead others; deliver value and performance; and evaluate the impact of their work.

HR Practitioners act as role models for managers and other employees in the organisation. What they accept or challenge, and what they are seen to accept or challenge provides a significant part of the development of an organisations culture. A good example is the way that transformational leadership[59] is seen as a positive contributor to both incident and absence reduction through the:

- Development and maintenance of effective and physically comfortable work environments.
- The maintenance of a healthy work climate leading to reduced health complaints.
- Initiatives to improve family and work commitment compatibility.
- Sympathetic, vigorous attempts to help people manage negative events.

Leadership behaviours[60] can have both a direct and indirect impact on positive health and safety performance, for example:

- A combination of transformational leadership (a clear vision for safety, employees motivated to achieve it, acting as a role model and showing concern for the welfare of employees) and transactional leadership (communicating and setting clear goals and monitoring and recognising positive safety behaviours) can balance direction with control.

- Adopting a coaching-oriented, supportive approach to safety which provides resources and encourages worker involvement can increase commitment and engagement.

- Actively championing safety can foster perceptions of a positive safety climate, which in turn can improve safety performance and influence 'bottom up' communication of safety concerns, and build trust.

- Consistent safety messages demonstrated at all management levels, from senior management to supervisors, fosters belief and safety culture.

References

[45] BP's "Beyond Petroleum" Campaign Losing its Sheen, Anne Landman, PR Watch, May 2010

[46] A History of BP's US disasters, The Telegraph, 15 November 2012

[47] A costly mistake, The Economist, July 2015

[48] Volkswagen Sustainability Report 2014

[49] Rana Plaza collapse: dozens charged with murder, The Guardian, June 1, 2015

[50] Quoted in: The role of managerial leadership in determining workplace safety outcomes, Angela O'Dea and Rhona Flin, University of Aberdeen, HSE, 2003

[51] Handbook of Human Resource Management Practice, Ibid.

[52] Health and safety responsibilities of company directors and management board members: 2001, 2003 and 2005 surveys Final report, Greenstreet Berman, HSE, 2005

[53] Health and safety responsibilities of company directors and management board members, Greenstreet Berman, HSE, 2003

[54] Health and safety responsibilities of company directors and management board members: 2001, 2003 and 2005 surveys Final report, Greenstreet Berman, HSE, 2005

[55] Leading Health & Safety at Work, Revision 1, HSE, 2013

[56] Leadership and worker involvement on the Olympic Park, Institute for Employment Studies, HSE, 2011

[57] Guidance on Risk Management, Internal Control and Related Financial and Business Reporting, FRC, 2014

[58] Analysis of Accidents by the London Olympic Committee, HSE, 2012

[59] The effects of transformational leadership on employees' absenteeism in four UK public sector organisations, Dr Nadine Mellor Professor John Arnold Dr Garry Gelade, HSE, 2008

[60] A review of the literature on effective leadership behaviours for safety, Chrysanthi Lekka and Nicola Healey, Health & Safety Laboratory, HSE, 2012

MANAGEMENT

Management duties are defined by the Management of Health & Safety at Work Regulations 1999. The Regulations set out the following duties for organisations:

- Establish a policy
- Manage risk
- Apply the Principles of Prevention
- Establish a system for managing safety (organise for safety)
- Conduct risk assessments
- Assess capabilities, and provide training and information
- Appoint competent persons
- Undertake health surveillance
- Establish emergency procedures

The key points are described below:

Policy

It is a legal requirement to have a Safety Policy if the organisation employs more than five people. This should comprise:

- A statement of general policy on health and safety at work,
- A responsibility section setting out who is responsible for what, and
- An arrangements section which sets out what the organisation is going to do in order to achieve the aims of the policy.

This should form the basis of systems to manage health and safety at work.

The Principles of Prevention

The Principles of Prevention set out a process through which the management of risks should be applied, starting with the most effective solution and working towards the least effective solution, thus:

(a) Avoiding risks;

(b) Evaluating risks which cannot be avoided;

(c) Combating risks at source;

(d) Adapting work to the individual, especially in workplace design, work equipment selection, and the choice of working and production methods, with a view, in particular, to alleviating monotonous work and work at a predetermined work-rate, reducing negative effects on health;

(e) Adapting to technical progress;

(f) Replacing the dangerous by the non-dangerous or the less dangerous;

(g) Developing a coherent overall prevention policy covering technology, organisation of work, working conditions, social relationships and the influence of factors relating to the working environment;

(h) Giving collective protective measures priority over individual protective measures; and

(i) Giving appropriate instructions to employees.

Following the sequence ensures that risks are removed e.g. through effective workplace design or equipment selection. Where risks cannot be avoided at source, there is a requirement to assess them, and put the necessary control measures in place.

A Safety Management System

There is no Approved Code of Practice associated with these regulations, although the HSE have published Guidance, often referred to as HSG65. A new version was introduced in 2013. This guidance is not a legal requirement, but employers need to adopt an approach that is broadly in line with its contents. The latest version of this guidance, introduced in 2013[61] is based on the Plan, Do, Check, Act model.

Plan

The Plan stage starts with a policy – stating the commitment of the organisation, and its vision in terms of where it is today and where it wants to be. The policy should establish a clear direction for managers and other employees to follow and be aligned with other organisational policies and systems. It should be shared with employees so that they can understand what the company is trying to achieve and see the senior management commitment to achieving it.

Planning ensures that employees have a co-ordinated approach to controlling risks, responding to changing circumstances, and sustaining positive health and safety attitudes and behaviours.

By the end of the Planning process, there should be:

- A clear and signed statement of intention;
- Clearly defined roles and responsibilities relating to who does what and how;
- Direction on how things will be done;
- What resources will be provided;
- Clarity on how performance will be measured; and
- How actions will be prioritised.

Internal processes for coping with change (e.g. the departure of a role holder within the safety management system) and arrangements for working with contractors and others affected by the organisation should also be defined.

Plans will be shared with workers and/or their representatives and communicated so that everyone understands what is expected of them. Lastly, the competence of role holders will have been measured against their roles and responsibilities, and solutions will have been identified and plans to address them put in place.

Do

The Do activity consists of three stages: Risk Profiling, Organising, and Implementing the Plan.

Risk Profiling provides a mechanism for identifying proportionate actions to address risks and prioritising them so that the greatest risks are addressed first. Risk is normally identified as a function of the likelihood that an event will occur and the severity of injury that will result. Profiling enables actions to be prioritised.

Organising the activity ensures that workers are clear on what is expected of them and others, and provides an opportunity for consultation on the activities so that everyone is clear. Organising also ensures that sufficient resources are in place and that the knowledge of a competent advisor has been sought.

Organising for safety is the term given to the process of control, co-operation, communication and competence necessary to promote positive health and safety outcomes:

- **Control** – leadership, management, supervision, performance standards, instructions, motivation, accountability, rewards and sanctions;
- **Co-operation** – between workers, representatives, managers, committees, and consultations, and employee involvement;
- **Communications** – through written and verbal processes providing information upwards, downwards, and across the organisation in a timely and comprehensible manner; and
- **Competence (and Capabilities)** – through recruitment, selection, training, coaching, and specialist advice, to provide the organisation with personnel with the knowledge, skills, and capabilities to work safely.

Implementing the plan includes the decision making process to establish the appropriate preventative and protected measures necessary, including the;

- Provision of suitable tools and equipment to do the job,
- Systems of inspection and maintenance to ensure that they remain suitable;
- Provision of training and instruction to ensure that all workers know what to do and how to do it; and adequate supervision to make sure that the arrangements are followed.

Check

Establishing processes for measuring performance and investigating when things go wrong are two important steps to ensure that agreed actions are appropriate to the risks and that they are being completed. Defining sensible performance measures and checking them regularly provides a mechanism for identifying what is working well, and where failings are occurring.

Active measures include health surveillance data; checks that workers are following instructions; identifying where breaches are regularly occurring; and process performance measures (including those related to the assessment of competence).

Reactive measures provide evidence of health and safety failings, and include information such as sickness absence records and accident or incident investigation reports. Investigations should explore the immediate, underlying and root causes of any event and should consider the extent to which information, instructions, training and supervision contributed to the event.

Regular reporting (appropriate to the level of risks involved and the size of the organisation) helps leadership and management to understand the level of risk exposure, and supports worker consultation and involvement processes.

Evidence from collected information also provides a mechanism to review the information, instructions and training provided to workers to ensure that they understand the hazards to which they are exposed and what the likely injuries or health problems might be if they do not follow the instructions.

Interventions arising from these processes should address the specific issues that were identified, but the next section ('Act') reviews that information to ensure that the management system is delivering the required outcome.

Act

The Act stage focusses on the management system itself, and consists of two elements: reviewing the performance on the management system, and taking action on lessons learned.

The performance review should check the overall validity of the health and safety system and ensure that it is effective. It provides an opportunity for failings to be addressed before a serious event occurs. The review should be planned, take place in accordance with the plan, and should be sufficiently comprehensive to ensure that the organisation is meeting both its statutory obligations, and those targets that it has set itself.

Understanding system failings provides an opportunity for organisations to learn – a key element of effective health and safety management.

Risk Assessment

Risk assessment is the mechanism through which hazards and their associated risks are identified and sensible and proportionate controls are established and implemented. Undertaking risk assessments at an early stage prevents the need for costly corrective action or replacement, and can contribute to a more effective solution for the organisation.

It is important to concentrate on significant risks, i.e. those that are most likely to cause the most harm. Many organisations use a formula system where likelihood and severity are scored out of 3, 5 or another value and are then multiplied together. These systems are not perfect and can cause a focus on numbers instead of content, but the numeric value can help organisations to prioritise investments, particularly where there are a number of safety improvements.

The risk assessment should examine the environment in which the work is being undertaken, the tasks being performed, and the individuals performing the activities.

In order for risk assessments to be suitable and sufficient:

- A proper check must have been made;
- The obvious significant risks addressed;
- Precautions were reasonable, and the remaining risk low; and
- Workers or their representatives were involved in the process.

Some workers may have particular requirements, for example: new and young workers, migrant workers, new or expectant mothers, people with disabilities, temporary workers, contractors and lone workers. These should be assessed as additional risks within the risk assessment and not in isolation.

A report by Health & safety Laboratories[62] highlighted the common pitfalls and failings of risks assessments as broadly being:

- No consideration of views from those with relevant knowledge;
- No use of [or lack of] good practice guidance;
- A failure to consider site specific data;
- A failure to consider all hazards, outcomes; or the effect of simultaneous risk;
- Understated risk;
- Over-reliance on consultants (who were used improperly);
- Justified pre-determined outcomes;
- Poorly considered the 'grossly disproportionate' concept; and
- Did not culminate in actions to reduce risks.

As long as duty holders are doing all that is reasonably practicable to protect people from harm, they have fulfilled their duty (personally) and the duty of the employer. Organisations have a duty to obtain advice from a competent person if in any doubt.

Whilst a contracted safety practitioner may be able to provide advice on the law, line managers, equipment manufacturers, and employees themselves may have a good insight into the risks and reasonably practicable solutions in a specific context. Some of the themes relating to risk assessments are explained in more detail below:

Combatting risks at source

Where risks cannot be avoided, they should be combatted at source. A great example of this is the way that some equipment may present risks associated with noise or vibration. Removing the noise or vibration is far more effective than techniques to control it.

Adapting work to the individual

The fourth principle places a specific duty on HR practitioners to:

> *'adapt the work to the individual, especially as regards the design of workplaces, the choice of work equipment and the choice of working and production methods, with a view, in particular, to alleviating monotonous work and work at a predetermined work-rate and to reducing their effect on health'.*

Environments, equipment and methods can contribute positively and negatively to employee performance, health, safety and well-being. Whilst concepts like monotony and pre-determined work rates are at odds with concepts like autonomy and variety that are seen as key to job satisfaction.

Adapting to technical progress

Adapting to technical progress requires two key elements – firstly, an attitude of continuous improvement towards working methods and safety, and secondly, an approach to continuous professional development so that progress is identified, captured, considered, and where appropriate, implemented.

Collective over individual protective measures

Adopting solutions that affect everybody reduces the risk of individuals not doing what they need to in order to protect their own safety. For example, a noise suppression system reduces the risks associated with a reliance on individuals to wear personal protective equipment.

Increasing a reliance on individual protective measures has an impact on supervision because of the greater need for measures to ensure workers are doing what is expected of them.

Giving appropriate instructions to employees.

Instructions, in the form of work processes, operating procedures, or safe systems of work, are used to ensure employees know how to perform work to minimise risk of harm. Combined with information and training, they provide the necessary knowledge that employees need to achieve competence.

Capabilities, Training and Information

The Regulations establish specific duties in relation to capabilities and training. These are:

- A duty on employers to take into account an employee's health and safety capabilities when entrusting them with tasks.
- The provision of information to employees on risks to their health and safety identified by the assessment; preventative and protected measures, particular fire risks, and additional risks arising from a shared building.
- A duty on employers to ensure that employees receive adequate health and safety training on appointment and before exposure to new risks arising from changes to responsibilities; the introduction of new work equipment, new technology or systems of work.
- Training should be repeated periodically, taking account of new or changed risks and take place during working hours.

The regulations also place duties on employees to:

- Use what is provided to them in accordance with training and instructions they have received.
- Raise concerns of serious and immediate danger or other shortcomings in an employer's protection arrangements for health and safety.

The London Olympic Games review[63] provided a good example of effective safety management in a high risk environment. They identified:

- High acceptance that work could be stopped for safety reasons;
- Supervisors put 'safety first', managers were good role models;
- Safety was a key message within the workforce induction;
- Operative safety meetings provided opportunities for issues to be raised and solutions discussed;
- A wide range of communication methods updated workers on health and safety, work progress, and encouraged feedback;

- Supervisor competence, particularly in communication skills and behavioural safety;
- Operatives felt safe and confident to raise issues and events, including near misses;
- Good performance was rewarded amongst individuals and contracting organisations, through simple and low cost incentives;
- Behavioural safety programmes focused on making safety 'personal' alongside, but separate from the site induction process;
- Operatives were trained to inspect and observe activities in areas other than their own and provide feedback;
- An emphasis on learning over blame ensured there were positive responses to accidents.

The HR Agenda

Specific legislation sets out duties such as the requirement to provide sufficient time and resources, and to provide work stations suitable for the person and the activity to be performed.

Statutory duties require that only competent people (ensuring that only those with the necessary knowledge, skills, experience or other factors) are appointed to undertake activities, and define planning and organisation processes, and the provision of information, instructions and training.

The statutory duty to consult, communicate, and co-ordinate requires employers to actively engage with their employees and their representatives. A review or audit of safety performance cannot be effective without a consideration of relevant HR information.

Across the HR function, there are a variety of duties that are encapsulated across the various Acts and Regulations, and which clearly establish duties and responsibilities for HR Practitioners. These are developed through the following sections, starting with a review of current organisation design, development processes, resourcing and recruitment, capability and competence, performance and reward, employee engagement, and HR service delivery and information.

References

[61] Managing for Health and Safety, HSE, 3rd Edition, HSE, 2013

[62] Good practice and pitfalls in risk assessment, Dr Sandra Gadd, Dr Deborah Keeley, Dr Helen Balmforth, Health & Safety Laboratories, HSE, 2003

[63] Leadership and worker involvement on the Olympic Park, Institute for Employment Studies, HSE, 2011

TODAY'S ORGANISATIONS

The way that an organisation is designed, in terms of the working environment, the type of activities performed, and the nature of workplace exposures, pre-determines the potential for harm and the likely consequences for the workers. The latest European Working Conditions Survey (2012)[64] and the European Report on New and Emerging Risks (2014)[65] describe the extent to which organisations expose employees to risks of significant harm.

These risks generally fall into two types – physical risks, with the potential to do actual bodily harm; and psychosocial risks, with the potential to cause harm to mental health. In some cases risks are at their highest level since records began.

The most common exposures reported across organisations are summarised below, along with the proportion of respondents that reported them:

Physical Risks		*Psychosocial Risks*	
Manual Handling	59%	*Dealing with difficult people*	65%
Chemical/Biological	52%	*Time pressure*	41%
Repetitive movements	50%	*Long/Irregular hours*	32%
Slips, trips and falls	49%	*Communication*	21%
Machinery and tools	48%	*Job insecurity*	16%
Tiring or painful positions	45%	*Lack of influence*	14%
Vehicles	44%	*Discrimination*	6%
Temperature	35%		
Noise	27%		
Vibrations	25%		

Exposure to Physical Risks

The physical risks to workers predominantly relate to musculoskeletal conditions or exposures to chemicals or substances at work. These are described above. Exposures to low temperatures, tiring or painful positions, and repetitive hand or arm movements are at their highest levels since records began 20 years ago.

Evidence suggests that working methods and new technologies, designed to optimise output, are requiring working practices which are causing employee harm and long term absence.

Exposure to Psychosocial Risks

Psychosocial risks are those that cause harm to mental health, usually in the form of stress, anxiety and depression. The European Report on New and Emerging Risks (2014)[66] identified:

- 60% of workers work to tight deadlines or work at high speed.
- 1 in 3 workers report a lack of autonomy at work.
- 1 in 4 workers report a lack of feedback on performance.
- 1 in 5 workers perceive a lack of management support
- 1 in 7 workers are concerned about job security.
- 1 in 10 perceive a lack of support from colleagues.
- 1 in 10 workers report that work conflicts with personal values.
- Less than 70% of workers are encouraged to participate in important decisions affecting them.
- Between 5% and 10% of workers do not know what is expected from them by their employer.

Health & Safety Statistics

The basic premise of cause and effect means that physical and psychosocial hazards cannot occur without consequence, and the data below provides some indication of the scale of the effects they cause.

Deaths

Around 13,000 deaths each year are caused by occupational lung disease and cancers attributed to work. In 2014/15 in the UK[67], there were 271 fatal injuries at work – 142 work related fatal injuries to employees and 129 work related fatal injuries to members of the public[d]. The sectors most affected were:

> *57% of fatal injuries occurred in the Service sector.*

- Service sectors[e] – 51 workers and 105 members of the public.
- Construction – 35 workers and 4 members of the public;
- Agriculture – 33 workers and 4 members of the public;
- Manufacturing – 16 workers and 2 members of the public
- Utilities - 6 workers and 2 members of the public; and
- Mining & Quarrying – 1 worker and 1 member of the public;

---

[d] These figures do not include deaths due to natural causes, injuries on the road, air or sea, nor do they include the armed services.

[e] The Service sector includes: Wholesale and Retail; Transportation; Human Health and Social Work; Recreation; and Other Service Activities

Ill-Health

The HSE data for 2014/15[68] shows that over 2 million workers (nearly 7% of the total workforce) are suffering from ill health conditions caused or exacerbated by work.

> *2 million workers suffer ill-health caused or made worse by work*

Of those 2 million workers, 800,000 employees have not worked for 12 months or more, with the implication that their wealth of knowledge, skills and experience has been removed from the organisations at which they were based. Of the remaining 1.2 million workers:

- 42% suffer from musculoskeletal disorders,
- 39% suffer from stress, anxiety or depression, and
- 19% suffer from illnesses predominantly linked to exposures at work.

Actual numbers are presented below:

	Condition started		Total
	<12 months ago	*> 12 months ago*	
Musculoskeletal disorders	169,000	383,000	**525,000**
Stress, depression or anxiety	234,000	206,000	**486,000**
Other Illnesses	112,000	137,000	**227,000**
Total	**535,000**	**705,000**	**1,238,000**

Injuries

The data presented below highlights the frequency of events happening at work. Every year[69]:

- 1 in 50 employees suffer work related injuries;
- 1 in 200 employees have an absence of one week or more following an accident at work (Labour Force Survey);
- 1 in 400 employees are involved in an accident that is reported to the HSE (HSE Data).

According to HSE data based on an analysis of reported incidents, the nature of injuries are as follows:

- Almost 40% of reportable injuries were caused by sprains and strains,
- 20% led to fractures,
- 16% led to contusions (bruises), and
- Almost 10% led to lacerations (cuts and open wounds).

It is similarly possible to analyse accidents by cause. According to the HSE, slips and trips, Falls and Manual handling incidents[70] account for approximately 2/3rds of all reportable accidents. The following table provides the data for 2014/2015[71] in more detail:

	All Reports[f]	Percent
Total	**76,054**	**100%**
Injured while handling, lifting or carrying	**17,262**	**23%**
Slip, trip or fall on same level	**21,328**	**28%**
Struck by (Total)	**16,852**	**22%**
Struck by moving, flying/falling, object	7,571	10%
Contact with moving machinery	2,918	4%
Struck by moving vehicle	1,555	2%
Acts of violence	4,808	6%
Falls from a height	**6,067**	**8%**
Struck against something stationary	**2,642**	**3%**
Exposure or contact with harmful substance	**814**	**1%**
Other[g]	**11,089**	**15%**

Analysing injuries to understand their frequency, their outcome, and their cause provides valuable information to assist those involved in organisation design to create organisations, structures, and operations that are free from risk of harm.

Addressing the Problems

Past and current organisations have produced a legacy of musculoskeletal and psychosocial conditions across the workforce. Whilst organisation design can help to reduce these conditions in the future, some action needs to be taken today to support those workers that are suffering from conditions they have already acquired.

Musculoskeletal Conditions

Musculoskeletal conditions are primarily caused by manual handling, ergonomics, repetitive tasks, slips, trips, or falls. Over half a million employees in work suffer from this condition (about 1 in 60 workers). According to the CIPD, musculoskeletal

---

[f] All reports includes over 7 day injuries and specified injuries under RIDDOR, excluding fatalities.

[g] The Other group includes entrapment, drowning, fire, explosion, electrical, animal bites, and other events.

conditions and back pain are second only to minor ailments as the major cause of absence from work.

Manual Handling

The European Reports described earlier indicated high levels of employees exposed to manual handling (59%). Over 17,000 employees suffered an injury culminating in an absence of 7 days or more last year, and the HSE estimate that approximately 40% of all musculoskeletal diseases (MSDs) are caused by manual handling.

Manual handling is responsible for about a quarter of all accidents culminating in absences of over seven days, but there are substantial sectoral variations. Handling causes:

- Over 50% of all lost time accidents in human health and air transport,
- 40% in social care and wholesale or retail distribution, and
- Between 30% and 40% in agriculture and manufacturing.

Manual handling has been the subject of legislation in the UK since 1992 when the Manual Handling Operations Regulations were introduced. Apart from minor amendments in 2002 relating to physical suitability, clothing, knowledge and training, the law has remained largely unchanged.

The HSE have published guidance on manual handling[72] which sets out what employers and employees need to do in order to work safely. There is no weight limit defined in the regulations. The regulations refer only to a 'load' which is described in the guidance as a discrete moveable object and can be wide and varied including patients (people and pets receiving medical care).

The Regulations set out a specific hierarchy of controls to be adopted by employers to reduce the risk of injury. These are to avoid hazardous manual handling operations so far as is reasonably practicable; assess any hazardous manual handling operations that cannot be avoided; and reduce the risk of injury so far as is reasonably practicable.

Avoiding manual handling is the first duty. This may be achieved by performing the work in another way – an example might be by moving the equipment to the load, instead of moving the load to the equipment. If this is not possible, automation may reduce effort.

Where a manual handling requirement remains, it must be risk assessed, control measures identified, defined, and incorporated in a safe system of work.

Risk assessments should include:

- The variety of manual handling activities and steps involved;
- The involvement of employees undertaking the work;

- The task, load, environment, and individual lifting capabilities, and any other relevant factors.

The task is often more complex than initial consideration might indicate, for example:

- Is the load lifted, held, or manipulated at a distance from the body;
- Does the task involve twisting;
- Does the task involve stooping down, or stretching up;
- Does the task involve significant lifting, lowering, or carrying distances;
- Does the task involve pushing or pulling the load;

There may be specific hazards arising from the load if it is heavy, has an awkward centre of gravity, is of a difficult shape, is slippery, involves a lift by more than one person (a team lift), or has sharp edges.

Environmental factors such as space constraints, floor condition, slopes or different floor levels, temperatures and lighting should also be considered. Employers engaged in the delivery, collection or handling of 'loads' at other premises have a duty to work with those in control of the other premises to reduce risks, and those in control of the other premises have a similar duty to protect the health and safety of workers at their site. Work design, job variety and work rotation can play a part by sharing the activity throughout the working day.

There is no reliable mechanism for undertaking health surveillance in relation to manual handling, and no specific duty in law for this to take place, however, records of accidents, sickness and ill health (from Safety and HR) can provide an indication of the scale of the problem. Careful analysis may show links between manual handling and ill health, including injuries apparently unrelated to any specific event or accident. Other possible indicators of manual handling problems include:

- High levels of absenteeism or staff turnover;
- Poor productivity and morale;
- Excessive product damage;
- Unwillingness by employees to perform a specific task or tasks;
- General dissatisfaction among employees concerned.

Ergonomics and Repetitive Tasks

The European Report on New and Emerging Risks presented evidence that 45% of workers are subjected to tiring or painful positions[h]. Rather than expecting people to adapt to a design that requires them to work in an uncomfortable, stressful or

---

[h] According to the Chartered Institute of Ergonomics and Human Factors[h], Ergonomics is a science-based discipline that brings together knowledge from other subjects such as anatomy and physiology, psychology, engineering and statistics to ensure that designs complement the strengths and abilities of people and minimise the effects of their limitations.

dangerous way, organisations must consider how the workplace can be designed to suit the people who use it (this is a statutory duty).

Factors to consider[73] include:

- **Awkward postures** – involving the head, neck, back, arms, wrist, hands and fingers;
- **Repetitive arm movements**;
- **Work-pace**;
- **Breaks** –including lunch breaks and time performing other work;
- **Duration** – time spent performing the task during a typical shift.
- **Force** – the level of force required;
- **Other factors** – such as lighting, exposure to vibration, temperature, etc.

Much of this work often lends itself to automation or re-organisation. Unfortunately, analysis of the impact of human activity, such as injury or longer term illness is not always factored into decisions when organisations are contemplating investments[74]. Analysing HR data on absenteeism, sickness and productivity, linked to morale and employee attitudes may support the development of a more accurate costing model.

Slips, Trips and Falls

About 1.5 million working days are lost each year to slips, trips and falls: 1 million days due to slips and trips, and 500,000 working days due to falls. The working days lost are so high, in part, because of the number of incidents that result in chronic conditions[75].

In 2013/14, there were 39 fatalities to workers caused by falls from height[76] and three fatal slips and trips. The industries in which fatal incidents were most common were construction, agriculture and manufacturing.

Conversely, of the 25 non-worker fatalities caused by slips, trips and falls, 17 occurred in the health and social care sector. 23 occurred to people aged 65 or over.

In terms of over seven day injuries, the following sectors showed the highest reported levels:

- slips and trips in human health & social (2,288),
- slips and trips in transport & storage (2,154),
- falls in transport & storage (479),
- falls in manufacturing (479).

Factoring in employee numbers, employees in the water supply, waste, and transport and storage industries were the most likely to suffer reportable slips, trips and fall events. The statistics show significant seasonal variation in over seven day injuries. Approximately 54% of slips and trips leading to an absence of more than seven days occur in the autumn and winter – when falling leaves, wet surfaces, ice and snow significantly increase the risk.

The most common causes of slips, trips and falls[77] are:

- Contamination (a leak or spillage) or poor cleaning regimes,
- Inappropriate flooring or footwear (footwear should be appropriate for the working environment),
- Uneven/blocked walkways (such as trailing cables or poor storage).

Other factors such as poor lighting can increase the risk of an incident occurring, whilst lean manufacturing techniques such as the use of 'white floors' reduce risks because they enable leaks and spillages to be quickly identified.

In 2007/8, the HSE ran a 'Watch Your Step'[78] campaign which consisted of the following key messages:

- Slips and trips are not funny;
- Simple and sensible precautions can eliminate most of the problems;
- Personal responsibility and worker participation are essential;
- Slips and trips should be treated seriously.

Whilst clever design, regular housekeeping and maintenance contribute to a reduction in the risk of slips, trips and falls occurring, the most effective way to reduce the risk is to instil a culture that does not create the risks to begin with and quickly clears up any spills.

Mental Health Conditions

Although 'stress' is often cited as being the major concern for employers, poor mental health can manifest in different ways, including stress, anxiety and depression, all of which can be caused or exacerbated by work. These terms are defined[79] below:

- **Anxiety** – A feeling of worry, nervousness, or unease about something with an uncertain outcome;
- **Depression** – A mental condition characterized by feelings of severe despondency and dejection, typically also with feelings of inadequacy and guilt, often accompanied by lack of energy and disturbance of appetite and sleep.
- **Stress** – A state of mental or emotional strain or tension resulting from adverse or demanding circumstances (The HSE refer to excessive pressure);

Whilst all three conditions can be caused by external factors such as the loss of a family member, a divorce, or moving house, almost half a million workers are currently suffering from stress, anxiety or depression caused or exacerbated by work.

Workers can also suffer psychosocial conditions as a consequence of discrimination, harassment or victimisation at work. The Equality Act has made it an offence for employees to be subjected to any of these activities by virtue of a protected characteristic. These are: Age; Disability; Gender reassignment; Race; Religion or belief; Sex; Sexual orientation; Marriage and civil partnership; or Pregnancy and maternity.

Psychosocial conditions can also exacerbate other conditions, for example there is a link between psychosocial conditions and musculoskeletal disorders. This could be because of a tensing of the muscles or because muscle pain and fatigue are idiopathic[i] symptoms related to mental health conditions. Whilst the origins of these symptoms are not well understood[80], there may be a relationship between feeling unwell and an increased awareness of other symptoms.

Despite the good work of some organisations, for many people there remains a stigma attached to mental health conditions and for this reason, employees do not always feel willing or able to share their condition with the organisation. Line Managers, Supervisors and colleagues are most likely to notice when an employee is showing signs that could indicate that they are suffering from a mental condition. Providing help to managers and employees to enable them to spot the condition is therefore an important training intervention to reduce the impact of the illness.

Workplace Interventions

There are three elements to addressing mental health at work. The first relates to workplace exposures, the second relates to employees abilities to withstand the pressures (resilience), and the third relates to the support provided by organisations when the pressure becomes too much.

Workplace Exposure

Exposure to psychosocial risk should be treated the same way as physical risk. Managers and employees should identify risks and implement control measures.

These can include:

- Job variety,
- Ensuring that employees have reasonable workloads,
- Monitoring and controlling working time,
- Providing training to support the process,
- Line manager awareness,
- Providing opportunities for employees to develop within the organisation,
- Evaluating piece-rate systems, and
- Positive employee engagement and good communications.

---

[i] Idiopathic symptoms are those relating to or denoting any disease or condition which arises spontaneously or for which the cause is unknown.

THE HUMAN RESOURCE PRACTITIONER'S GUIDE

There is evidence that employees in emotionally demanding occupations[81], may suffer from negative stressors to the extent that they suffer burnout[j].

Emotionally demanding occupations often bring with them a roller coaster of emotions as the positive emotions gained from positive events juxtapose with sadness and disappointment; difficult client meetings; verbal abuse; and/or difficult colleague, subordinate or third party interactions.

In 2011, at the height of the banking crisis, according to Jim Armitage of the London Standard[82], approximately one quarter (£150 billion) of Lloyd's loans were funded by short term loans of just one month. Lloyds had a daily, multi-billion-pound scramble to keep a third of the nation's mortgages afloat. Going public would have almost certainly deepened the banking crisis. After the pressure began to ease, the Lloyds Chief Executive took six weeks sickness absence, citing the toll the crisis had taken and the insomnia he had suffered as a result.

Other examples such as call centre personnel[83] are identified as having suffered increased levels of anxiety and depression. In the case of call handlers: temporary contracts, script reading, and regular performance monitoring (including eavesdropping) all increase the likelihood of depression and anxiety. These employees also indicated effects on personal wellbeing and a desire to leave the organisation.

Stress can be caused by 'perceptions' rather than actual events which can make it difficult to link to a particular event or cause, and can appear in physiological, emotional, mental, or behavioural differences or changes in an employee as diverse as weight gain or weight loss.

Resilience

The Local Government Association (LGA) have published a guide for councillors[84] on stress management and personal resilience. Resilience is often seen as an effective means of reducing personal stress and combines the abilities of being able to identify, and then deal with stress. Their guidance defines resilience as the ability to bounce back from tough times, to triumph in the face of adversity and to display tenacity, but not at the expense of reason. The LGA advocates the use of the Nicholson McBride Personal Resilience Tool which sets out 5 elements:

- **Optimism** – encourages people to feel positive about themselves, about other people, and the world's general direction of travel.
- **Solution Orientation** – the ability to see and anticipate problems coming a long way off and to prepare accordingly.

---

[j] Burnout is described as physical or mental collapse caused by overwork or stress.

- **Individual Accountability** – a strong sense of self-worth and self-regard which gives people a belief in their own abilities.
- **Openness and Flexibility** –to tolerate and thrive on ambiguous situations.
- **Managing Stress and Anxiety** – identifying and dealing with stress.

The book suggests that particularly useful skills like time management, assertiveness and positivity can all play an important part in building 'resilience' and helping people to cope with excessive levels of work pressure.

The US Army use a different set of measures. Their five elements, which provide an alternative, though equally valid approach, are as follows:

- **Social** – Trusted and valued relationships that foster good communications and the comfortable sharing of ideas, views and experiences.
- **Emotional** – Responding to life's challenges in a positive way, and demonstrating self-control, stamina and good character.
- **Family** – Being in a family unit that is supportive, healthy and secure.
- **Spiritual** – Having a purpose, core values, beliefs, identity and vision.
- **Physical** – Balancing sleep, activity and nutrition to improve personal performance, resilience and readiness.

These two sets of measures appear very different, reflecting the difference between the organisations. Understanding how resilience applies in a particular organisation, and sharing that practice with others will help them to cope more effectively.

Rehabilitation

The Institute for Employment Studies [85] have produced a report on best practices to facilitate rehabilitation. The report identifies the following steps when supporting an employee absent due to mental health with a view to facilitating a return to work:

- Early contact with the employee;
- Early health assessment;
- A good quality health assessment;
- Developing an agreed rehabilitation plan;
- The availability of therapeutic interventions;
- Flexible return to work options;
- Work adaptations and adjustments.

They also identify a series of management activities that will support the identification and resolution process. These are:

- The existence of a written policy and guidelines;
- Oversight of the rehabilitation process;
- Roles and Responsibilities integrated to produce a cohesive solution;
- Stress awareness amongst line management;
- Good awareness of the return to work and rehabilitation policies;

- Effective monitoring of sickness absence.

Adopting these activities was found to reduce length of absence following a period of work related stress; accelerate the process of getting the individual fit, healthy, and back to work; preventing unnecessary or unwanted turnover; and supported the identification and resolution of potential problems or issues on an organisational or departmental scale.

Workplace Interventions

The CIPD has published a Toolkit[86] to help HR practitioners to increase stress awareness and support the development of a managing stress policy. The toolkit includes content on stress awareness; the business case; strategy and policy development; auditing approach; stress reduction interventions and solutions; and effectiveness evaluation.

The HSE[87] identifies six factors that relate to stress at work. These are Demands; Control; Support; Relationships; Role; and Change Management. These are different to the CIPD causes: Relationships; work-life balance; overload, job security; control; resources and communication; pay and benefits; and other job aspects. Any and all of these elements can cause stress.

The HSE model is well supported through independent research including the research by the University of London[88], showing the organisational benefits to be gained from a proactive approach to stress. These were:

- Better performance when objectively measured, when self-rated, or rated by others
- Better team performance
- Less absenteeism and turnover intention
- Less withdrawal behaviours

One solution which is common to both the CIPD and the HSE tools is the use of a survey to establish the prevalence of stress and the causes of stress in the workplace. The HSE Indicator Tool[89] is a particularly easy to use questionnaire but may not suit the specific circumstances of your organisation (particularly given the different ways that organisations evaluate resilience).

In order for policies to be effective, they need to address all the possible mental health conditions that can arise, both from work, and elsewhere, and effective methods of support to assist managers and employees to identify the causes of, and employees suffering from mental health conditions. Policies need to reduce risk and provide early interventions to minimise the risk or duration of absence.

Violence

According to the HSE, work related violence is described as 'any incident in which a person is abused, threatened or assaulted in circumstances relating to their work'[90]. This wide variation identifies the significance of abuse or threatening conduct on mental health and physical health. Violence in this context can arise from managers, peers, subordinates, or members of the public.

Violence can occur in any sector although those sectors with a higher level of public interaction are most at risk. These include health and social care, wholesale and retail, transport and distribution and other service functions. These are the functions that have grown the most in the UK economy.

Employers have a duty to protect the health, safety and welfare of their employees and this includes protecting them from violence so it is important for employers to understand the scale of the problem within their organisation.

Employees may not always be open about their exposure to violence in the workplace which can make it difficult for employers to identify the existence or scale of a problem, this is because violence is seen as a part of the job. Encouraging employees to report violence is the only effective way to address this, although evidence from industry bodies or similar organisations can provide an indication about the existence of the problem.

The HSE identify workers as being at increased risk of violence or aggressive behaviour if they are:

- Working alone;
- Working after normal working hours;
- Working and travelling in the community;
- Handling valuables or medication;
- Providing or withholding a service;
- Exercising authority;
- Working with people who are emotionally or mentally unstable;
- Working with people who are under the influence of drink or drugs;
- Working with people under stress.

Certain factors are likely to contribute to an increased risk of violence, such as inherent predispositions, impatience, frustrations, anxiety, and resentment, and these may be exacerbated by drugs and alcohol.

It is often the case that many of these events may happen at once – e.g. in the case of an employee who is working and travelling in the community, working alone, outside of normal working hours, working with people who are emotionally or mentally unstable and who may be under the influence of drink or drugs, with whom they may need to exercise a level of authority.

Violence can lead to protracted absences and in extreme cases, can cause physical or psychosocial disability. Victims may need specialist support or counselling which can be provided by specialist organisations, including the police, victim support, or specialist counsellors. Insurers may finance or partly finance this expenditure.

Example 1: Health and Social Care

Employees, visitors and contractors can all be at risk from violence in health and social care as the pressure of circumstances and/or the prevalence of medical conditions can lead people to react to circumstances. Whilst it is usually the patient or client that is violent, it could also be a family member of other visitor who is anxious or worried[91]. A suitable and sufficient risk assessment may need to consider both the activities of the organisation and the individual client. If the person is under, or is going to be under a regime of care, an assessment should be undertaken and regularly reviewed as a part of the care management plan. This should include:

- Inherent dispositions including physical/psychosocial state/history of violence;
- The impact of prescribed medication or other drugs or alcohol;
- The role the carer is performing and how that is likely to be perceived; and
- The impact of changing circumstances.

Control measures in this setting are likely to include:

- **Careful analysis of the roles being undertaken** by the organisation and how those roles might come into contact with clients or patients that may present a risk of violent behaviour.
- **Provision of information, instruction and training** to employees that relates to the organisation including the systems and procedures that it uses to reduce the risk of violence; and to the information relating to patients and clients under its care.
- **Work organisation**, particularly the manner in which clients and patients are supported and their care is managed, perhaps through communications that reflect the particular needs of the person under their care.
- **Particular support for lone workers** which could include meetings at alternative locations where this is viable, regular reporting in where that is not possible (and response strategies when reports are not received), or alternative working practices where particular patient or client circumstances warrant it, e.g. two-person (escorted or multi-agency) visits.

Training should include the causes of violence, identifying the warning signs, interpersonal skills (e.g. de-escalation), and internal processes and procedures that reduce the risk of violence at work and ensure that where violence does occur, that it is reported.

Example 2: Licensed and Retail Premises

Licensed and retail premises present particular risks[92] to staff because of exposure to the public. These risks can be increased where the premises may be smaller and consequently have lower employee levels.

The main causes of violence are disagreements between members of the public, or between members of the public and the establishment. In pubs and clubs, alcohol and drug use contributes to a heightened level of risk. Employees handling large amounts of cash, having high levels of face to face contact, and providing extended opening hours, are likely to have a heightened risk.

Risks can be reduced through the following interventions:

- **Changing the work environment** – giving particular consideration to visibility, lighting, building exteriors, movement of people, queueing times; and the use of security devices and closed circuit television (CCTV).
- **Changing working practices** – particularly in relation to cash handling, opening hours, staffing numbers particularly at peak times or periods times of increased vulnerability.
- **Providing employee training** – dealing with the particular risks, customer service, handling complaints, security awareness, conflict, spotting potentially violent individuals, procedures for handling violence, and reporting crime.
- **Strictly adopting legal recourse** –using the legal options available.
- **Partnering with other organisations** – including the police, local authority, trade union, local chamber of commerce, or other businesses

Vulnerability and Violence

Particular groups of staff may be more vulnerable, for example young workers, trainees, or temporary workers that may have received less training and have less experience; early morning or late evening workers (e.g. key holders); employees dealing with complaints or disputes, and lone workers. A more comprehensive list of affected workers is provided in the HSE guide: Preventing violence to retail staff[93].

Employees with protected characteristics may find themselves at a higher risk of violence. The Equality Act applies to third party harassment, as well as harassment by managers and other employees. In 2013/14, there were 44,480 hate crimes recorded by the police[94]. These included 37,484 (84%) race hate crimes; 4,622 (10%) sexual orientation hate crimes; 2,273 (5%) religion hate crimes; 1,985 (4%) disability hate crimes; and 555 (1%) were transgender hate crimes.

Organisations have a duty to make reasonable adjustments for persons with protected characteristics.

References

[64] Eurofound, Fifth European Working Conditions Survey, Publications Office of the European Union, Luxembourg, 2012

[65] European Survey of Enterprises on New and Emerging Risks, 2014

[66] European Survey of Enterprises on New and Emerging Risks, 2014

[67] http://www.hse.gov.uk/statistics/fatals.htm

[68] Health and Safety Statistics Annual Report for Great Britain 2014/15, ONS

[69] Health and Safety Statistics Annual Report for Great Britain 2014/15, ONS

[70] HandS-On Statistics Data Tool, HSE website, retrieved August 2015

[71] http://www.hse.gov.uk/statistics/causinj/kinds-of-accident.htm

[72] Manual handling. Manual Handling Operations Regulations 1992 (as amended). Guidance on Regulations L23 (Third edition) HSE Books 2004

[73] Assessment of Repetitive Tasks of the upper limbs (the ART tool): Guidance for health and safety practitioners, consultants, ergonomists and large organisations, HSE, 2010

[74] The Health & Safety Laboratory has developed a tool to risk assess repetitive tasks (called ART) and more information can be found at www.hse.gov.uk/msd/uld/art.

[75] Manual handling. Manual Handling Operations Regulations 1992 (as amended). Guidance on Regulations L23 (Third edition) HSE Books 2004

[76] Slips & trips and falls from height in Great Britain, HSE, 2014

[77] Slips and trips mapping tool An aid for safety representatives, HSE,

[78] 'Watch your step' - A promotional campaign including workplace inspections, HSE, 2007

[79] Definitions taken from the Oxford Dictionary, on-line version, August 2015

[80] Attention, awareness and occupational stress, Prepared by Liverpool John Moores University, HSE, 2008

[81] The nature, causes and consequences of harm in emotionally-demanding occupations, Birkbeck College University of London, HSE, 2008

[82] Lloyds boss Antonio Horta-Osorio earned his pay in stress alone, Jim Armitage, London Standard, 14/05/15

[83] Psychosocial risk factors in call centres: An evaluation of work design and well-being, Prepared by the University of Sheffield, Health and Safety Laboratory and UMIST for the Health and Safety Executive, 2003

[84] Stress management and personal resilience, Councillor workbook, Local Government Association, 2012

[85] Best practice in rehabilitating employees following absence due to work-related stress, The Institute of Employment Studies, HSE, 2003

[86] Stress: CIPD Toolkit, Robertson and Cooper, CIPD Publishing

[87] Managing the causes of work-related stress A step-by-step approach using the Management Standards, HSE, 2007

[88] A business case for the Management Standards for stress, University of London, HSE, 2006

[89] HSE Management Standards Indicator Tool User manual, HSE

[90] Violence at work, A guide for employers, HSE, 1996

[91] http://www.hse.gov.uk/healthservices/violence/index.htm, retrieved August 2015

[92] Managing work-related violence in licensed and retail premises, HSE

[93] Preventing Violence to Retail Staff, HSE, 1995

[94] Hate Crimes, England and Wales, 2013/14 Byron Creese and Deborah Lader, Kevin Smith (Ed.) Home Office Statistical Bulletin, 16 October 2014

DESIGNING ORGANISATIONS

Organisation Design is the mechanism through which organisations structure themselves to achieve their goals. The CIPD defines organisation design as a process comprising:

- Assessment of needs,
- Creation of an organisation design,
- Planning, Implementation, and Review.

The outcome is likely to be a revised organisation which more effectively addresses the 'business' need through a combination of governance structures and work processes that achieve organisational goals.

The Business Case

These requirements (Assessment-Creation-Plan-Implement-Review) form the basis of the business case which will typically include:

- The justification for the activity;
- Forecast volumes and values;
- Required outputs and/or capacity requirements;
- Structure, accountabilities and spans of control; and
- Systems and communication flows.

Organisations increasingly use principles and standards to define how they expect this vision to be realised. These, balanced with the performance targets, form the basis of the governance systems, structures, and processes that shape the design.

Ownership structures assign risk within the entity and control structures reduce the risk arising from day to day activities by defining how work is planned, organised, controlled, monitored and reviewed. They also define the policies, procedures and systems necessary to safeguard stakeholders' interests and ensure that statutory and other compliance regimes are met, e.g. through safety, quality and environmental systems adopted to assure control.

Work processes and operating procedures define the way that work is undertaken, the interaction between people and technology, and the selection of operating and safety equipment. They also define the way in which change is managed within the organisation.

Until now organisation design has focussed on organisational (hierarchical) requirements. The practical aspects of organisation design are similarly shaped by the business case. These include elements such as what equipment to use, where to locate, how to manage any raw materials, and finished products, etc.

The planning, implementation and review phases ensure those involved understand the consequences of the change; boundaries and controls are clear and implementation went to plan. HR practitioners often work with the organisation, providing support to managers and employees affected by the changes, and review the outcomes to ensure that expectations were delivered and relevant lessons were learned.

Implications for Organisation Design

13,000 annual deaths are predominantly associated with exposures to hazardous substances as were 227,000 illnesses at work. A further one million workers suffer from musculoskeletal disorders (525,000) or mental health conditions (486,000) caused or exacerbated by work.

Modern technologies and advances in science and engineering have provided opportunities for risks to be eliminated, for the use of alternative substances (substitution); or for different engineered solutions to be applied, all of which isolate employees from potential harm.

Asbestos is still present in many workplaces built before the year 2000 and lead is still used regularly today in construction and manufacturing processes. Both of these chemicals are considered highly hazardous. HR practitioners do not need to understand the specifics of these chemicals or their accompanying regulations unless they are directly involved in decision making relating to the work activity, but their knowledge of how organisational factors like fatigue and human behaviour impact work will help to reduce risks. They must also be able to challenge line managers to apply the principles of prevention to safeguard employee health and safety.

Measures introduced to control some risks can sometimes create new risks, for example processes to reduce chemical exposure may increase work at height (e.g. inspecting enclosed silos for the storage of bulk chemicals). These are sometimes referred to as the unforeseen consequences. It is therefore important to consider risk assessment as an iterative process.

Equipment selection defines the nature of the production activity, which in turn establishes level of risk, and therefore the supervision; information, instruction, training; maintenance and inspection requirements of the organisation, all of which impact employee numbers and costs.

The design stage provides the greatest opportunity to avoid risks, to combat risks at source, and to replace the dangerous with the non-dangerous and less dangerous. These are all specific duties defined in the Management of Health and Safety at Work Regulations.

Hierarchical Structures

Hierarchical structures need to reflect the requirements for leadership, management and supervision based on the risks associated with the activity and the capabilities and competence of those performing the work.

Large hierarchical structures can cause messages to get lost or watered down, and block messages from going up or down the organisation. Departmental objectives can sometimes conflict with organisational goals, and performance expectations can conflict with how the organisation expects its workers to behave. In extreme cases competing priorities can significantly increase corporate risk.

Recent events demonstrate how these risks have been realised by organisations with rogue teams or employees who believed they were working in the organisation's best interest, and who were often well rewarded and acknowledged for their achievements. The hierarchy therefore needs to optimise:

- Flow of materials and information up, down, and across the organisation;
- Balance between variety and autonomy, and direction and control;
- Use of knowledge and skills, technologies; and other resources;
- Balance of functional and geographic supervision; and
- Controls to prevent or minimise exposure to harm arising from work.

Management and Supervision

The HSE make it clear that the degree of supervision should be proportionate to the findings of a risk assessment.

In some cases an employer might simply instruct an employee how to do the work and then periodically check that all is well, for example if the work is routine, the precautions straightforward, and all the arrangements for safety can be properly controlled by the person carrying out the work.

Where an employer identifies a greater level of risk, it may be necessary to appoint a competent person to supervise the work and who, in some cases, may need to remain present while the work is being undertaken.

It will be the supervisor's role to ensure that systems and processes operate properly, the necessary safety precautions are taken, and that anyone in the vicinity is aware of the work being done.

HR practitioners can support organisational design processes through an awareness of current trends and themes in organisational flexibility, work system design and high performance working practices. These approaches should recognise the importance of strong active leadership, worker involvement, and review processes.

Organisations establishing agile, flexible and responsive structures to meet their needs are increasing the number of temporary 'vulnerable' workers in work. This has implications for recruitment, induction, information, instruction and training, and for management and control systems.

Good organisation design supports resourcing, learning and development, performance management, reward, and employee involvement processes, and improves organisational behaviour, including a positive safety culture and a mature approach to change and effective risk management.

Failings in organisation design produce unworkable arrangements, poor working environments and unacceptable employee exposures that can culminate in work which is repetitive, tiring or painful. There may be inadequate welfare facilities. Equipment may be inadequate or not subject to the required inspection and maintenance regimes. Collectively these will increase the likelihood of accidents, worker fatigue, health problems, and work pressures, which in turn can lead to stress, anxiety and depression.

Job Design

Good job design ensures safe environments for employees to work, in a manner that contributes to their sense of overall well-being, personal growth, fulfilment and self-worth. This is best achieved through a combination of security, autonomy, variety, equity, recognition and strength of working relationships. A difficult challenge is to simultaneously provide strong direction and control alongside autonomy and variety. This can be managed through flexible job descriptions that define the organisational expectations of the role, including a statement about how that role is expected to contribute to wider organisational performance.

Roles need to be clear, with defined responsibilities and accountabilities. This clarity helps organisations to define the necessary training and competence requirements. Research into 16 major incidents found that a lack of clear roles and responsibilities contributed to the tragedy in half (8) of the cases.

There are specific duties assigned from a variety of other regulations, for example the Electricity at Work Regulations require competent persons to follow electrical safety rules. Both the Control of Noise Regulations and the Control of Vibration Regulations require organisations to consider other working methods that remove the risk, or otherwise limit the duration or magnitude of exposure. Armstrong[95] suggests that jobs can be enhanced by the following four approaches:

- Job rotation,
- Job enlargement,
- Job enrichment,
- Self-managing teams (or autonomous working groups).

Job rotation, as well as increasing variety, can be used to reduce exposure to working environments that present risk, for example by splitting work involving noise or vibration exposure across a wider group of people, so minimising individual exposures.

Job enlargement and enrichment can be used to increase variety and autonomy, whilst self-managing teams can also support the equity, recognition, and strength of relationship factors that contribute to employee wellbeing.

HR practitioners can use their experience to analyse work activities and work volumes to create jobs that provide a balance between optimising the productivity and efficiency demands of the organisation on the one hand, and providing the intrinsic and extrinsic motivation requirements of the employee on the other.

Job Descriptions, Role Profiles, and Safe Systems

The Employment Rights Act 1996 provides the right for an employee to receive 'the title of the job which the employee is employed to do or a brief description of the work for which he is employed'.

The reality, however, is that there are many good reasons why a more detailed set of expectations should be provided to the employee, for example:

- Employees can more easily identify with a task and better understand its significance when it is given to them formally and as a part of a wider presentation of the structure;
- Duties to ensure that employees are treated equally often commence with an evaluation of the job;
- Training Matrices and Competence Frameworks are of more value when they show the gaps at a 'job' level;
- It is difficult to discuss performance if it is not possible to evidence that a particular activity is the duty of an individual, or if the standard or expectation is not clearly set down.

The Job Description is the most common way in which a collection of activities are presented, although the term Role Profile is sometimes used interchangeably. Role Profiles differ from the Job Description in the way that they feature a reference to the Person Specification or set down, not only what activities should be performed, but how those activities should be performed.

Terms like safe operating procedures, safe systems of work, and method statements are used by operational and safety professionals to denote the right way to perform a task or activity based on the outcome of a risk assessment which has considered the hazards to which persons might be exposed, assessed the risks, and established a set of necessary control measures.

Safe systems of work/safe operating procedures generally reflect routine operational activities performed regularly. Method statements are used for specific incidences of work and describe the activity, location, and people involved. Occasionally, method statements may be generic, in which case a further assessment needs to be undertaken to ensure that the specific hazards are properly considered.

> An example of this might be the removal of a gear box from a production line – whilst the generic method statement may set out how to remove the equipment, this particular gear box may be at height, it may be larger than usual, it may require specialist equipment, and the work may be undertaken by a different team to normal - none of these elements may be present in a generic method statement.

There are specific legal duties and responsibilities on employers to ensure that employees have received suitable and sufficient information, instruction and training relevant to their role, particularly in relation to specific hazards (which are discussed in more detail subsequently).

Furthermore, organisations assign employees with roles arising from Business, Quality, Safety and Environmental Management Systems. To ensure these are effectively incorporated into other HR management systems, these are often incorporated in Job Descriptions.

Having a clearly established set of jobs, roles, and job families helps employers to ensure that they have captured their duties in a way which satisfies their legal responsibilities.

Working Arrangements

No review of Organisation Design would be complete without a consideration of how a structure is resourced, particularly with flexible approaches to working time, an increase in employees working alone, and a resurgence in employees working at home.

Working Time

The Working Time Directive provided an option for European member states to adopt a maximum of 48 hours to be worked on average per week. The UK were unique in Europe in adopting this standard with many other countries adopting limits of between 35 and 40 hours.

Employers can agree longer reference periods for the calculation of average working time, and employees can exempt themselves from working time limits altogether. This allows employers to become more agile and respond to demands with a greater degree of flexibility. There is however a risk that typical hours of work are extended and this increases tiredness and diminishes work life balance.

The Working Time Regulations 1998[96] (as amended) established:

- Maximum weekly working time limits of 48 hours in any seven day period when averaged over a reference period (normally 17 weeks) excluding holiday, sickness, maternity or other specified leave.
- Limits on night work (hours between 22:00 and 06:00) of 8 hours in 24 hours when averaged over a reference period. Where work involves special hazards or heavy physical lifting, the limit is 8 hours in any 24 hour period.
- A right to a medical assessment prior to commencing night work, and an opportunity to undergo regular medical assessments thereafter.
- A right to be transferred off night work where possible in the event that a medical practitioner advises against an employee working such turns.
- A right for those engaged in monotonous work to adequate rest breaks.
- Daily rest periods of 11 consecutive hours, although this may be split up.
- Weekly rest periods of one 48 hour, or two 24 hour periods in 14 days.
- An uninterrupted rest break of 20 minutes away from the workstation where an adult worker's daily working time is greater than 6 hours.
- Entitlement to 20 days paid annual leave (increased to 28 days).

The regulations apply specific limits on night work that involves special hazards or heavy physical lifting, but shift patterns in any event may be flexed due to operational demands. Some consideration should be given to the nature of work and whether the hours are likely to ensure the highest levels of productivity and performance. Inherent in that should be a consideration of whether any special hazards or heavy lifting is incorporated in the role.

The investigation following the incident at Buncefield highlighted a significant difference between planned and actual work. It is important that HR departments are not blinkered to the differences once shift swaps and overtime have been taken into account.

Shift Working

The HSE published guidance on shift work[97] to help employers to:

- Consider the risks of shift work and the benefits of effective management.
- Establish systems to manage the risks of shift work.
- Assess the risks associated with shift work in your workplace.
- Take action to reduce these risks.
- Check and review your shift-work arrangements regularly.

The Risks of Working Shifts

There is evidence that working shifts outside standard daytime hours, particularly those covering the night or with early morning starts can result in…

- Disruption of the internal body clock
- Disturbed appetite and digestion
- Social and domestic problems
- Fatigue
- Sleeping difficulties
- Reliance on sedatives or stimulants

…which in turn can affect performance, increase the likelihood of errors and accidents at work and have a negative effect on health. These in turn can cause secondary effects. Sleep deprivation and fatigue can:

- Reduce performance and increase errors;
- Affect vigilance and monitoring;
- Affect decision making;
- Affect situational awareness;
- Increase reaction times;
- Undermine tracking abilities and memory.

It is perhaps unsurprising therefore, to see that the risk of errors, accidents, and incidents has been found to be higher on night shift, to rise with increasing shift length over eight hours, to increase over successive shifts (particularly night shifts), and to increase when there are not enough breaks.

Shift working has also been linked with a variety of health factors, including:

- Gastrointestinal problems such as indigestion, abdominal pain, constipation, chronic gastritis and peptic ulcers;
- Cardiovascular problems such as hypertension, coronary heart disease;
- Increased susceptibility to minor illnesses such as colds, flu and gastroenteritis;
- Reproductive problems and an appreciable but not definitive link with breast cancer[98] in female shift workers;
- The exacerbation of existing health problems such as diabetes, asthma, epilepsy and psychiatric illness.

In essence, employees who work shifts have higher levels of sickness and absenteeism, at least in part, because of the shifts themselves.

The Benefits of Effective Management of Shift-Working

Reducing the problems associated with shift work can contribute to:

- Lowering sickness and absenteeism;
- Decreasing lost-time incidents;
- Reducing the risk of fatigue-related accidents;
- Reducing the likelihood of compensation claims;
- Increasing work efficiency;
- Improving product quality;
- Reducing staff turnover.

These factors can form a business case to establish internal systems to manage the risks of shift work and gain management commitment, engagement with those responsible for managing shift working arrangements, get safety representatives buy-in and gain employee support.

Assessing the Risks of Shift Work

Engaging with those who have a vested interest in shift working will ensure greater involvement and contribute to a better understanding of the specific issues prevalent at each workplace and agree ways of making improvements.

Some typical examples follow:

- Scheduling mentally and physically demanding work to optimal times;
- Work activity variations to reduce demands and promote alertness;
- Permanent versus rotating shifts (and fast v. slow rotations);
- Shift timings, durations, variety; split-shifts; rest periods and rest days;
- Facilities, lighting and temperature;
- Supervision;
- Overtime, shift swaps and stand-by duties;
- Training, information and communication (e.g. shift hand-over);
- Occupational Health;
- Lone Working.

The HSE has published a set of good practice guidelines but these may not reflect the best practice for your site or organisation. Organisations that operate shift patterns should review their shift patterns against the good practice. Understanding where good practice can be met will help to improve performance, identifying where good practice cannot be met should lead to a review of the reasons why and the implications that might have.

The 34 good practice points follow over the next two pages. They have been reproduced under the terms of the UK Open Government licence:

Working Shifts: Good Practice Guidelines from the HSE 1

- Plan a workload that is appropriate to the length and timing of the shift.

- If reasonably practicable, schedule a variety of tasks to be completed during the shift and allow workers some choice about the order they need to be done in.

- Avoid scheduling demanding, dangerous, monotonous and/or safety-critical work during the night, early morning, towards the end of long shifts and during other periods of low alertness.

- Avoid placing workers on permanent night shifts.

- If possible, offer workers a choice between permanent and rotating shift schedules.

- Where possible, adopt a forward-rotating schedule for rotating shifts rather than a backward-rotating schedule.

- Either rotate shifts very quickly, e.g. every 2-3 days or slowly, e.g. every 3-4 weeks and avoid weekly/fortnightly rotating shift schedules.

- If not strictly necessary for business needs, try to avoid early morning starts before 7.00 am.

- Where possible, arrange shift start/end times to be convenient for public transport or consider providing transport for workers on particular shifts.

- Limit shifts to a maximum of 12 hours (including overtime) and consider the needs of vulnerable workers.

- Limit night shift or shifts where work is demanding, monotonous, dangerous and/or safety critical to 8 hours.

- Consider if shifts of a variable length or flexible start/end times could offer a suitable compromise.

- Avoid split shifts unless absolutely necessary to meet business needs.

- Encourage and promote the benefit of regular breaks away from the workstation.

- Where possible, allow workers some discretion over when they take a break, but discourage workers from saving up break time in order to leave earlier.

- In general, limit consecutive working days to a maximum of 5-7 days and make sure there is adequate rest time between successive shifts.

- Where shifts are long (> 8 hours), for night shifts and for shifts with early morning starts, it may be better to set a limit of 2-3 consecutive shifts.

Working Shifts: Good Practice Guidelines from the HSE 2

- When switching from day to night shifts or vice versa, allow workers a minimum of 2 nights' full sleep.
- Build regular free weekends into the shift schedule.
- Provide similar facilities and opportunities for shift workers as those available for your daytime workers.
- Ensure that workplace lighting is adequate and adjustable by workers.
- Ensure that the workplace temperature is adjustable and allows workers to carry out their tasks in reasonable comfort.
- Consider increasing supervision during key periods of low alertness, e.g. during the night, early morning, towards the end of long shifts and other periods of low alertness.
- Make sure supervisors and team members with responsibility for shift-working arrangements are aware of the risks associated with shift work and can recognise shift work-related problems.
- Control overtime and shift swapping by monitoring and recording hours worked and rest periods. Discourage workers from taking second jobs.
- Make provision in the work schedule to allow adequate rest for those workers carrying out standby/on-call duties or overtime.
- Provide training and information for workers, their families and management on the risks associated with shift work and on coping strategies. This may help workers to cope better with shift work.
- Make provision to release staff for foreseeable training, development and communication needs.
- Encourage interaction between workers and provide a means of communication for lone workers.
- Agree on, and ensure timing and procedures for transmitting information to the next shift team are followed at all times.
- Encourage workers to inform their doctor about their working arrangements.
- Promote healthy living strategies such as diet and exercise.
- Ensure that free health assessments are provided for night workers.

Ensure that the workplace and its surroundings are well lit, safe and secure and that workers are free from the threat of violence.

Lone Working

The HSE has published specific guidance[99] for employers with employees that work alone. The HSE describes lone workers as those 'who work by themselves without close or direct supervision' but this description covers a wide group, working across almost every sector of work.

Whilst good practice might be to try to avoid lone working altogether, sometimes this will be inevitable. Typical examples include those working in units such as small workshops, shops and petrol forecourts; some homeworkers; and those personnel who work outside normal working hours, such as cleaners, caretakers, technicians and maintenance staff.

It also includes workers on large sites who, by virtue of the size of the site or means of operation, are alone for long periods, such as workers in engineering, construction, agriculture and forestry; and mobile workers such as sales representatives, estate agents, postal staff, and medical or social workers.

The guidance identifies some activities where at least one other person should be present. These include, as examples, work in confined spaces, near exposed live electric conductors, or in health and social care dealing with unpredictable client behaviour and situations.

Where a lone working requirement is identified, it should be risk assessed (either separately or as a part of the work activity) because of the unique factors that arise due to 'lone working'.

The HSE recommend the following considerations:

- Does the workplace present a specific risk to the lone worker, for example due to temporary access equipment, such as portable ladders or trestles that one person would have difficulty handling?
- Is there a safe way in and out for one person, e.g. for a lone person working out of hours where the workplace could be locked up?
- Is there machinery involved in the work that one person cannot operate safely?
- Are chemicals or hazardous substances being used that may pose a particular risk to the lone worker?
- Does the work involve lifting objects too large for one person?
- Is there a risk of violence and/or aggression?
- Are there any reasons why the individual might be more vulnerable than others and be particularly at risk if they work alone (for example if they are young, pregnant, disabled or a trainee)?
- If the lone worker's first language is not English, are suitable arrangements in place to ensure clear communications, especially in an emergency?

The risk assessment should pay particular attention not only to the operational circumstances of the role, but to dealing with emergencies. For example, specific consideration should be given to the provision of first aid, including any requirement to self-treatment.

Person specifications, recruitment processes and pre-employment medicals (where used) should identify the lone working status as some personal factors may need to be considered. Certain disabilities may preclude an employee from some activities, which could lead to a decision that the employer needs to defend as a proportionate means of achieving a legitimate aim.

Information, instruction and training play an important role in the safety of lone workers, particularly in relation to dealing with unexpected or infrequent events. A deeper or broader level of skill or knowledge may also be necessary in relation to the tasks being undertaken and the operating environment, given the additional complexity or effort involved in gaining advice, or a second opinion.

Supervision and monitoring should reflect the circumstances of the job holder, the risks associated with the role, and the nature of the working environment. This could be in the form of regular contacts, radio or telephone communications. In the case of health and social care, home visits sometimes occur in places with limited radio signals. In these circumstances, alternative arrangements should be considered.

Working Environments

Organisations have a duty to provide workplaces that are suitable for the person and the activity. This specifically includes workers with disabilities, for whom employers have a duty to make reasonable adjustments.

In the majority of cases workplaces are governed by the Workplace (Health, Safety and Welfare) Regulations 1992 and the supporting Approved Code of Practice (ACOP) which sets out how the requirements should be achieved in the workplace[k].

Ventilation, Lighting, and Temperature

Ventilation, lighting, and temperature should be suitable for all working spaces (the entire building). It might be useful to think of environments such as the inside of lift spaces, boiler rooms, etc.

Specific considerations include:

- The sufficiency of ventilation based on the work processes, and where mechanical systems are necessary, the location of air inlets, the need for

---

[k] Note that the Workplace Health, Safety and Welfare ACOP does not apply to construction sites, home-workers, those working on a ship, or those working below ground at mines.

filtration; and regimes of inspection, testing, maintenance, and cleaning, not least because of the risk of legionella or contamination;

- The adequacy of lighting, and the provision of artificial lighting at individual work stations and at places of particular risk. Consideration should be given to selection, maintenance, cleaning, including emergency lighting.
- Working temperatures should be reasonable given the nature of the work and should not normally be below 16 degrees Celsius (13 degrees for work involving a high degree of manual effort). There is no specified maximum temperature. Thermometers should be provided to enable the temperature to be measured[1].

Specific Risk: Heat Stress

Heat stress is more likely to occur in places where work involves high temperatures, for example in thermal power plants, production sites, such as foundries or kilns, or service activities where heating is a key element e.g. laundry services. It can also occur in environments where generated heat does not quickly dissipate such as boiler rooms or mines.

People that work in these conditions often become acclimatised to the working environment, but organisations should consider the implications for employees that do not regularly experience these conditions and new employees.

The symptoms of heat stress are: an inability to concentrate, muscle cramps, heat rash, severe thirst - a late symptom of heat stress, fainting, heat exhaustion - fatigue, giddiness, nausea, headache, moist skin, and heat stroke - hot dry skin, confusion, convulsions and eventual loss of consciousness.

These are particularly significant because many people that work in hot environments also work alone and may not appreciate the effect that heat is having on them.

Work Rooms and Work Stations

Work rooms and work stations should provide enough space to allow people to work and move around with easy access to and from their workstations. Workstations should be suitable for the person and work for which they are intended, including seating and footrests where necessary; and enable the worker to leave swiftly in the event of an emergency.

---

[1] Specific guidance applies to employers whose operations include hot or cold processes, e.g. metal working or food preparation.

There is an indication of 11m^3 given as a minimum per person, although high ceilings may have an impact on whether that is reasonable, and the guidance does not apply in all circumstances[m].

Floors and Traffic Routes

Floors and traffic routes should be of sound construction with adequate strength and stability; free from holes, slopes or uneven or slippery surfaces; with adequate drainage and no steeper than necessary.

They should be kept free of obstructions, leaks and spillages should be fenced off, cleared up quickly, and covered up in the meantime. Risks from snow and ice should be minimised, particularly outside stairs, ladders and rooftop walkways.

Open sides of staircases should be securely fenced with a hand rail on at least one side; in some circumstances on both sides; and where the staircase is particularly wide, down the centre.

Windows should be constructed in such a way as to minimise risk to health or safety arising from their opening, closing, adjusting, or cleaning (taking into account the equipment).

Employers have particular duties in relation to workplaces that have translucent features (e.g. glass walls), sliding doors and gates, or escalators/moving walkways.

Traffic routes should be designed so that pedestrians and vehicles can circulate in a safe manner. So far as is reasonably practicable:

- They should be suitably indicated and suitable for the persons or vehicles using them. In practice this means sufficient in number, in suitable positions, and of sufficient size given the volume of traffic;
- There must be sufficient separation of any traffic route for vehicles from doors or gates or from traffic routes for pedestrians which lead onto it;
- Where vehicles and pedestrians use the same traffic route, there should be sufficient separation between them.

Suitable measures must be taken to ensure that pedestrians or vehicles can use traffic routes without danger to the health or safety of persons at work near it.

Facilities for Welfare

Specific duties are placed on employers to ensure provision for:

- Persons to eat meals with enough tables and seating for those likely to use them at any one time and an adequate supply of drinking water, marked by an appropriate sign.

---

[m] Specific exceptions are detailed in the Workplace (Health, Safety & Welfare) ACOP

- Suitable and sufficient sanitary conveniences at readily accessible places[n].
- Washing facilities[o] should be provided in the immediate vicinity of conveniences and changing rooms, with hot and cold running water (as far as practicable), including a means of cleaning (soap) and drying.
- The protection of non-smokers from discomfort caused by smoke;
- Suitable facilities for pregnant or nursing mothers to rest;

Suitable in this context means adequately ventilated and lit, clean and in orderly condition, and with means of separation of men from women. Sufficiency is defined in the Approved Code of Practice[p].

Equality in Working Environments

The Approved Code of Practice (ACOP) for Workplace Health, Safety and Welfare establishes a requirement that workplaces meet the health, safety and welfare needs of each member of the workforce, which may include people with disabilities. 'Suitable' means suitable for everyone, including people with disabilities. Specifically, it sets out requirements in relation to traffic routes, work stations, rest areas, and other facilities for use by disabled persons.

Maintenance and Cleaning

Equipment, devices and systems at work must be cleaned and maintained in efficient working order and good repair. Particularly in relation to equipment relating to the workplace, e.g.: ventilation and lighting systems:

- Potentially dangerous defects should be rectified immediately;
- Equipment that could fail and put workers at risk should be properly maintained and checked at regular intervals.
- Cleaning should be sufficient to prevent dirt and waste from building up.

Working at Home

In recent years there has been a retrogressive trend towards the cottage industries of the past combined with a growth of new technologies that has made new ways of working possible. There are a wide variety of activities that are now undertaken by employees working from home. These include: clothing, soft-furnishing, greetings card and electrical manufacture; domestic ironing; local authority administration, and services for utility and telecommunications companies.

---

[n] The Approved Code of Practice (ACOP) for Workplace Health, Safety and Welfare sets out actual requirements

[o] Washing facilities should include showers if required by work activity or health reasons.

[p] Legislation (legionella) requires water systems to be regularly operated and maintained.

This is not, however, without risks, for example, telecommunications workers can be exposed to abusive telephone calls and other psychosocial hazards which working from home can exacerbate, whilst those involved in manufacture may be exposed to fumes, chemicals, or other substances, for which the employer needs to provide personal protective equipment. The HSE have provided some guidance on the subject[100].

Organisations are responsible for the equipment that they supply to homeworkers and have the same duties to ensure that it is serviced, maintained and used in the correct manner, as is the case for any other workplace. Research from Health & Safety Laboratories[101] has identified good practices, such as:

- Homeworkers should have one or two contacts within the organisation for maintaining regular communications. This can be enhanced by photographs of contacts, dedicated phone lines and voicemail systems.
- Conducting risk assessments for every incidence of homeworking with the involvement of the homeworker to address each homeworker's specific needs, e.g. pets and small children.
- Regular (monthly or quarterly) inspections, or following significant changes (e.g. pregnancy or house move) supplemented by home visits.
- Special consideration needs to be given to line management, who may not be used to working in such an environment of high trust, empowerment and independence, with limited control. This should include awareness of the potential consequences of lone working such as stress or isolation.
- Encourage reporting of accidents, incidents and near misses through data collection methods that link this data to diaries or records of hours worked.
- Risk assessments should be explicit in terms of what constitutes and what does not constitute the 'workplace'.
- Upfront investment in understanding how home working might work effectively, contributes substantially to the sense of commitment and value from the employee, and may reduce lost time due to ill health or injury.

Hazardous Environments

Some workplaces present specific hazards, such as those involving construction, work at height, confined spaces, or those involving exposure to noise, vibration, or pressure systems. Employers requiring employees to operate in these environments are subject to more rigorous legislation.

Construction

In 2014/15, there were 35 employee deaths in Construction (approximately a quarter of all employee deaths) despite the sector employing a little over 6% of the working population.

In November 2014, the HSE published the results of a campaign[102] over 1,748 repair and refurbishment sites. During their visits they found unacceptable conditions and dangerous practices at 40% of sites visited, and one in five received Notices or Prosecutions as a result. Work at height was highlighted as particularly poor during the campaign and 42% of all notices related to work at height and falls. 200 sites were ordered to stop work immediately.

These figures become all the more significant when the nature of the campaign becomes apparent. The HSE were focussing on health, rather than safety risks, and 35% of the notices served related to asbestos, exposure to harmful dusts, noise and vibration, manual handling and insufficient welfare.

Research into construction work has been particularly critical of factors such as poorly defined work schedules, the long-hours culture, worker fatigue, and the impact they have on decision making, productivity and safety.

A report by Loughborough University and UMIST[103] identified causal factors in Construction Accidents. These included:

- Insufficient consideration of health and safety by clients and designers;
- A focus on price in contract negotiations rewarding organisations that adopt short cuts on safety;
- A focus on health and safety documentation from a 'compliance' perspective producing documents that do not contribute to safe working;
- Long sub-contractor chains hampering effective control, communication and co-ordination and providing little assurance of competence;
- Poorly designed work schedules resulting in frequent change and increased pressure;
- A long hours culture resulting in fatigue, compromised decision making, reduced productivity and reduced safety;
- Bonus payments and other reward mechanisms compromising safety;
- Skills shortages culminating in a reliance on inexperienced and unskilled workers, coupled with problems in demonstrating competence;
- Problems with personal protective equipment availability, performance, and comfort; and
- Training which is seen as a solution to all problems, but often with only superficial content.

To juxtapose the typical problems with construction, the following good practices were identified during the Construction of the London Olympic Park in 2012[104]:

- The client had a significant impact on project health and safety;
- Early and ongoing planning, coordination and contractor involvement were crucial;
- Principal Contractors shared ideas and lessons learned;
- There was a culture of challenge to all significant decisions;
- Worker engagement helped to motivate the workforce and get key messages across;
- Behavioural health and safety initiatives changed culture for the better;
- Clients took a leadership role;
- Allowing and encouraging workers to report 'unsafe' activities;
- Integrating teams of designers and contractors early and often;
- A Focus on getting the right competences in individuals and organisations; and
- Forums for sharing knowledge between organisations and sharing office facilities.

The Construction (Design and Management) Regulations 2015

The Construction (Design and Management) Regulations 2015 (CDM) applies to all construction[q] work and the definition of construction work is very wide. CDM is increasingly being recognised as a requirement for maintenance works, particularly in engineering construction sites where invasive activities result in, for example, the removal or replacement of pipework.

This is a relatively new piece of legislation. There is currently no ACOP for construction activity, although the HSE are keeping this position under review. New guidance[105] has been published.

CDM sets out specific roles for the Client, the Designers (and Principal Designer) and the Contractors (and Principal Contractor). In some cases, the Client could fulfil all these roles.

---

q 'Construction' includes… construction, alteration, conversion, fitting out, commissioning, renovation, repair, upkeep, redecoration or other maintenance, de-commissioning, demolition or dismantling of a structure… preparation for an intended structure, including site clearance… preparation of the site or structure for use or occupation at its conclusion… assembly [or disassembly] on site of prefabricated elements… removal of a structure, or of any product or waste resulting from demolition or dismantling of a structure… and installation, commissioning, maintenance, repair or removal of mechanical, electrical, gas, compressed air, hydraulic, telecommunications, computer or similar services which are normally fixed within or to a structure.

Duties of All Persons under CDM

All persons with duties or roles under CDM must co-operate with others working on or in relation to the project on the site, or at an adjoining site, to the extent necessary to enable others to fulfil their duties.

Managers and Contractors required to give information or instructions to others must ensure that the information and instructions are comprehensible and provided as soon as practicable.

Client Duties

The client has a duty to make suitable arrangements for managing a project; to allocate sufficient time and resources, and ensure those arrangements are maintained and reviewed throughout the project. The client must:

- Provide Pre-Construction Information as soon as is practicable to every designer or contractor appointed or being considered for appointment.
- Ensure that a Construction Phase Plan is drawn up before construction begins. The Construction Phase Plan is more than a Project Plan and sets out the health and safety arrangements and site rules, taking into account specific activities and controls.
- Ensure that the Principal Designer prepares a Health and Safety File that is reviewed, updated and revised from time to time.
- Take reasonable steps to ensure that Principal Designers and Principal Contractors are complying with their duties.

Client organisations with responsibility for the appointment of Designers and Contractors must take reasonable steps to ensure that they have the skills, knowledge and experience, and (if they are an organisation) the organisational capability necessary to fulfil the role.

Duties of Principal Designers and Principal Contractors

Principal Designers must plan, manage and monitor the pre-construction phase. Principal Contractors must plan, manage and monitor the construction phase, particularly when design, technical and organisational aspects of simultaneous or successive works are being planned, with a view to estimating the period of time required to complete the work.

Principal Contractors must:

- Organise co-operation between contractors,
- Co-ordinate implementation by contractors of legal requirements,
- Ensure employers and self-employed persons apply the principles of prevention consistently and follow the Construction Phase Plan,

- Ensure that a suitable site induction is provided to those, take reasonable steps to prevent access by unauthorised persons, and ensure that reasonable facilities are provided for the use of those working on the site.

Duties of Designers

Designers have a duty to take into account the Principles of Prevention to eliminate, so far as reasonably practicable, foreseeable risks to persons:

- Carrying out or liable to be affected by construction work;
- Maintaining or cleaning the structure; or
- Using a structure designed as a workplace.

Where the risks cannot be eliminated, they should be reduced or controlled and information should be provided to the Principal Designer and included in the Health and Safety File.

Duties of Contractors

Contractors must plan, manage and monitor construction work by contractors under their control in accordance with the instructions of the Principal Designer and Principal Contractor and in accordance with the Construction Phase Plan.

A contractor must not employ or appoint a person to work on a construction site unless that person has, or is in the process of obtaining, the necessary skills, knowledge, training and experience to carry out the tasks allocated to that person in a manner that secures the health and safety of any person working on the construction site.

Work at Height

Work at Height presents particular risks. HSE published data for 2014/5 shows there were 7,571 major incidents or reported lost time injuries arising from moving, flying, or falling objects, and 6,067 reported incidents of falls from height, both were amongst the top four causes of reported injuries in the workplace.

An analysis by Bomel (2005)[106] identified that whilst fatalities are most likely to occur in the agricultural and construction sectors, the largest number of major injuries occurred in the service industries, followed by manufacturing and construction.

The Work at Height Regulations

Work at height is subject to the Work at Height Regulations 2005. The legislation places absolute duties on employers to protect both employees and other persons under their control.

Under the Work at Height Regulations, employers also have a duty to prevent injury to any person, take suitable and sufficient steps to prevent, so far as is reasonably practicable, the fall of any material or object.

Employers have a duty to ensure that all work at height is:

- Properly planned, supervised and carried out in a manner which is, so far as reasonably practicable, safe. Planning in this context includes provisions for emergencies and rescue and includes consideration of the effect of weather conditions.
- Undertaken by a competent person (including organisation, planning, and supervision), or if he is being trained, under the supervision of a competent person.
- Properly risk assessed, so that work at height will be avoided, or if it cannot be, that suitable and sufficient measures will be put in place to prevent a fall. Where the risk of a fall cannot be eliminated, work equipment will be provided to minimise the distance and consequences of the fall.
- Undertaken by personnel that have received such additional training and instruction and/or take other additional suitable and sufficient measures to prevent, so far as is reasonably practicable, any person falling a distance liable to cause personal injury.
- Assisted by work equipment[r] that takes account of working conditions, distances, consequences of fall, the duration and frequency of use, the need for easy and timely evacuation in the event of an emergency, any additional risks posed by the equipment itself, and any other relevant provisions.
- Carefully managed where there is a risk of fragile surfaces such that suitable support or protection is provided, and where a risk of fall still remains, suitable and sufficient measures are taken to limit the distance and consequences of a fall.

When the risk of fall cannot be eliminated, employers have a duty to take suitable and sufficient steps to prevent any person from being struck by falling objects. This includes a duty to ensure that no material shall be thrown or tipped from height where it could cause injury and a duty to prevent employees from entering a 'danger area' where they could be struck by a falling object. This area should be protected, so far as is reasonably practicable, by devices preventing access to the area. These areas should be clearly indicated.[s]

---

[r] There are detailed requirements for the selection and inspection of work equipment including guard rails, toe rails, working platforms, nets, personal fall protection, and ladders.

[s] Specific rules relating to the wearing of turbans is described in the 'resourcing' section of this book.

Confined Spaces

The HSE define a confined space as a place which is substantially enclosed (though not always entirely) and where serious injury can occur from hazardous substances or conditions within the space or nearby.

The Confined Spaces Regulations

The Confined Spaces Regulations 1997 identify clear duties for employers including the design and construction of confined space, the need to risk assess confined space activities, the minimisation of access, safe working, emergency procedures, the use of plant and equipment, and training for those involved in planning, undertaking work, or undertaking emergency activities arising from works. The regulations are supplemented by an ACOP[107] which describes methods that can be used to achieve compliance with the Regulations.

The regulations describe a confined space as any place which as a consequence of its 'enclosed nature there arises a reasonably foreseeable specified risk'.

The specified risks are:

- Serious injury to any person at work arising from a fire or explosion;
- Loss of consciousness of any person at work arising from an increase in body temperature or asphyxiation arising from gas, fume, vapour or lack of oxygen;
- Drowning of any person at work arising from an increase in the level of liquid or the asphyxiation arising from, or the inability to reach a respirable environment due to entrapment by a free flowing solid (e.g. powder).

As well as a risk of increase in body temperature, there is a similar risk of a decrease in body temperature that could lead to hypothermia in some restricted spaces (although hypothermia is not a specified risk in the Confined Spaces Regulations).

Confined spaces do not have to be closed on all sides, they do not have to be small, they do not have to be hard to enter or exit, and they do not need to be unusual working locations.

In order for a space to be classified as a confined space, these risks do not need to be present, they need to be foreseeable. If, for example, the work area contains, or may contain a flammable substance, and work is being undertaken in the space that could introduce an ignition source, then there is a serious foreseeable risk from a fire or explosion and the space should be regarded as a confined space under the regulations.

There is a simple process to determine whether a location is a confined space under the Regulations:

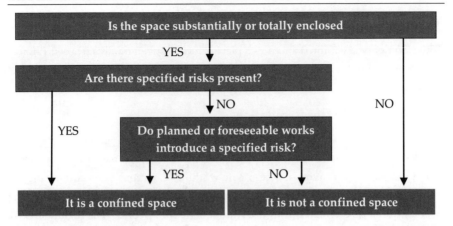

For example, open topped vats, ships' holds[t], and spray painting booths may all be confined spaces under the Regulations.

Employers must ensure compliance with the regulations for their own activities, and so far as reasonably practicable for the activities of others where the provisions relate to matters under the employers control. This requires liaison and coordination with contractors working on site.

It also means that employers engaging others to work in confined spaces must take all reasonably practicable measures to ensure that contractors are competent to undertake the work they are required to perform.

The ACOP establishes a requirement on the duty-holder to consider what measures can be taken to enable the work to be carried out properly without the need to enter the confined space. The measures might involve modifying the confined space to avoid the need for entry, or to enable the work to be undertaken from outside the space. In many cases it will involve modifying working practices.

Specific rules relate to the design of confined spaces, but the key points are that the structure should be sturdy, and enable ease of access and egress (especially in an emergency), the suitability of access and working platforms, and the design of space to reduce the need for entry.

The Regulations are clear: '*No person at work shall enter a confined space to carry out work for any purpose unless it is not reasonably practicable to achieve that purpose without such entry.*' There may be a need to limit the time period that individuals are allowed to work in a confined space, e.g. where RPE is used, or under extreme conditions of temperature and humidity, or if the confined space is so small that movement is severely restricted.

---

[t] Whilst ships undertaking normal activities are not covered, ships in port are covered by the regulations.

Noise

Noise comes from a variety of sources and causes damage that cannot be cured. Whilst many people with significant hearing loss will not consider themselves disabled, deafness can be a disability under the Equality Act.

Age is the biggest single cause of hearing loss[108]. Most people begin to lose a small amount of their hearing from around 40 years of age. This hearing loss increases as you get older. By the age of 80, most people have significant hearing problems. In some cases, people can suffer hearing loss as a result of a genetic condition, through viral infections such as mumps, measles or rubella.

Head injury (trauma), certain cancers, strokes, and other illnesses can also cause temporary or permanent hearing loss. Some treatments and medicines, such as radiotherapy for nasal and sinus cancer, certain chemotherapy medicines and certain antibiotics can also damage the cochlea and the auditory nerve, causing sensorineural hearing loss. People with diabetes, chronic kidney disease and cardiovascular disease are also at increased risk of hearing loss. Sensorineural hearing loss is permanent and hearing aids are often required to improve hearing in these cases.

Although hearing can be lost as a consequence of a sudden, extremely loud noise (acoustic trauma), it is normally prolonged exposure to noise that causes hearing loss. Research estimates that two million people are exposed to noise levels at work which are harmful, and this is reflected in civil claims for loss of hearing.

Workers are more likely to suffer noise induced hearing loss if they work with noisy machinery or equipment or work close to other loud sounds e.g. at night clubs or music events. In many cases, hearing loss can be prevented by the actions of employers and workers such as the selection of quieter equipment, the introduction of acoustic enclosures and the provision of personal protective equipment.

The Control of Noise at Work Regulations

Noise Regulations and the supporting guidance were updated in 2005[109] to reduce pre-existing exposure limits and introduce new limits for certain circumstances. The Regulations place requirements on employers to assess the noise risks by identifying the hazards, estimating exposures, and identifying necessary measures to control them.

It is the duty of the employer to ensure that his employees are not exposed to noise above the daily or weekly personal noise exposure limit values[u] (with hearing

---

[u] The daily or weekly personal noise exposure limit values are 87 dB; and/or a peak sound of 140 dB

protection). If the exposure limit value is exceeded, the employer must immediately reduce exposure to noise to below the exposure limit value; identify the reason for that exposure limit value being exceeded; and modify the organisational and technical measures taken to prevent it being exceeded again.

Where workers are exposed to the upper exposure action values[v], employers are required to provide hearing protectors and ensure they are used.

The employer shall also establish and implement a programme of organisational and technical measures which are appropriate to the activity to reduce exposure to as low a level as is reasonably practicable.

Employees are legally required to wear hearing protection in these areas.

Every employee shall make full and proper use of personal hearing protectors, and any other control measures provided. If he discovers any defect in any personal hearing protectors or other control measures, he must report it to his employer as soon as is practicable.

The employer shall ensure so far as is practicable that anything provided by him is fully and properly used and is maintained in *'an efficient state, in efficient working order and in good repair'*.

It is not good practice for employees to wear hearing protection for the duration of their shifts so any opportunity to increase job rotation or variety to reduce exposure throughout the shift is good practice.

Supervision should ensure equipment is used correctly. Regular checks and defect reporting systems should be established to ensure that faults are quickly identified and corrected. Checks should include inspection of equipment, noise sampling, health surveillance and the reporting of results.

Employees do not always like wearing hearing protection so the HSE encourage the following steps:

- There should be a clear commitment to using personal protection in the organisation's safety policy and signs and warning notices should indicate where and when hearing protection should be worn;
- Employees should receive information, instruction and training on the risks to which they may be exposed and the actions they should take;
- Clear responsibilities should be assigned to the person responsible for the hearing protection programme and the distribution of hearing protection, which should include the recording of hearing protection issue, arrangements for ensuring that people know where and how to use them,

---

[v] The daily or weekly upper exposure action values are 85 dB; and/or a peak sound of 137 dB or more

the recording of any problems encountered through their use; and a programme of regular spot checks.

If an employer carries out work which is likely to expose employees to noise at or beyond the lower exposure action values[w], he must arrange for a suitable and sufficient risk assessment to be carried out by a competent person. This should include an observation of the work activity, reference to information about probable noise levels, and if necessary, noise measurement.

The employer shall ensure that risk from the exposure of his employees to noise is either eliminated at source or, where this is not reasonably practicable, reduced to as low a level as is reasonably practicable. At this level, hearing protection has to be provided for those that ask for it but the law does not make it compulsory.

Where the exposure of an employee to noise varies markedly from day to day, an employer may use weekly personal noise exposure in place of daily personal noise exposure for the purpose of compliance with these Regulations.

Once the lower exposure action limit has been met or exceeded, the employer must provide personal hearing protection to any employee that is exposed, the area should be designated as a hearing protection zone, and should be demarcated and identified by means of the correct signage[x].

Access to the hearing protection zone should be restricted to those who necessarily need to visit to perform their work. Hearing protection should be put on prior to entry and should be worn all the time the person is in the protection zone. This may have an impact on walkways and traffic routes which should then be re-considered.

Vibration

According to the European Agency for Safety and Health at Work[110], exposed workers are overwhelmingly male and typically either drivers of mobile machines, operators of hand-tools, or people working in the vicinity of stationary machines.

Approximately 25% of European workers are exposed to vibration for a quarter of their working time or more[111].

The HSE provides a wider and more sector based description of exposed workers in the construction, engineering, motor vehicle repair, quarries, and agriculture as having a higher likelihood of employee exposure to hand-arm vibration.

---

[w] The daily or weekly lower exposure action values are 80 dB; and/or a peak sound of 135 dB or more

[x] Safety signs are defined in the Health and Safety (Safety Signs and Signals) Regulations 1996. There is a separate BS EN ISO 7010 British standard for safety signage although, whilst this is best practice, it is not a legal requirement.

Construction, quarries and agriculture are also likely to have employees with the greatest exposure to whole body vibration.

The Control of Vibration at Work Regulations

Exposure to vibration is regulated by the Control of Vibration at Work Regulations 2005. Under this legislation, employers have a duty to take into account the latest technical advances and organisational measures to reduce the exposure of workers, contractors and visitors. Parts of the legislation were only implemented in July 2014.

The legislation establishes exposure limits for both hand-arm vibration[y] and whole-body vibration[z]. Employees should not be exposed to vibration in excess of the daily exposure limit value, unless all of the following conditions are met:

- The average exposure over one week is less that the exposure limit value,
- The risk from the pattern of exposure is less than the risk from constant exposure below the limit,
- The risk level is reduced to the lowest reasonably practicable level, and
- The worker is subject to increased health surveillance.

Employers are required to undertake risk assessments of any activities that are likely to expose workers to vibration. The risk assessment will include an assessment of work activities to establish the probable and/or actual level of exposure to which workers are subjected. The risk assessment should also consider the potential impact of vibration on work equipment, the stability of structures and the security of joints.

The risk assessment should consider information supplied from equipment manufacturers, the availability of replacement or vibration reducing additions to the equipment being used and a wider consideration of vibration exposure during work breaks or the consequences of other factors such as temperature and weather.

As with noise, the duty on employers is not just to achieve exposure levels below the occupational action levels, but to eliminate the vibration at source or to reduce it to as low a level as is reasonably practicable.

The Regulation sets out the following principles of prevention where the vibration cannot be removed at source:

- Other working methods which eliminate or reduce exposure to vibration;
- Choice of work equipment of appropriate ergonomic design which, taking account of the work to be done, produces the least possible vibration;

---

[y] For hand-arm vibration— (a) the daily exposure limit value is 5 m/s2 A(8); (b) the daily exposure action value is 2.5 m/s2 A(8)

[z] For whole body vibration— (a) the daily exposure limit value is 1.15 m/s2 A(8); (b) the daily exposure action value is 0.5 m/s2 A(8)

- The provision of auxiliary equipment which reduces the risk of injuries caused by vibration;
- Appropriate maintenance programmes for work equipment, the workplace and workplace systems;
- The design and layout of workplaces, work stations and rest facilities;
- Suitable and sufficient information and training for employees;
- May be used correctly and safely, in order to minimise their exposure to vibration;
- Limitation of the duration and magnitude of exposure to vibration;
- Appropriate work schedules with adequate rest periods;
- The provision of clothing to protect employees from cold and damp.

The HSE have developed free to use calculators for the purpose of determining whole body vibration exposure[112] and hand-arm vibration exposure[113]. Employees identified in health surveillance as suffering conditions associated with vibration should receive the same treatment as those identified as suffering the effects of noise.

Pressure Systems

In 2012/13, there were 93 reports of dangerous occurrences of a failure of any closed vessel including boiler or of any associated pipework, in which the internal pressure was above or below atmospheric pressure. There were 55 reports in the first half of 2013/14.

On 1 October 2013, the classification changed to "The failure of any closed vessel or of any associated pipework (other than a pipeline) forming part of a pressure system." There were 40 reports under the new criteria in the second half of 2013/14.

Pressure systems cover a wide variety of pressure vessels, piping, safety and pressure accessories. The list includes:

- Pressurised process plant including steam heating and boiler systems;
- Compressed air systems (fixed and portable);
- Pressure cookers;
- Heat exchangers and refrigeration plant, including heat exchangers consisting of pipes for the purpose of cooling or heating air;
- Pipes, tubing, fittings, expansion joints, hoses, or other pressure-bearing components as appropriate including pressure gauges, level indicators, valves, steam traps and filters;
- Components attached to pressurised parts such as flanges, nozzles, couplings, supports, and lifting lugs;
- Safety accessories and devices designed to protect pressure equipment against the breaches to allowable limit, these include safety valves, bursting discs etc., as well as limiting devices which either activate the means for

correction or provide for shutdown or shutdown and lock out, such as pressure switches or temperature switches etc.

The main hazards from pressure are likely to be impact incidents arising from either the equipment itself or the release, or burns caused by contact with the liquid or gas stored under pressure. Incidents involving pressure systems are most likely to be caused by poor design, poor equipment selection, manufacture, installation, maintenance, repairs or modifications; by poor inadequate systems of work, or operator error.

Because of the significant risks associated with pressure systems, their use is governed by several Regulations and an Approved Code of Practice[114] which applies to designers, manufacturers, and employers (duty-holders) that own a mobile system, i.e. one that can be easily moved, such as an air compressor taken from site to site, or use an installed system, i.e. one that is not a mobile system, such as a steam boiler.

The main regulations covering pressure equipment and pressure systems are the Pressure Equipment Regulations 1999[115] (PER99) (as amended by the Pressure Equipment (Amendment) Regulations 2002) and the Pressure Systems Safety Regulations 2000[116] (PSSR00).

Pressure Equipment Regulations 1999 Amended 2002

PER99 implemented the European Pressure Equipment Directive which established requirements for design, manufacture and conformity assessment of pressure equipment and assemblies with a maximum allowable pressure greater than 0.5 bar to meet specified standards. The regulations define the different tests applicable based upon the nature of the equipment and circumstances of use.

A competent person can advise on the specific requirements in relation to any plant or equipment on site. A failure to ensure that equipment conforms to the European standard is an offence although due diligence may be a defence.

Pressure Systems Safety Regulations 2000

PSSR00 imposes duties on owners and users of pressure systems in relation to their use at work and the risks to the health and safety of those that may be exposed to them. The aim of these Regulations is to prevent serious injury from the hazard of stored energy as a result of the failure of a pressure system or one of its component parts.

The Pressure Systems Safety Regulations apply if the vessels or pipework containing steam at any pressure, a fluid or mixture of fluids which is at a pressure >0.5 bar above atmospheric, or a gas dissolved under pressure in a solvent (acetylene).

Relevant fluids do not include hydraulic oils. Hydraulic systems, whilst using high pressures, do not store energy in the system and so are not covered by this legislation.

Large pressure vessels are subject to additional controls including regular examination in accordance with a written scheme, the maintenance of particular records and the requirement to define action in case of imminent danger. Before using any qualifying pressure equipment (new or otherwise), a written scheme of examination must be in place, and an examination undertaken.

Workplace Equipment

Regulations on construction sites, work at height, confined spaces, noise, vibration and pressure systems focus on working environments. The next consideration relates to the hazards associated with workplace equipment.

There is a variety of equipment used at work, starting with the common place display screen equipment you may use on your desk, to more complex equipment used for lifting and transport around the site. All equipment is subject to the Provision and Use of Work Equipment Regulations, but certain equipment requires additional and specific activities to be performed to ensure workers do not come to harm.

The Provision and Use of Work Equipment

The Provision and Use of Work Equipment Regulations 1998 (often referred to as PUWER) and its associated ACOP[117] define work equipment as *'any machinery, appliance, apparatus, tool or installation for use at work'*. As such it covers all equipment from hammers to large scale production lines and everything in between. It does not matter whether the equipment is used exclusively at work, or whether the equipment is supplied by an employee.

The regulations establish particular responsibilities in relation to equipment selection and use. Employers must select equipment which is suitable for the use for which it is intended, and must also ensure that it is used in accordance with manufacturer's instructions. In this regard, particular consideration should be given to the environment in which the equipment will be used.

Equipment design can increase safety and simultaneously improve operational performance, e.g. by positioning lubrication points and inspection screens in easily accessible places and using technologies that are likely to reduce blockages or reduce the need for human intervention.

The ACOP requires employers to consider the ergonomic risks inherent in equipment design. This extends beyond the requirements of the operator, for whom operating positions, height and reach distances should be considered, to include freedom of movement between equipment installations.

The ACOP also requires equipment to be designed and constructed in such a way as to ensure safety in the form of energy and substances used or produced, e.g. the ventilation of exhaust gasses.

All work equipment should be subject to a suitable and sufficient risk assessment. The risk assessment should take full account of any manufacturer's recommendations, the advice of others, such as trade associations and consultants, as well as other sources, such as published advice on health and safety.

The Regulations identify specified hazards – articles or substances falling from or being ejected by the equipment; the rupture or disintegration of parts; work equipment catching fire or overheating; or the unintended or premature discharges or explosions – there is an absolute duty on employers to control these risks.

Where risks are identified, they should be eliminated, or if that is not possible, employers should:

- Take engineering (physical) measures to control the risks such as the provision of guards; but if the risks still cannot be adequately controlled;
- Take appropriate management measures to deal with the remaining risk such as following safe systems of work, and the provision of information, instruction and training.

Where a risk assessment identifies a significant risk to the operator, or other employees from the installation and use of equipment, inspection should be undertaken at the following intervals:

- Where the safety of work equipment depends on the installation conditions, it should be inspected after installation and before first use, and after re-assembly at any new site / location;
- At suitable intervals, where work equipment is exposed to conditions causing deterioration liable to result in dangerous situations;
- Each time exceptional circumstances (e.g. major modifications, known or suspected serious damage, substantial change in the nature of use) are liable to have jeopardised the safety of the work equipment.

Inspection

Inspection processes, and the appropriate organisational structures to undertake and oversee it, should be in place to ensure the effective operation of safety-related parts which are necessary for the safe operation of work equipment and, in some cases, this may require testing or dismantling. However, not all safety-critical features on a particular item of work equipment may require inspection at the same intervals.

An inspection can vary in its extent, and is likely to comprise a combination of:

- Quick checks before use (e.g. electric cable condition on hand-held power tools, functional testing of brakes, lights on mobile machinery, etc.)
- Weekly checks (e.g. presence of guarding, function of safety devices, tyre pressures, and the condition of windows, mirrors and CCTV on mobile plant)
- More extensive examinations, undertaken every few months or longer (e.g. general condition of a ladder, close examination of a safety harness, portable appliance testing, etc.).

Records of inspections should be retained and made available to an HSE Inspector on request. Records are not normally required to be made for the simplest pre-use checks.

The use of checklists can assist but these, and the records made, should be tailored to the particular type of work equipment. Requiring too much detail can lead to a superficial 'tick box' approach or even, in some cases, the inspection activity ceasing altogether.

Organisations should ensure that people who determine the nature of the inspections required and who carry out inspections are competent to do so. The necessary level of competence will vary for inspections, according to the type of equipment and how / where it is used.

The nature of these inspections does not have to be determined by the same person who undertakes them, provided the person determining them is competent. This can often be done in-house by experienced staff, taking account of:

- the manufacturer's recommendations
- industry advice
- their own experience of the equipment, its use, the particular factors of the workplace and the people using the work equipment

Maintenance

Once selected and installed, the employer must ensure that equipment is maintained in an efficient state, in efficient working order and in good repair. Regular maintenance also contributes to improved efficiency (cost to operate), productivity (output rates), and asset life (reducing capital investment)[118].

Maintenance schedules should highlight the safety critical components, devices or parts which may need a higher and more frequent intervention. Manufacturer's instructions provide a useful guide to the use and maintenance of equipment, but this should not be considered in isolation. It is unlikely that a risk assessment will be suitable and sufficient if it does not take into account:

- The intensity of use,
- The operating environment,
- The variety of operations,
- Knowledge and experience from the organisation or industry body, and
- The severity of risk from malfunction or failure.

Where there is a significant risk of harm arising from failure of equipment, it is unlikely that a policy of reactive maintenance (founded primarily on breakdown repair) will be reasonably practicable. In these cases, planned preventative maintenance, condition monitoring and other maintenance techniques may be more appropriate. These require regular maintenance inspections which need to be factored into the activities of the organisation.

There is no specific requirement within PUWER for a log to be kept, but they are increasingly used by organisations to support maintenance planning activities and can contribute to planned and preventative maintenance strategies. Where an equipment log is kept, it is a legal requirement that this is kept up to date.

The employer must also ensure that maintenance operations on work equipment can be undertaken safely. Manufacturer's instructions should make recommendations on how to safely undertake maintenance of their work equipment and, unless there are good reasons otherwise, these should be followed.

Equipment must be capable of being made safe to enable interventions such as repair, maintenance, clearing blockages, performing checks, or replacing consumable parts. The safest way to ensure these interventions is through isolation[119].

Where possible, equipment should be shut down and isolated (with residual / stored energy through the safely release of pneumatic pressure or gravitational / rotational energy, the disconnecting of the equipment from the energy source, along with means to prevent inadvertent reconnection (e.g. by locking off). Formal systems of work, such as a permit to work, are required in some cases to safely manage high-risk maintenance operations.

In some cases, it may be possible to avoid particular significant hazards during maintenance by adopting particular control measures. These may include:

- Physical measures, e.g. providing temporary guarding, slow speed hold-to-run control devices, safe means of access, personal protective equipment, etc.
- Management measures, e.g. safe systems of work, supervision, monitoring
- Personnel competence (training, skill, awareness and knowledge of risk).

Authorisation

Where work equipment involves particular risks to those using, repairing, modifying, maintenance or inspection, that work should be restricted only to those authorised to do so once they have received suitable and sufficient information, instruction and training.

The advent of technology has helped employers to reduce risks to employees through, for example, the remote diagnosis of manufacturing plant and equipment[120], whilst light curtains and light beams have increased safety for operators[121]. Both of these technologies present risks as well as benefits and care should be taken in relation to the design, installation and reliance by Operators. Furthermore, some equipment is subject to specific additional regulation, for example power presses or chain saws.

Lifting Operations and Lifting Equipment

Lifting at work is governed by the Lifting Operations and Lifting Equipment Regulations 1998 (often abbreviated to LOLER). The Regulations have an Approved Code of Practice (ACOP)[122] that clearly sets out the duties of employers and workers who own, operate or have control over lifting equipment.

This applies to all businesses and organisations whose employees use lifting equipment, irrespective of whether they own the equipment. LOLER applies to all lifting equipment used for work purposes. This includes:

- Cranes;
- Lift trucks and telescopic handlers;
- Hand pallet trucks;
- Passenger and goods lifts;
- Rope and pulley systems, including climbing ropes;
- Person lifts and hoists, such as those used in hospitals and care homes;
- Pull-lifts;
- Vacuum and other suction based lifting equipment;
- Vehicle inspection hoists;
- Scissor lifts and mobile lifting platforms;
- Automated systems for lifting raw materials or finished goods;
- Tractor and excavator attachments used for lifting purposes;
- Loader cranes and tail lifts attached to road vehicles;
- Loading arms for refuse collection, including skips;
- Vehicle transporters including tilt and slide recovery trucks; and
- Air cargo transfer vehicles.

LOLER also applies to the accessories used as a part of a lifting operation, for example the slings, eyebolts, chains, ropes, shackles, grabs, magnets, and vacuum lifters. It does not apply to escalators, conveyor belts, roller shutter doors, or fall arrest equipment (although these are likely to be subject to PUWER).

The ACOP provides guidance on the importance of ergonomic design. This includes operating positions, operating environments, handling weights, heights, reach distances, etc. that are compatible with human dimensions. Poor design in this regard will contribute to injury and illnesses such as work related upper limb disorders.

All equipment used for lifting must be fit for purpose, appropriate for the task, suitably marked (to show safe working loads or number of people) and, in many cases, subject to statutory periodic thorough examinations. Records must be kept of all thorough examinations and any defects found must be reported to both the person responsible for the equipment and the relevant enforcing authority.

Planning, Supervision and Execution

Employers undertaking lifting operations or providing lifting equipment for others to use must manage and control the risks to avoid any injury or damage[123]. Work must be planned properly; supervised appropriately and carried out in a safe manner.

The degree of planning will vary considerably, depending on the lifting equipment and the complexity of the lift. The plan should include the determination of equipment, means of access and egress, proximity hazards (e.g. vehicles, overhead power lines, etc.), protection from slips, trips and falls, operator protection, visibility, the effects of the weather (wind, visibility, lightning, ground conditions, etc.), the strength and stability of lifting equipment (particularly in relation to mobile plant and site assembled equipment), the risk of overturning, overloading, and the risk of a fall of material from height.

There are published Standards for specific lifting operations, for example BS 7121: Safe use of cranes, or BS EN 14439: Safety requirements for tower cranes. British Standards use the term 'appointed person' to define a competent person who undertakes planning of lifting operations.

Where the equipment is used to move persons, specific consideration should be given to the risks of crushing, trapping, falling or persons being struck by the equipment, in both normal operations and malfunction. This is particularly significant where the lifting equipment is being used to move vulnerable persons for example in care homes or hospitals.

Safe and successful lifting operations depend, in large part, on the continued safety of the lifting equipment and accessories that are used. Failures in this kind of equipment can result in significant or fatal injuries.

In addition to the requirements for safe design and construction, all lifting equipment should also be checked and maintained as necessary to keep it safe for use, so:

- Users may need to undertake simple pre-use checks (e.g. on lifting chains and slings), or make checks on a daily basis;
- In some cases, inspections and checks should be made on a regular basis, often weekly, but this may be on a monthly or quarterly basis;
- Employers should ensure that lifting equipment is subject to statutory thorough examinations.

Thorough Examinations

Thorough examinations are required throughout the lifetime of the equipment and accessories to ensure that they remain safe for use, and to detect and remedy any deterioration in good time.

These should take place:

- Before first use (unless the equipment has an EC Declaration of Conformity less than one year old and the equipment was not assembled on site), or after assembly and before use at each location (e.g. tower cranes)
- Following exceptional circumstances - liable to jeopardise the safety of lifting equipment, which may include: damage or failure, being out of use for long periods, or following major changes, which are likely to affect the equipment's integrity (e.g. modifications, or replacement/repair of critical parts)
- At intervals specified by LOLER or in accordance with an examination scheme, drawn up by a competent person to ensure that normal wear and tear has not caused deterioration likely to result in dangerous situations.

These checks are necessary to verify that the lifting equipment can continue to be safely used.

Display Screen Equipment

It is easy to neglect office and control room personnel because of the perception that they are not exposed to risk. In many cases there will be fewer risks of injury associated with office work than for example, production operations or maintenance, however illnesses associated with fatigue, eye strain, upper limb disorders, and backache can and do cause extended periods of absence.

The DSE Regulations came into force on the 1st January 1993. The definition of a display screen is wide and encompasses any alphanumeric or graphic display screen, regardless of the display process involved, provided it is used for, or in connection with work (regardless of who provided it). It does not include small display screens, for example on cash registers, but it does include laptops.

The HSE guidance provides useful information to help employers to understand and implement the regulations[124]. The regulations apply to employers whose workers regularly use DSE as a significant part of their work, i.e. for continuous periods of an hour or more (and as a consequence could extend in some cases to the use of 'tablets' at work).

Employers must carry out a suitable and sufficient risk assessment of the workstations for the purpose of assessing health and safety risks to which employees and operators are exposed. Once completed, they should review and update the risk assessment from time to time.

The HSE have provided a helpful checklist[125] to help organisations with their risk assessment duties. The checklist covers risks associated with the keyboard, mouse, display screen, software, furniture and environment.

Where risks are identified, the employer has a duty to reduce the risks to the extent that is reasonably practicable. There are, however, specific duties with which an employer must comply:

- Periodic breaks or changes of activity;
- Information to users and operators on all aspects of health and safety relating to their work stations arising from the risk assessment;
- In the case of employees:
  o an entitlement to an eye test by a competent person as soon as practicable after their request and subsequent tests at regular intervals, or when a user experiences visual difficulties;
  o corrective appliances appropriate for the work being undertaken;
  o health and safety training on any workstation upon which he may be required to work;
- Information on periodic breaks or changes of activity, eye tests, corrective lenses, and training.

Workplace Transport

This section addresses the risks of workplace transport, i.e. the use of transport at the work site. It does not include transport on the public highway. There are approximately 50 deaths and 5,000 injuries as a consequence of accidents involving workplace transport every year[126].

In the case of workplace transport, there is no single piece of legislation and the duties are defined from several pieces of legislation, including those relating to noise and vibration, the Workplace (Health, Safety and Welfare) Regulations, the Construction (Design and Management) Regulations, and the Work at Height Regulations.

In order to help organisations to consider the risks associated with workplace transport, they have divided the hazards into groups which have been modified slightly to aid understanding.

Site design

- Suitability for the intended purpose;
- Separation/segregation of vehicles and pedestrians;
- Proximity to people, processes, and other hazards;
- Drainage to protect against the weather and risks of spillages;
- Free from pot-holes, uneven surfaces, steep slopes, or obstructions;
- Marking, lighting, and where appropriate ventilation;
- Made of suitable material, and gritted to prevent slips or skids; and
- Avoid restricted access for example by limited headroom or sharp bends;

Site activities

- Particularly parking and reversing;
- Coupling and uncoupling, and other loading/unloading activities; and
- Specific activity hazards such as height limits or other conditions;

Safe vehicles

- Suitability for the activity and environment in which they operate;
- Visibility –for the driver looking outside and for others to see the vehicle;
- Seat restraints and other aids, e.g. reversing sensors; and
- As with other work equipment, inspection and maintenance.

Workplace Exposures

Two earlier sections have concentrated on working environments (e.g. height, confined spaces, etc.) and equipment (the provision and use, and some specific equipment such as display screen, or those used for lifting).

The next section concentrates on workplace exposures, including chemical, biological and explosive substances, radiation, electricity and other major accident hazards.

Chemicals

Workplace exposures caused 13,000 deaths in 2015 and caused or exacerbated illnesses for 220,000 employees currently in work.

Although these figures are largely attributable to exposures that may have happened historically, there were 814 reported injuries caused by contact with harmful substances last year. There are approximately 800 reported accidental releases or escapes of substances liable to cause harm each year, although in 2012/2013 it peaked at 1,141 cases[127].

Control of Substances Hazardous to Health Regulations

The use of substances at work is regulated by the Control of Substances Hazardous to Health Regulations 2002 (as amended) (COSHH), and the Approved Code of Practice and Guidance document[128].

COSHH applies to chemicals, substances or preparations (combinations of substances) which may be ingested, inhaled, absorbed by, or come into contact with the human body. It includes naturally occurring and man-made materials which create a risk to health. In some cases, for example all dust, irrespective of source, in excess of particular concentrations can be harmful to health.

The legislation also includes specific provisions in relation to carcinogens[aa], mutagens, and asthmagens. As a consequence, the legislation is more onerous than other health and safety legislation in the way that it places duties on employers to:

- Assess exposure,
- Use control measures,
- Monitor exposure,
- Conduct health surveillance,
- Provide information and training, and
- Establish emergency procedures not just for employees, but also (so far as is reasonably practicable), to provide interventions (except health surveillance) for other persons on the premises.

Special arrangements also apply to visiting employers to co-operate with the site to ensure that occupiers and contractors know and understand the exposure to which their employees may be exposed and the risks associated with those exposures.

The assessment must consider:

- The nature of the substance and its physical attributes,
- When and how exposure can occur,
- The existing controls,
- The work activity (including work performed by sub-contractors at the workplace),
- The physical, chemical and biological properties of the substance, the hazards involved,

---

[aa] Carcinogen – a substance with the potential to cause cancer in living tissue

Mutagen – an agent which causes genetic mutation

Asthmagen - any substance causally-related to the development of asthma symptoms

- The people exposed,
- The types and extent of exposure,
- The potential health effects and any other requirements.

The Registration, Evaluation, Authorisation and restriction of Chemicals (REACH)[129] system is used to control chemicals in the EU. It became law in the UK on 1st June 2007. This requires organisations producing chemicals to register them. Some of this information is likely to be found on a chemical safety data sheet, which suppliers have a duty to provide (this is a requirement under REACH).

By-products or substances produced as a consequence of operational processes undertaken by the employer will not be the subject of a chemical data sheet. As such, the employer must use his knowledge and experience to determine the likely by-products of their activities and their properties.

The regulations set out specific substances which are prohibited for particular uses. Even where substances are not prohibited, work cannot commence until:

- Steps to prevent or control exposure have been adequately identified and implemented;
- Systems for the correct use and effective maintenance, examination and testing of the control measures have been established;
- Exposure monitoring and health surveillance requirements have been identified and put in place;
- Procedures for dealing with accidents, incidents and emergencies have been established; and
- Information, instruction and training has been provided to employees.

The HSE has established a series of seven good practice principles to reduce the risks associated with substances at work. These are:

- The design and operation of processes and activities to minimise emission, release and spread of substances hazardous to health.
- Take into account all relevant routes of exposure – inhalation, skin and ingestion – when developing control measures.
- Control exposure by measures that are proportionate to the health risk.
- Choose the most effective and reliable control options that minimise the escape and spread of substances hazardous to health.
- Where adequate control of exposure cannot be achieved by other means, provide, in combination with other control measures, suitable PPE.
- Check and review regularly all elements of the control measures for their continuing effectiveness.
- Inform and train all employees on the hazards and risks from substances with which they work, and the use of control measures developed to minimise the risks.

The HSE provides specific guidance on COSHH risk assessments[130].

Employers must maintain equipment (engineering controls and protective equipment) in an efficient state, in good working order, and in a clean condition. Some equipment, for example local exhaust ventilation (LEV), is subject to specified statutory frequencies of inspection. Examinations, tests and repairs should be recorded and form a part of the assessment of the equipment.

Employers also have a duty to provide storage facilities for PPE. The location of storage should support the need for inspection, test and repair.

Carcinogens and Mutagens

Carcinogens and mutagens should not be used if the employer can use a suitable non-hazardous or less hazardous product in their place. Consideration should be given to both the use of chemicals and the by-products of production.

Specific rules relate to the volume, storage, labelling, and disposal of carcinogens and mutagens. Appropriate signage must be used in areas where they are used, stored, or transported. Non-essential personnel must be excluded. Workers must not eat, drink, smoke, or apply cosmetics in the restricted area, and warning signs must be appropriately displayed.

Exposure Limits

The Regulations specify workplace exposure limits (WELs) for a variety of substances. WELs are not black and white to the extent that exposure below the limit is safe, whilst exposure above the limit is dangerous, they do however provide a useful guide to exposures which can be incorporated as a part of work design, including working hours to reduce exposures. Not all chemicals have WELs, so good practice is to establish a suitable limit based on industry knowledge and experience.

In the case of some substances, the regulations provide short term exposure limits (STELs) because of their acute effects. Organising jobs to prevent, or minimise exposures can help to keep employees within WELs and STELs if planned correctly, although consideration should be given to both standard and non-standard operations.

Personal protective equipment (PPE) and Respiratory protective equipment (RPE) should be seen as a last resort, when other control measures cannot effectively ensure protection. Where there is no option but to adopt PPE/RPE, care must be taken to ensure that the PPE/RPE is suitable and sufficient for the purpose.

Where PPE and RPE is required, careful consideration should be given to the impact of one on another – for example the wearing of a face mask and a hard hat. Additional consideration should also be made of the effect of the protective equipment on the task being performed. For example, masks can be uncomfortable in hot work areas, which may reduce the duration that work can be undertaken in the environment. Some respiratory equipment operates using a battery to ensure a continuous supply of fresh air. These can be heavy and impede work at height or in confined spaces.

Facilities for washing, changing, eating, drinking

Suitable facilities should be provided in appropriate locations based on the outcome of COSHH risk assessments to enable employees to meet and maintain standards of hygiene, avoid the risk of spread of substances, and reduce the risk of ingestion. These should include adequate facilities for washing, changing facilities, resting, eating and drinking.

Information, instruction and supervision should ensure that employees understand how and when facilities should be used to reduce the risk of harm. However, employees should be trained so that they understand why the facilities should be used.

Monitoring

Employers must ensure through visual checks and observations that employees are working in accordance with defined control measures, for example to ensure that the correct procedures are being followed and that the correct PPE/RPE is being worn.

Monitoring systems will help employers to understand the effectiveness of controls and prompt remedial actions as necessary. Employers should also stay up to date with new working practices. Monitoring should take place at regular intervals or following significant changes to processes, equipment or materials.

In some cases, for example in relation to identifiable personal exposures, records should be kept for 40 years. In all other cases, records should be kept for 5 years.

There are a variety of techniques that can be used based on the nature of the hazard. These include air monitoring, personal monitoring, wipe sample monitoring, and biological monitoring[131]. Testing of containment systems may include environment testing (outside of the confined area) or seal, filter, joint or pipework integrity testing.

In order to be effective, a risk assessment must define what monitoring should happen, how frequently it should occur, and who should be monitored. Both the determination and the monitoring should be undertaken by competent persons.

Health Surveillance

Employers must ensure that their employees who are, or liable to be exposed to a substance hazardous to health, receive suitable health surveillance. Some specified risks may define the frequency of health surveillance. Where they are not specified, a suitable frequency should be determined based on industry knowledge and experience. Individual health records should be retained for 40 years and be made available to employees and/or the regulator on request. Medicals should take place during working time and at the cost of the employer.

Where a medical examination discovers an identifiable disease or adverse health condition as a consequence of an exposure, the employee should be informed by a suitably qualified person. The employer should also review the risk assessment, the control measures in place, and provide a review for employees who have been similarly exposed.

The employer should also consider re-assigning the employee to alternative work where there is no further risk of exposure to that substance, taking into account any advice from a medical practitioner.

Health surveillance is particularly appropriate where there have been previous cases of work related ill health; where there is a high reliance on PPE/RPE; and/or where there is evidence of previous ill health across the industry.

Accidents, Incidents and Emergencies

In order to protect employees from accidents, incidents and emergencies, the employers must ensure that:

- Safety procedures including appropriate first aid facilities have been put in place,
- Relevant safety drills have been prepared and tested at regular intervals, including:
    - evacuation of some or all personnel,
    - the isolation or making safe of specific plant and equipment,
    - general fire drills, and
    - steps by nominated personnel to help disabled staff leave the building,
- Information on hazards, hazard identification, and emergent hazards is available to workers, and
- Suitable warning and communication processes are in place to enable an appropriate response.

Employers should regularly inform, instruct and train employees on emergency procedures.

The employer must also ensure that the information is available to the emergency services to enable their own response, taking suitable and sufficient measures to protect their own personnel.

Employers must ensure that immediate steps are taken to mitigate the circumstances of any event, restore the situation to normal, and inform employees who may be affected. Until the site is returned to normal, access should be restricted to those persons essential for repairs, and only then, when they have the correct PPE and other safety equipment. Additional duties apply in the event where there may have been a release of a biological agent.

Biological Agents and Infections

In 2014/15, there were 411 reports of dangerous occurrences of an accident or incident which results, or could have resulted in the release or escape of a biological agent likely to cause severe human infection or illness, although over the last five years, the figure is typically 350 instances per annum.

COSHH also applies to biological agents, which are classified into four 'hazard groups' according to the following infection criteria:

- Their ability to cause infection;
- The severity of the disease that may result;
- The risk that infection will spread to the community; and
- The availability of vaccines and effective treatment.

Infections can be a major cause of absence in industries with high levels of human contact such as health and social care and education; high levels of animal contact, such as farming and agriculture; or as a consequence of the environment in which employees are operating.

If employee activities include deliberate work with biological agents, work should be undertaken in contained use activities. If the risk assessment concludes that there is a risk of exposure to a biological agent for which effective vaccines are readily available, these should be offered.

The Health & Safety at Work Act requires that these vaccines are provided free of charge. The use of vaccines cannot be mandatory and should not be considered as sufficient controls in their own right.

Below are some of the biological hazards which are more likely to occur in the workplace, through the activities performed, or by virtue of travel requirements of employees. They are intended to provide an indication of the types of biological hazard, but the list is not comprehensive.

Legionnaires' disease

Legionnaires' disease is the collective term given to a number of pneumonia like illnesses caused by the Legionnaires' bacteria which lives in water sources. Legionella contaminates water systems such as cooling towers, evaporative condensers, hot and cold water systems, and whirlpool spas.

Risks increase where water is stored or re-circulated and where the temperature is between 20° and 45° centigrade, where impurities in the water may accelerate bacterial growth, and where water droplets may be produced and dispersed over a wide area[132].

Specific duties[133] are defined in the Approved Code of Practice on Legionnaires' disease which includes:

- The development of a risk assessment,
- Specific duties assigned to the 'competent' person,
- Control scheme requirements and the requirement to review them, and
- Duties and responsibilities on those involved in the supply of water systems.

This must extend across the entire system, and not be limited to the cooling towers in isolation.

The risk assessment duty includes a requirement not only to assess the water systems for risks, but also to consider whether vulnerable people may be at risk from contamination. This should be prepared by a competent person who understands the potential risk sources and effective control measures (including monitoring, inspection and maintenance). Records should be kept and the risk assessment should be reviewed regularly.

Control measures are likely to include physical interventions (ensuring that taps are run for periods to release water stored between 20° and 45° centigrade), the use of chemical treatments (and the handling, storage, and disposal of those chemicals) including the provision of information to workers that may handle them, system testing regimes, defined limits and actions to be taken when limits are exceeded.

Records of the controls should be maintained, as well as their application. Records should include system schematics, results of testing, and details of physical and chemical interventions – showing dates, activities and results.

Where the control system is outsourced, steps should be taken to ensure that the person responsible for managing that arrangement is competent to understand what is required from the contractor. Where the requirement is met internally, the internal employee and his manager/supervisor should understand what actions are required and the importance of ensuring that those actions take place and are suitably recorded.

In 2002, there was a serious outbreak of Legionnaires' disease[134] at the Forum 28 arts and leisure centre owned by Barrow Borough Council. Seven members of the public died and 180 suffered ill-health. The average age of those seven was 66 years which reflected the significance of the need to consider the people that may be exposed to any risk.

A public enquiry identified six key failures which were published so that the lessons could be learned by others:

- *Poor lines of communication and unclear lines of responsibility*

  Specifically, a general lack of leadership and direction within the council and poor communication meant health and safety, in particular the risks from legionella, were not appropriately controlled.

  The responsible person needs to have sufficient authority, competence and knowledge of the system.

- *Failure to act on advice and concerns raised*

  Although a contractor had raised a concern, the HSE had sent information, and an auditor had reported a general lack of health and safety risk assessments, these concerns did not result in remedial action being taken.

- *Failure to carry out a risk assessment*

  A specific risk assessment should have been produced for legionella and as a consequence, a suitable control scheme was not drawn up.

- *Poor management of contractors and contract documentation*

  The failure to effectively manage contractors was a significant factor in the cause of the outbreak. This failing included a lack of formal documentation, the absence of an agreed specification of works, and a lack of routine checking of what contractors were doing, and how they were doing it.

- *Inadequate training and resources*

  Vacancies in the organisational structure and a lack of training for those responsible for health and safety meant that those responsible were not competent to fulfil the tasks required.

- *Individual failings*

  Specific failings by different individuals were identified by the investigation. In one case, failures:

  o *To use knowledge in the procurement process,*

  o *To respond to concerns that were raised, and*

  o *To not escalate concerns to another*

  …led to a personal prosecution to take reasonable care for the health and safety of herself and other persons who may be affected by her acts or omissions at work.

Influenza

Influenza (Flu) is one of the most common forms of infection. It commonly occurs between the beginning of December and the end of January and can occur in as many as 15,000 employees over that period. There are occasionally outbreaks of higher incidence. The most recent significant outbreak was in 2010/2011 when numbers were six times normal levels.

Most years, influenza is likely to be maintained within 'normal' levels. However, the high level of absence over a short period, particularly in organisations where absences can have a significant impact on organisational performance, has encouraged organisations to consider voluntary flu jabs for their employees.

In one case study, following the introduction of the flu injection, sickness absence amongst those taking up the injection reduced by around 25% (compared to the group that did not take up the injection), which represented an organisational saving of 540 staff days (more than two staff years) and an estimated saving of £217,000.[135]

There is a small risk of a UK influenza pandemic, and in 2011, the government issued their UK influenza pandemic preparedness strategy.[136]

Risks from Animals

Working with, in proximity to, or in areas where animals may have been present introduces a risk of exposure to a number of infections. This group of infections are called Zoonoses[bb] of which there are around 40 conditions. The HSE estimate that 300,000 workers are potentially exposed. Typically, these workers can be engaged in any of the following industries:

- Veterinary care
- Laboratory work
- Human health and social care
- Farm workers, including animal husbandry
- Food preparation and processing, including dairy workers, chefs and other kitchen personnel
- Animal processing industries including textiles, leather, rendering and manufacture using animal derivatives
- Storage and distribution, including postal services (bio-threats)
- Border control – especially those engaged in animal quarantine
- Local Authorities (Regulation)
- Refuse disposal and street cleaning
- Outdoor and rural leisure industry including nature conservation
- Sewage and waste water workers

[bb] Zoonoses are diseases that can be transmitted from animals to humans

- Construction, demolition and building renovation
- Other outdoor workers, for example telecommunications engineers.

The most commonly reported infections are those that cause diarrhoea and vomiting. These include campylobacteriosis, salmonella and cryptosporidiosis.

Many infections cause skin conditions and because many of these can be quite mild, it is believed that there is a high level of under-reporting.

Blood borne viruses

This group includes hepatitis, human immunodeficiency virus (HIV) and acquired immune deficiency syndrome (AIDS), but also includes Chicken Pox, Tuberculosis, Measles, Mumps and Rubella.

Although they are normally referred to as blood borne viruses, they can also be found in other bodily fluids. They are mainly transmitted by exposure to contaminated fluids, but can also be transmitted by a sharp instrument, for example a needle, blade or broken glass.

Workers in the following sectors are most at risk:

- Custodial services
- Education
- Mortuary, embalming or crematorium work
- Health and medical care including emergency services, first aid, hospital, medical, and dental care
- Hairdressing, beauticians, body-piercing
- Dentistry, acupuncture, chiropody and other health care
- Military
- Plumbing and sewage working
- Cleaning and maintenance work associated with any of the sectors described above.

There is no obligation on employees to inform employers that they have a blood borne virus, or to take a medical test for it. If an employer is aware that an employee is suffering from a blood borne virus, that information must be treated confidentially and should not be passed on without the employee's permission. If an employee is aware that he has a medical condition, he should take care to protect the health and safety of others. Many employees with BBVs can carry on work normally.

In the case of HIV and AIDS, there is no requirement to demonstrate a physical or mental impairment that has a substantial and long term adverse effect on the ability to carry out normal day-to-day activities[137]. Some people including those with cancer, multiple sclerosis, and HIV/AIDS are automatically protected by the Equality Act.

Tuberculosis has been subject to a two decade long rise in the UK, but has recently shown signs of abatement. In 2014, there were 6,520 cases of TB[138], of which 72% occurred in non-UK born people, most of whom had been in the country for two years or more, suggesting a latent reactivation[139]. Approximately 2/3rds of cases were found in people in work or education. Some concern has been raised about the future trend for this illness as a consequence of the immunisation policies of countries from which migrant workers are arriving.

Chicken Pox is relatively common in the UK and can cause serious harm to expectant mothers (including pneumonia, and in rare cases, encephalitis or hepatitis), miscarriage, or to the unborn child (including foetal varicella syndrome).

Measles, Mumps or Rubella, particularly because fears over the MMR vaccination during the last 25 years have created, according to Public Health England, '*Sub-optimal levels of vaccination*' in 10 to 16 year olds, that over the next five years will enter employment. As with chicken pox, Rubella and Measles are particularly significant where there is a risk of infection to an expectant mother.

Risk assessments should pay particular attention to the risks of vulnerable personnel, to personnel that spend a lot of their time off site, and where there are increased risks to or from members of the public[140]. Identifying the nature of the hazards, their sources, and means of transmission will support the assessment of control measures.

Typical control measures should include:

- Minimising risk of contamination to begin with, by reducing the amount of direct exposure;
- The prohibition of eating, drinking and smoking in working areas;
- Prevent puncture wounds, for example by controlling the use of sharp equipment, perhaps by changing working methods, or substituting equipment;
- Ensure breaks in exposed skin or other access points to the human body are blocked, for example by the use of masks, goggles, water resistant protective clothing and suitable footwear;
- Ensure that adequate hygiene practices are in place and that practices are regularly supervised;
- Use effective decontamination procedures and dispose of contaminated waste properly.

SARS and MERS

Severe Acute Respiratory Syndrome[141] and Middle East Respiratory Syndrome (Coronavirus)[142] are unlikely in the UK but may present a risk to employees travelling to regions including China, Korea and Saudi Arabia.

Care should be taken to ensure that employees travelling to regions with increased risk of harm understand the potential risks associated with travel and that they are provided with precautions and information. Advice in respect of general hazards associated with international travel and any specific medical precautions can be obtained from the Foreign Office website at https://www.gov.uk/foreign-travel-advice.

Dangerous Substances

In 2012/13, there were 184 reports of dangerous occurrences of an explosion or fire occurring in any plant or premises which results in the stoppage of that plant for more than 24 hours. There were 258 reports of sudden, uncontrolled releases of flammable substances.

The UK introduced the Dangerous Substances and Explosive Atmospheres Regulations (DSEAR) in 2002. A more recent Approved Code of Practice (ACOP) 2013[143] sets out the duties in relation to design, storage, control and safe maintenance.

The regulations set minimum requirements for the protection of workers from fire and explosion risks related to dangerous substances and potentially explosive atmospheres. The Regulations apply to employers and the self-employed at most workplaces in Great Britain where a dangerous substance is, or could be present.

The DSEAR regulations use words in common language but apply a very specific meaning, such that:

- A **hazard** is confined to the properties of a substance that can potentially lead to fire, explosion or other similar energetic effects which could affect a person's safety.
- The **risks** relate to those caused by fires, explosions or similar events such as burns, blast injuries, or asphyxiation caused by smoke or fire gases, but not to other risks associated with the substances;
- **Physical properties** relate to boiling points, auto-ignition temperatures, flammability, corrosivity, reactivity, volatility, flashpoint and electrical conductivity, thermal and mechanical sensitivity, and oxidising properties; **chemical properties** relate to reactivity, heat of reaction, self-acceleration and de-composition properties.
- **Workplaces** and **Premises** have a wide definition and include vehicles, vessels and installations, and may include private roads, industrial estates and in some cases, the public highway (where work is being undertaken producing dangerous substances as a part of the work activity).

They do not include areas used for the medical treatment of patients; the use of gas appliances burning fuel which are used for heating or hot water production (not exceeding 105°c) or other domestic gas installations; the manufacture, handling or use of explosives, mines, quarries, boreholes, offshore installations; ships; or other means of transport subject to international agreements (unless the vehicle is intended to be used in a potentially explosive environment).

Whilst many of these workplaces are exempt from the DSEAR Regulations, they are subject to their own legislation such as the Manufacture and Storage of Explosives Regulations 2005, Mines and Quarries Act 1954, Quarries Regulations 1999 or the Borehole Sites and Operations Regulations 1995.

Risk Assessment

DSEAR places particular duties on employers to assess and control risks from dangerous substances. New works should not commence until a risk assessment has been carried out and the required measures[cc] have been implemented, although for good reason, it is sensible to carry out a risk assessment as part of a wider plant design programme to reduce the risk of additional or remedial costs. Risk assessments should consider the risks to employees, contractors and other persons that may be affected by the employer's activities. Whilst dangerous substances bought into the workplace as raw materials may be the most obvious source of hazard, dangerous substances can be present in the workplace from a number of sources:

- By-products of a process or activity (including the production of fumes), or as a result of an accident or incident;
- From contractors or other departments for use in maintenance, cleaning and repair work; or
- Natural occurrence in the workplace.

In order to be suitable and sufficient, risk assessments must cover the hazardous properties of the substance(s), its safety data sheet information, and the:

- Work processes to be undertaken, including maintenance, and their interactions;
- The storage location, particularly ensuring incompatible substances are not stored in close proximity;
- Where that substance may come into contact with other substances (deliberately or otherwise) the impact of their interaction (a chemical reaction hazard assessment);
- Arrangements for the safe handling, storage and transport of dangerous substances and of waste containing dangerous substances;

[cc] Required measures are those necessary to ensure that the risk is eliminated or reduce so far as is reasonably practicable.

- The impact of implemented measures on the risks associated with the substance;
- The likelihood that an explosive atmosphere will occur and its persistence;
- The likelihood that ignition sources (including electro-static discharges) will be present and become active and effective;
- The scale of the anticipated effects of a fire or an explosion;
- Any places which are or can be connected via openings to places in which explosive atmospheres may occur; and
- Any additional safety information that may be necessary in order to complete the risk assessment.

Risk assessments should also consider scenarios which could occur, for example the impact of hot work on vessels containing substances which might not combust at normal operating temperatures, some chemicals may not be classified as flammable or combustible but could ignite under certain circumstances, combustible dusts may be dispersed to give rise to explosive atmospheres or latent smouldering hazards, and some substances may decompose under conditions causing risk of fire.

The risk assessment should consider the skills, knowledge and experience of employees and their representatives, the training and supervision of employees, activities in adjacent areas or premises (particularly where they could provide an ignition source) and the possible misuse of dangerous substances. The most effective way to eliminate the risk is to substitute the process or raw materials for a safer alternative. The ACOP provides detailed information on

- the substitution, control and mitigation measures (including design, storage, ventilation, containment, control of ignition sources, segregation of incompatible substances, barriers, transport (on site), and handling waste).
- Hot work including preparation and procedures including cleaning, gas freeing or inerting, and the use of gas welding and cutting equipment.
- Redundant plant and equipment including its disposal.

Where the risk cannot be eliminated, the employer must, so far as is reasonable, apply measures to control the risks and mitigate the detrimental effects. The ACOP sets out specific information in relation to specific tasks and operational risk. In any event, employers should establish a system of work that ensures that the control measures for a particular activity are properly understood and implemented and that an appropriate level of control is in place. The ACOP provides specific information in relation to:

- Cleaning activities;
- Operating Procedures for low, medium and high risk activities; including safety method statements;

- Non-routine activities;
- Access restrictions and 'EX' signage for hazardous areas;
- Clothing, personal protective equipment and Footwear (that cannot produce an electro-static discharge); and
- Arrangements to deal with Accidents, Incidents and Emergencies.

Safety Method Statements

The safety method statement, whether it is prepared in-house or by outside contractors, should be clear, concise and contain the following information:

- A description of the task and where it is to be carried out;
- The sequence and method of work;
- The hazards identified during the risk assessment;
- The skills required to deal with the hazards;
- The precautions necessary to control the hazards;
- References to specific safety procedures covering known hazards;
- Details of any isolations and any related control procedures;
- Details of tools and equipment to be used;
- Methods of disposal of wastes and debris; and
- Details of the state or condition in which the plant or equipment will be left at the end of the activity.

Major Accident Hazards

In 1976, a chemical plant near Seveso, Italy failed to effectively close down their plant at the end of a week's production. This failure culminated in the release of a harmful chemical which killed over 3,000 animals and led to the deliberate slaughter of a further 77,000 animals otherwise destined for the food chain. Almost 500 people suffered skin lesions as a result of the exposure.

Not only was the incident significant because of the scale of harm done (there had been worse incidents before the event), but also because of the lack of knowledge amongst the local community of the potential harm that could be caused by an incident at the site.

These factors led to the European 'Seveso Directive' which was introduced into UK Legislation through the Control of Major Accident Hazards Regulations 1999 (COMAH99). These regulations specifically addressed process safety on the one hand, and public information on the other through:

- The identification of sites producing, processing, or storing dangerous substances;
- Necessary control measures to prevent major hazards;
- Mitigation measures that limit the effects of any accidents which do occur.

The directive has been updated following further incidents in Europe and has been recently reviewed in the UK culminating in a new Regulation (The Control of Major Accident Hazards Regulations 2015 – COMAH15). The main updates include an updated list of substances, increased emergency planning duties (including the co-operation of designated authorities in tests of the emergency testing plan), stronger requirements for public information, a stronger 'domino effect' duty, and stronger requirements on competent and local authorities. The HSE have published guidance to support the new Regulations[144].

Major accidents occur when *uncontrolled developments* at an establishment to which the regulations apply lead to a *serious danger* to human health or the environment (inside or outside the plant) involving one or more of the *dangerous substances* defined in the regulations. Organisations (called Operators) with major accident hazards, must meet a high standard of safety.

Operators must establish a *Major Accident Prevention Policy* (MAPP) and a *Safety Management Plan* for implementing it. The MAPP should include internal and external emergency plans to contain and control incidents so as to minimise the consequences, and to:

- Limit damage to human health, the environment and property;
- Implement the necessary measures to protect human health and the environment;
- Communicate the necessary information to the public and to the services or authorities concerned in the area; and
- Provide for the restoration and clean-up of the environment following a major accident. Emergency plans should be tested and reviewed.

Good practice should be considered as a minimum. Sources of good practice include Approved Codes of Practice and standards produced by organisations such as the British Standards Institution (BSI), the Comité Européen de Normalisation (CEN), and the International Organization for Standardisation (ISO).

Radiation

In any given year, there are typically 20 reports of malfunctioning of radiation generators. These are recorded under the RIDDOR classification:

"The malfunction of a radiation generator or its ancillary equipment used in fixed/mobile industrial radiography, the irradiation of food or the processing of products by irradiation, which causes it to fail to de-energise at the end of the intended exposure period, or equipment used in fixed/mobile industrial radiography or gamma irradiation, which causes a radioactive source to fail to return to its safe position by the normal means at the end of the intended exposure period".

There are two types of radiation – ionising radiation and non-ionising radiation.

Ionising Radiation

Ionising radiation occurs as either electromagnetic rays (such as X-rays and gamma rays) or particles (such as alpha and beta particles). It occurs naturally (e.g. from the radioactive decay of natural radioactive substances such as radon gas and its decay products) but can also be produced artificially.

Workers in the medical sector, industrial radiography, and nuclear power generation are most likely to come across ionising radiation, although it can also be found in mining.

Work with ionising radiation is governed by the Ionising Radiation Regulations 1999[145] and the Work with Ionising Radiation Approved Code of Practice[146].

Employers must not use equipment intended to produce x-rays unless they have the prior approval of the HSE. The nature and method of approval varies based on the circumstances. Before any new activity involving ionising radiation is carried out, a suitable and sufficient risk assessment must be produced to reduce so far as is reasonably practicable the extent of exposure.

Employers have a duty to take all necessary steps to ensure, so far as is reasonably practicable that employees are not exposed to ionising radiation. The ACOP sets out specific interventions that should be considered to reduce risk, level, or unintended exposures to ionising radiation.

Exposure to radiation by patients undergoing medical examination are covered by Ionising Radiation (Protection of Persons Undergoing Medical Examination or Treatment) Regulations 1988.

Welfare Facilities

Specific washing and changing facilities must be provided to employees over and beyond the requirements of the Workplace (Health, Safety and Welfare) Regulations to ensure that any radioactive contamination is not ingested or spread to areas beyond the controlled area.

Where there is a significant risk of contamination in controlled working areas, facilities must be provided outside of the area for eating, drinking, smoking, etc.

Medical Surveillance and Personal Dosimetry Monitoring

Medical surveillance should include assessment of classified workers once appointed, periodic reviews at least annually, special surveillance of those whose doses have been exceeded, determining whether special conditions are necessary (perhaps because of the use of PPE or other activities), and a final assessment on cessation of work.

Employers must ensure that monitoring provision is established for workers who are or may be exposed to radiation. Advice should be sought from the Radiation Protection Advisor on the use of personal dose meters, and the nature and frequency of other assessments which might include urine, or part/full body monitoring, along with any special additional assessments in the event of unplanned exposure.

Employers also need to ensure that employees are informed of these arrangements and their administration.

Non-ionising radiation

Non-ionising radiation (NIR) is the term used to describe the part of the electromagnetic spectrum covering two main regions: optical radiation (ultraviolet (UV), visible and infrared), and electromagnetic fields (EMFs) (power frequencies, microwaves and radio frequencies).

Non-ionising radiation affects a substantial proportion of the working population, because it includes exposure to ultraviolet sun rays for outside workers as well as those working with communications equipment, lasers and tanning equipment.

Working Outside

Outside workers are exposed to ultraviolet rays from the sun that can cause sunburn, which can include peeling and blistering of the skin. Prolonged exposure leads to accelerated ageing of the skin, and can cause skin cancer. There are 40,000 cases of skin cancer diagnosed in the UK every year. It can also harm the eyes.

Employees can suffer reactions to sunlight if they have been exposed to some chemicals (for example wood dyes or preservatives) or to particular plants[147]. Employees should be encouraged to cover up (preferably with appropriate breathable but tightly woven fabrics), wear a hat that provides cover for the ears and back of the neck, stay in the shade where possible, use sunscreen of a minimum factor of SPF15 for areas that cannot be easily covered, and regularly check the skin for signs of damage[148].

Employers should routinely provide training to employees on the points above, consider the scheduling of work to minimise exposure – for example by staging non-outdoor activities for times when the sun is at its strongest, providing shaded rest areas, and providing drinking water to avoid dehydration.

Dependant on the nature of work, employees in these environments can also suffer heat stress (see heat stress) which can present significant risks because often outside workers are alone (see lone workers).

Electro-Magnetic fields

According to the HSE, It has been known for a long time that exposure of people to high levels of electromagnetic fields can give rise to acute effects[149].

The effects that can occur depend on the frequency of the radiation. At low frequencies the effects will be on the central nervous system of the body, whilst at high frequencies heating effects can occur, leading to a rise in body temperature. In reality, these effects are extremely rare and will not occur in most day-to-day work situations.

Optical radiation

According to the HSE[150], Optical radiation is another term for light, covering ultraviolet (UV) radiation, visible light, and infrared radiation.

The greatest risks to health are posed by:

- **UV radiation from the sun.** Exposure of the eyes to UV radiation can damage the cornea and produce pain and symptoms similar to that of sand in the eye. The effects on the skin range from redness, burning and accelerated ageing through to various types of skin cancer.
- **The misuse of powerful lasers.** High-power lasers can cause serious damage to the eye (including blindness) as well as producing skin burns.

Tanning equipment

Tanning equipment uses NIR to stimulate the human body to produce a tan, or in some cases to produce Vitamin D to help build bone strength[151].

It nonetheless presents particular hazards similar to those described for working outside but in a more concentrated manner. These can include burns, skin dryness and itching, premature ageing of the skin and skin cancer (particularly in under 35s). The equipment can also cause eye irritation, conjunctivitis or cataracts if suitable goggles are not worn.

Electricity

In 2013/14, there were 376 reports of electrical short circuits or overloads leading to a plant stoppage of over 24 hours, or significant risk of death reported to the HSE. Accidents at work resulting in lost time arising from electrical injuries are not classified as such so it is very difficult to obtain detailed data for the number of incidents.

A response from the HSE to a freedom of information request[152] in 2014 showed 7 employees suffered death from electrocution whilst at work during that year.

A report undertaken by Bomel Limited for the HSE published in 2010[153] analysed 56,597 'electricity related' accidents reported between 1996 and 2003.

The authors estimate that there were 173 electricity related fatalities (approximately 10% of all fatalities) in the period; over 12,000 major industry accidents; and over 44,000 accidents resulting in an absence from work of more than three days. Electrical construction and installation are the highest causes of major incidents and fatalities.

The Electrical Industry is obliged to report incidents involving members of the public under the Electrical Safety, Quality and Continuity Regulations 2002 (ESQCR). In 2014/15 there were 5 fatal injuries, 407 serious (but non-fatal) events, and 12,076 other events in Great Britain (including short circuits, unauthorised access, etc.)[154].

This level of reporting is in part down to the quality of reporting procedures, but is also indicative of attempted cable thefts or interference with electrical networks (attempted electricity theft).

The main accidents likely to occur are electric shocks (which can be fatal), muscular contractions, deep burns, and damage to eyes caused by intense ultraviolet radiation.

Electrical incidents can cause fires or explosions igniting flammable materials.

Electricity is invisible and because work is normally undertaken by those with electrical skills, training, knowledge and experience, and normally without incident, the risk is not always recognised. Accidents are normally caused by a belief that the network was dead (isolated) or because workers did not have adequate training, equipment, or other precautions in place[155].

Electricity at Work Regulations

The Electricity at Work Regulations 1989 requires systems to be of such construction as to prevent danger. Equipment must be properly designed, constructed, installed and maintained so that it does not present a risk of electric shock, burns, fire or explosion when properly used.

An important factor to consider is the nature of the environment of the electrical installation. For example, heavy engineering (presenting a risk of mechanical damage) and wet or humid conditions. Certified explosion-protected equipment must be used in places where there could be potentially explosive atmospheres.

It is important that care is taken to consider the whole system. Switch disconnectors should be capable of being locked off, or use a similar method to secure them in the off position; circuits and equipment should be capable of local isolation where possible so that sections of the system can be isolated as necessary; and devices used for isolating circuits must be clearly marked to show their relationship to the equipment they control, unless there can be no doubt that this would be obvious to anyone who may need to operate them.

Modern equipment complies with a series of safety standards but in old buildings; there is still a risk that older electrical systems can be in place, including open-type switchboards and fuse boards.

Before work takes place on electrical equipment, it is important to assess the risks because a loss of energy may affect other plant and equipment.

Managers should establish a system of rules and procedures wherever electrical work is to be carried out, or ensure that contractors brought in to do electrical work have appropriate rules and procedures. These should be written down and everybody involved must be made aware of them. These will form the basis of task-specific risk assessments. The rules and procedures should reflect the nature and extent of the risk.

Safety rules should set out the principles and general practices clearly and in a compact format. Those carrying out the work should be instructed to carry the safety rules with them. Workers should know the limitations of their work allowed under the safety rules.

Detailed procedures for safe working on particular equipment, or under particular circumstances, should be the subject of separate documents, including task-specific risk assessments or method statements, which should be readily available when required.

If something unforeseen occurs during a working procedure, there should be a review of the work. Even a properly trained, competent worker may not always be aware of what to do when things go wrong. The worker should have been trained to recognise that there may be a need to change to a new system of work.

It will normally be necessary for the worker to know how to refer a changed situation to the correct people, by communicating both up and down the management structure in the organisation.

Managers and Supervisors must:

- Ensure that everyone knows how to work safely and without risk to their health and that all workers follow the safety rules and control measures identified in risk assessments.
- Be involved in planning the work and in the risk assessment process;
- Coordinate the work where more than one group is involved;
- Discuss the necessary precautions and emergency procedures with the workers;
- Clearly define the roles and responsibilities of the supervisors and workers, including those of any contractors who may be employed;

- Ensure that supervisors are competent to supervise the work, with the level of supervision being appropriate to the danger and the competence of those carrying out the work;
- Identify those people who are competent and have knowledge and experience of the electrical system to be worked on.

Anyone who does not have the competence, knowledge and experience of the electrical system will need a greater level of supervision, or will need to be given adequate training to make sure that they have the correct skills, knowledge and risk awareness for the task.

Unauthorised, unqualified or untrained people must not be allowed to work on electrical systems.

Live working should be avoided wherever possible. Many accidents occur to personnel working on live equipment that should have been isolated. The risk assessment should consider the nature of the work and the competence of the people who will be carrying out the work, including their ability to avoid danger, taking into account the available precautions.

The risk assessment should inform managers and supervisors whether it is reasonable in all the circumstances to work live. The decision should not be taken lightly. At this stage the economic and operational factors should be evaluated against the risks involved before making a decision, bearing in mind that the risks associated with working live can be very serious. Minor inconveniences arising from working with the equipment dead, sometimes arising from commercial and time pressures, will very rarely outweigh the risks associated with live work.

Live working can only be justified if suitable precautions have been taken. These are likely to include:

- Temporary insulation, protective enclosures, or screens;
- Temporary barriers with signs to keep unauthorised personnel from harm;
- Mechanisms to ensure adequate clearances are established and maintained;
- Assurance that employees understand the task and system and are appropriately trained and experienced;
- Suitable workspace including lighting, and adequate space, free from trip hazards;
- Use, maintenance and storage of robust insulated tools, probes and fused leads;
- Avoidance of lone working;
- Provision and use of the correct personal protective equipment.

Planning should include the identification of the equipment and the importance of the accuracy of the information cannot be underestimated. Many electrical accidents are due to a failure to plan ahead. Planning should consider the management, supervision, implementation and completion of the work, and should lead to a formal system of work based on information in the safety rules and a task-specific risk assessment.

Organisations should consider the work to be done, along with the:

- Hazards of the system/equipment and the risks associated with the work;
- People doing the work, their competence and the level of supervision necessary;
- Precautions to be taken and the system of work to be employed;
- Possibility that the nature of the work may change, e.g. non-invasive becoming invasive.

The planning process should also consider the level of supervision required, factoring in the amount of training and experience workers have had to do the specific jobs, the requirement for working live.

The need for accompaniment should also be considered, and whilst there is a greater need for live work, it may still be necessary for working dead, particularly in close proximity to live plant. The accompanying person should be trained to recognise danger, to switch off and, if necessary, to give assistance in the event of an emergency.

Managers and supervisors should ensure that workers understand the correct working methods, related to the specific work in hand. They have a responsibility to provide the protective equipment identified in the task-specific risk assessment and make sure that it is:

- Suitable for the use for which it is provided;
- Maintained in a condition suitable for that use; and
- Used properly.

Managers should check that workers are following the rules and correct procedures. Sometimes, some or all of these checks may be delegated to the supervisor of the work. Regular and systematic management checks of the work are necessary, particularly if work is being carried out off-site.

Procedures should include equipment identification, disconnection, isolation, caution notices (lock-out, tag-out), ensuring the equipment is dead, earthing, and any special arrangements for high voltage work.

Electrical permit to work systems increase safety and often work alongside existing permit to work systems.

Electrical Permit to Work Systems

HSE Guidance is that the electrical permit to work systems should include:

- The person the permit is addressed to, i.e. the leader of the group or working party, who will be present throughout the work;
- The exact equipment which has been made dead and its precise location;
- The points of isolation;
- Where the conductors are earthed;
- Where warning notices are posted and special safety locks fitted;
- The nature of the work to be carried out;
- The presence of any other source of hazard, with cross-reference to other relevant permits;
- Further precautions to be taken during the course of the work.

At the time the person in immediate charge of the operation accepts the permit they become responsible for ensuring that all the specified safety precautions are followed, and that:

- Only permitted work is done; and
- The work is confined to the area defined in the permit.

If the permit is issued to the leader of a group, the leader accepts responsibility for the people in the group and should explain to them – before the work begins – the scope of work and the means by which safety has been achieved.

If the person issuing the electrical permit-to-work will also be doing the work, it is strongly recommended that someone else makes an independent check of the precautions taken. The person doing the work should then issue a permit to themselves. This routine helps to ensure that the full safety procedure is applied.

The recipient of an electrical permit-to-work should keep it for reference while the work is in progress and to prevent inadvertent cancellation and re-energisation of the equipment.

When the work is complete, whoever the permit was issued to should sign it to declare that any additional earths and tools have been removed and people in the group have been withdrawn and instructed not to approach the equipment again. The person closing the permit should also indicate whether or not the equipment is fit for service. The permit is then returned, preferably to the designated competent person who originally issued it, for cancellation before the equipment is re-energised.

PAT Testing

The Electricity at Work Regulations 1989 require that any electrical equipment that has the potential to cause an injury is maintained in a safe condition. The Regulations do not specify what needs to be done, by whom or how frequently.

The HSE has provided guidance on the frequency of user checks and formal inspections, and to those who have control over, or use, portable electrical equipment. A part of this guidance is a maintenance plan for the different types of equipment including user checks, inspections and testing to reduce the risk of incidents.

Records of checks should be maintained. Labels are not a legal requirement but are a good indicator of the most recent checks and inspections which can help a management process.

User checks and formal visual inspections can be carried out by a 'competent' employee. In this context, the HSE guidance defines 'competent' as having suitable training, skills and knowledge for the task to prevent injury to themselves or others. The guidance also sets out when testing by someone with a higher level of competence is necessary.

Portable electrical equipment should be used in accordance with manufacturers' instructions, and for the use, and in the environment intended. The HSE have published a schedule of inspections as a part of their guidance. It is not compulsory. Organisations should use a schedule that reflects the nature of the equipment, environment and tasks they undertake.

References

[95] Handbook of Human Resource Management Practice, Michael Armstrong, Kogan Page, 2014

[96] Working Time Regulations 1998 – see legislation.gov.uk for full list of amendments

[97] Managing Shift Work - Health and safety guidance, HSE, 2006

[98] Shift work and breast cancer: a critical review of the epidemiological evidence, The Institute of Cancer Research, HSE, 2003

[99] Working alone - Health and safety guidance on the risks of lone working, HSE, 2013

[100] Homeworkers: Guidance for employers on health and safety, INDG226, HSE, 2011

[101] Health and safety of homeworkers: Good practice case studies, Rachel O'Hara, Julian Williamson, Alison Collins, Danny Higginson, HSL, 2004

[102] http://press.hse.gov.uk/2014/forty-per-cent-of-construction-sites-fail-health-and-safety-spot-checks/

[103] Causal factors in construction accidents, Loughborough University and UMIST, HSE, 2003

[104] London 2012: The Construction (Design and Management) Regulations 2007 Duty-holder roles and impact Frontline Consultants, HSE, 2007

[105] Managing health and safety in construction: Construction (Design and Management) Regulations 2015, Guidance on Regulations, 2015

[106] New perspectives on falls from height – Identifying high profile areas for intervention Prepared by BOMEL Limited for the Health and Safety Executive, 2005

[107] Safe work in confined spaces Confined Spaces Regulations 1997 Approved Code of Practice and guidance, HSE, 2014

[108] http://www.nhs.uk/Conditions/Hearing-impairment/Pages/Causes.aspx retrieved August 2015

[109] Controlling noise at work The Control of Noise at Work Regulations 2005 Guidance on Regulations, HSE, 2005

[110] Workplace exposure to vibration in Europe: an expert review, European Agency for Safety and Health at Work, 2008

[111] Eurofound, Fifth European Working Conditions Survey, Publications Office of the European Union, Luxembourg, 2012

[112] http://www.hse.gov.uk/vibration/wbv/calculator.htm

[113] http://www.hse.gov.uk/vibration/hav/vibrationcalc.htm

[114] http://www.hse.gov.uk/pubns/priced/l122.pdf

[115] http://www.legislation.gov.uk/uksi/1999/2001/contents/made

[116] http://www.legislation.gov.uk/uksi/2000/128/contents/made

[117] Safe use of work equipment Provision and Use of Work Equipment Regulations 1998, Fourth Edition, HSE, 2014

[118] For more information, refer to the Institute of Asset Management website: https://theiam.org/

[119] The safe isolation of plant and equipment, Second Edition, HSE, 2006

[120] Safety in the remote diagnosis of manufacturing plant and equipment, HSE, 1995

[121] Application of electro-sensitive protective equipment using light curtains and light beam devices to machinery, HSE, 1999

[122] Safe use of lifting equipment, Lifting Operations and Lifting Equipment Regulations 1998 Approved Code of Practice and guidance, Second Edition, HSE, 2014

[123] Lifting equipment at work A brief guide, HSE, 2013

[124] Working with display screen equipment (DSE) A brief guide, HSE, April 2013

[125] http://www.hse.gov.uk/pubns/ck1.pdf

[126] A guide to workplace transport safety, HSE, 2014

[127] Dangerous Occurrences reported in Great Britain 2009/10 - 2013/14r1

[128] The Control of Substances Hazardous to Health Regulations 2002 (as amended), Approved Code of Practice and guidance, HSE, 2013

[129] http://www.hse.gov.uk/reach/

[130] A step by step guide to COSHH assessment, HSE 2004

[131] Biological monitoring in the workplace A guide to its practical application to chemical exposure, HSE, 2010

[132] Legionnaires' disease A brief guide for duty-holders, HSE, 2012

[133] Legionnaires' disease The control of legionella bacteria in water systems, Fourth Edition, HSE, 2013

[134] Report of the public meetings into the legionella outbreak in Barrow-in-Furness, August 2002, HSE, March 2007

[135] http://www.hse.gov.uk/business/casestudy/barts.htm, retrieved 24th August 2015

[136] UK Influenza Pandemic Preparedness Strategy, Department of Health, 2011

[137] Equality Act 2010: What do I need to know? Disability Quick Start Guide, Government Equalities Office, HMSO, 2010

[138] Tuberculosis in England 2015 report (presenting data to end of 2014), Public Health England, October 2015

[139] http://www.tbalert.org/about-tb/statistics-a-targets/uk-stats-and-targets/

[140] Infection at work: Controlling the risks: A guide for employers and the self-employed on identifying,

assessing and controlling the risks of infection in the workplace, Advisory Committee on Dangerous Pathogens, HMSO, 2003

[141] http://www.hse.gov.uk/biosafety/diseases/sars.htm

[142] Disease Outbreak News, World Health Organisation, 30 June 2015

[143] Dangerous substances and explosive atmospheres Dangerous Substances and Explosive Atmospheres Regulations 2002 Approved Code of Practice and guidance, HSE, 2013

[144] The Control of Major Accident Hazards Regulations 2015 Guidance, HSE, 2015

[145] http://www.legislation.gov.uk/uksi/1999/3232/contents/made

[146] Work with ionising radiation Ionising Radiations Regulations 1999 Approved Code of Practice and guidance, HSE, 2000

[147] Advice for outdoor workers from the Health and Safety Executive and the Health Departments in England, Scotland and Wales, HSE, 2007

[148] Sun Protection advice for employers of outside workers, HSE, 2001

[149] http://www.hse.gov.uk/radiation/nonionising/electro.htm

[150] http://www.hse.gov.uk/radiation/nonionising/electro.htm

[151] Ferguson installed tanning booths so united players top up their Vitamin D levels, Adam Shergood, Mail On line, 19 December 2012

[152] http://www.hse.gov.uk/foi/fatalities/in-year-names.htm, retrieved August 2015

[153] Identifying the incidence of electricity-related accidents in Great Britain BOMEL Limited, HSE, 2010

[154] ESQCR-Safety-related incidents reported in Great Britain under ESQCR, ONS, 2014/15

[155] Electricity at work Safe working practices, HSE, 2013

DEVELOPING ORGANISATIONS

Changes to an organisation's customer base, technological advances, new leadership, and many other factors change the way that organisations operate. Organisations develop new products, target new markets, or introduce new ways of working.

Mergers and acquisitions do not always happen when you want them to, and often do not leave time for executives to carefully consider how the new structure will be embedded into the existing organisation. Divestments similarly impact organisations more widely as the need for support functions diminishes.

Many organisations conduct reviews as a part of a three or five year plan. This enables the organisation to structure itself around its long term vision and mission. Establishing a clear vision for the organisation (where it wants to be) and a mission (how it is going to get there), helps to define tactical and operational priorities which underpin the two questions that focus the organisation: what it needs to do, and how it needs to do it.

Conducting a gap analysis between how the organisation is working currently, and how it needs to work provides a basis to establish change. Performance data and reports are important to this activity. A range of HR metrics can provide a useful indication of what is working well and what is causing problems (See Service Information for more details).

Partial reviews are often undertaken every year to validate the structure and introduce gradual changes. These are often linked to the budgetary process, and so can sometimes reflect more immediate or short term goals, such as a requirement to reduce headcount or cut costs.

As the new organisation starts to become clear, and before final decisions are made, it is important to engage in consultations with other employees because:

- Employees will have views on the development of the organisation that could contribute to further or better improvements (they have a good understanding of what is happening on the ground);
- Employees that believe that they are involved in the process are more likely to support the changes; and
- If there are to be any job losses as a result, being able to demonstrate that you consulted with employees at the earliest possible opportunity will improve the quality of a defence should you end up at tribunal.

When there are changes to working conditions, or the introduction of new technology or equipment, there is a statutory duty to talk to employees or their representatives. This duty arises from both the Safety Representatives and Safety Committees Regulations (in unionised organisations) and the Health and Safety

(Consultation with Employees) Regulations (for non-unionised organisations or for employees that are not represented by unions).

Discussions with employees should include proposed changes to the organisation structure, new ways of working and the means of achieving them – the project plan.

Armstrong[156] quotes research from Whittington and Molloy that successful organisation design is a consequence of seven activities:

- Top management support (personal and political commitment)
- Business case led activity considering wider impacts
- Substantive employee engagement in the change process
- Communicating with external stakeholders
- Involvement of HR from the beginning of the process
- Effective project management teams
- Use of skilled change management teams

Top Management Support

Top management support is key to the success of any organisation development project. Their attitude determines the level of support and effort within the organisation to see it through to completion.

As a result, there can be a lot of pressure on the author to present a best-case scenario. It is an important requirement to ensure that the business case sets out the realistic costs and the project risks, as well as the potential costs arising from those risks[157].

Business Case

The business case sets out the justification for the activity (or change), often in the form of forecast financial performance showing investment phasing, revenue and costs. Its acceptance is seen as a key stage of the project – normally triggering the commencement of the process.

A well thought out business case can contribute to reduced start-up costs because the legal requirements will be factored into the initial cost. These include:

- Work equipment – including inspection and maintenance activities necessary to keep the equipment in an efficient state, efficient working order, and in good repair;
- Workplace health, safety and welfare – including all the necessary facilities required for the number of employees anticipated; as well as
- Any other requirements arising from the health and safety regulations.

Cutting corners can cause additional costs and delays whilst mistakes are put right. In extreme cases, they can cause projects to be terminated, or introduce additional and unacceptable risks into the workplace.

In 2014 the National Audit Office (NAO) provided a clear indication of what can happen when business case in a way that reflects reality. According to the NAO[158], just 42% of projects were rated as highly likely or probable to deliver on time and on budget. 16% of major projects had significant doubts concerning their deliverability.

> *'Problems occurred because departments initially underestimated the project's complexity. Delivery schedules therefore had to be revised. In some cases, the whole project was re-scoped because it was deemed unachievable or impractical in its original form... less than half of the portfolio is considered likely to be delivered successfully, in terms of both project numbers and whole life costs'.*

Involving a wide variety of people in the development of the business case increases the likelihood that the necessary elements of the activity will be considered. Costs like salaries, recruitment, training and personal protective equipment, amongst others need to be included alongside the costs of machinery and equipment, guarding and fire protection as well as the costs of storage and handling of materials necessary for the fulfilment of the activity.

There may be additional costs associated with employee health, safety or welfare which also need to be factored in, including health surveillance for activities with specific risks. These costs have an impact on start-up and annual operations.

Stakeholder Involvement

In September 2014, the Financial Reporting Council published its Guidance on Risk Management, Internal Control and Related Financial and Business Reporting[159]. Their guidance says:

> *Good stewardship by the board should not inhibit sensible risk taking that is critical to growth. However, the assessment of risks as part of the normal business planning process should support better decision-taking, ensure that the board and management respond promptly to risks when they arise, and ensure that shareholders and other stakeholders are well informed about the principal risks and prospects of the company. The board's responsibility for the organisation's culture is essential to the way in which risk is considered and addressed within the organisation and with external stakeholders...*
>
> *The board has ultimate responsibility for risk management and internal control, including for the determination of the nature and extent of the principal risks it is willing to take to achieve its strategic objectives and for ensuring that an appropriate culture has been embedded throughout the organisation.*

Management of Change

According to the CIPD[160], management of change processes often fail because:

- Systems and processes are not aligned with changes to the organisational structure;
- Poor project management or change management;
- Poor communications, and a lack of engagement; and/or
- Over-management or lack of effective leadership.

In some industries[161], for example those entailing high risks or high potential consequences of failure, all modifications – whether involving procedures, plant and equipment, people or substances – will be subject to more formal management procedures.

Even where this occurs, the focus is often targeted on plant or process changes, and is not always followed, or extended, to cover changes to people. All impacts should be considered before implementation takes place.

Factors that are crucial to the success and safe implementation of a change include:

- Consideration of corporate history;
- Communication between different departments;
- Recognition of authorised personnel;
- Accurate recording and monitoring of changes to plant and process.

Many of these themes are seen as being outside of the domain of the HR practitioner. Often because they are seen as being the responsibility of the Line Manager and/or safety professional. Many of these activities should be performed by a competent person in the eyes of the regulator, i.e. a safety professional.

Good Practice from High Risk Industries

The Chemical Industries Association Safety Advisory Group outlines the following good practice for modification / change procedures:

- Members of staff must be aware of the hazards associated with the work they carry out and be able to determine that the risks involved are acceptable;
- Risk assessment must be carried out to determine the possibility and consequence of the hazards being realised; if necessary, appropriate precautions must be taken to minimise the risk; and
- All modifications – whether involving procedures, plant and equipment, people or substances – should be subject to formal management procedures.

The procedure should draw reference to:

- Evidence from previous incidents – their cause and means of preventing them;
- The intrinsic link between process definition and the validity of the hazard evaluation;
- The options that are available in the design of safety measures;
- Preventative measures; and
- Protective measures.

Good industry practice requires that process and plant modifications should not be introduced without having first undertaken a safety, engineering and technical review. This review should be traceable and identify changes proposed to the following factors:

- Process conditions;
- Operating and Engineering methods;
- Safety;
- Environmental conditions; and
- Engineering hardware and design.

A form of risk assessment should then identify what hazards have been created by the change that may affect plant or personnel safety, and what action can be implemented to reduce or eliminate the risk.

Typical hazards that may be introduced which need to be considered are fire, explosion and loss of containment.

Changes may affect other parts of the plant which may be quite remote from the source of the change. Therefore all parts of the plant should be considered in undertaking hazard identification and risk assessments.

The Role of Human Resources

According to Armstrong[162], HR have a broader, more holistic view of the organisation and an 'understanding of organisational [and individual] behaviour' and so are well placed to support the development of effective organisations.

HR also has a wealth of tools available to support the transition, including an understanding of trends in the nature of work, approaches to job design, organisation structure, resourcing, recruitment, training, competence, performance management, and reward.

References

[156] Handbook of Human Resource Management Practice, Michael Armstrong, Kogan Page, 2014

[157] Components of a PRINCE2 Business Case, PRINCE2, 2015

[158] Major Projects Authority Annual Report 2012-13 and government project assurance, Report by the Comptroller and Auditor General to the Cabinet Office and HM Treasury, NAO, February 2014

[159] Guidance on Risk Management, Internal Control and Related Financial and Business Reporting, FRC, 2014

[160] http://www.cipd.co.uk/hr-resources/factsheets/change-management.aspx

[161] The Chemicals Industry Association Safety Advisory Group

[162] Handbook of Human Resource Management Practice, Ibid.

RESOURCING & RECRUITMENT

Resourcing processes define organisations. The type of people hired, the manner in which they are hired, and the terms on which they join, define organisational culture. If culture matters, resourcing matters.

Resourcing

Most organisations have a framework or organisation design that predetermines the job, the hours, and the structure in which the employee will work. Creating more flexible structures or working arrangements can help organisations to get the most from their staff or widen the breadth of potential job seekers. Often it is necessary to flex or shape jobs to reflect the knowledge, skills and experience of the most suitable candidate. The health and safety duty is to adapt work to the individual.

Approaches to resourcing should reflect the environment in which the organisation operates. Whilst organisations in established sectors may benefit from structures that are solid and robust, some organisations may require a resourcing model that is more fluid and responsive. Under these circumstances the ability to change organisational structure, through the use of temporary or zero-hours contracts, or through changing roles and responsibilities in response to the skills and capabilities of job holders, may provide the organisation with the necessary flexibility to succeed.

> *The Department for Business Innovation and Skills (BIS) published guidance on zero hour contracts in 2015[163].*

Resourcing plans should include external sourcing and internal succession planning to ensure that there is a ready supply of personnel to meet the needs of the organisation based on an assessment of knowledge, skills, qualifications, behaviours and other factors to ensure fair and objective decisions.

The focus of the resourcing plan is on identifying current and future gaps; taking into account workforce demographics, attrition and scarcity; and developing plans to support business continuity.

Understanding the likelihood and impact of vacancies arising helps organisations to manage the risks associated with carrying vacancies or the loss of key workers. The HSE[164] and Health & Safety Laboratories[165] found that fatigue linked to high working hours caused by vacancies was a contributory factor in the Buncefield explosion. Effective resourcing strategies can significantly mitigate the risks associated with vacancies and 'time to fill'.

Building organisation structures that contain career and succession maps, provide a level of 'bench-strength' or substitution, which can help organisations to fill gaps efficiently, whilst retention plans can help to reduce the risk of employee departures.

According to the CIPD[166]:

- Average labour turnover has returned to 2009 levels, with 1 in 7 employees leaving organisations.
- Four fifths of respondents found that competition for talent has increased.
- Two thirds reported that required job skills are changing, and three quarters reported recruitment difficulties.

In this context, the importance of an effective resourcing strategy is key to business continuity, and talent management is a deliberate and tactical approach to support succession and retention of key workers, significantly reducing organisational risk.

Incorporating Hazards in the Resourcing and Recruitment Processes

Some environments and activities carry increased hazards. In these circumstances, it is particularly important to ensure that employees have the necessary knowledge, skills, experience and other attributes to work safely, so as not to cause harm to themselves or others.

Work that is comfortable to one person may be challenging to another, and vice versa. Ensuring that there is a correct fit between the pressures of the work and the inclination of the individual is key to achieving retention and maximising job performance.

Whilst the duty is to adapt work to people, it is not always reasonably practicable to fit the job (environment or activity) to the person, and fitting the person to the role may be both the safest and most effective solution. There are statutory requirements that must be met through resourcing and recruitment processes.

Appointing Persons – Statutory Requirements

There is a statutory requirement for the organisation to hire suitable and competent persons to undertake particular activities. For example:

- To hire a competent person to assist the organisation to effectively execute its responsibilities under the Health & Safety at Work Act.
- Where chemicals are handled, the competent person must know the work activity and understand the chemical processes involved[dd].

[dd] Where more than one competent person is appointed, the employer should nominate someone to co-ordinate, consult, compile, assure quality, record, communicate and implement the risk management measures and monitor their effectiveness, as well as consider the need for reviewing the assessment.

- Statutory equipment inspections (e.g. Lifting Equipment or Pressure Systems) must be undertaken by a competent and ideally independent person.

- Construction clients responsible for appointing a designer or contractor to carry out work on a project must take reasonable steps to ensure they have the skills, knowledge and experience, and if they are an organisation, the organisational capability, necessary to fulfil the role they are appointed to undertake.

  Furthermore, a contractor must not employ or appoint a person to work on a construction site unless that person has, or is in the process of obtaining, the necessary skills, knowledge, training, and experience to carry out the tasks allocated.

- For work at height and lifting operations, planners must have the practical and theoretical knowledge and experience to make a relevant assessment of requirements, whilst those undertaking the work should be competent, or be supervised by competent personnel if they are under training.

  There is evidence that suggests that future work at height 'accident victims' can be identified through assessment tests that measure attitude to risk[167].

- Work in confined spaces for workers with particular pre-existing medical conditions may significantly increase risk, for example claustrophobia, respiratory conditions or physical capabilities (e.g. wearing heavy breathing apparatus).

- Exposures like noise and vibration cause progressive damage. HSE Guidance is that if an employee has suffered exposure related harm, alternative work without that exposure should be considered.

- Driving vehicles is subject to HSE guidance that requires organisations to have checking processes in place to ensure (i) that drivers are at least 16 years of age (HSE recommend 17), 17 (on the public highway), and 18 if driving at ports, (ii) have a mature and responsible attitude and (iii) a level of physical and mental fitness[ee].

These examples highlight the importance of understanding the role. Without this understanding, it is not possible to discuss the requirements during the recruitment process. If this information is not shared, it will be impossible for the candidate to

---

[ee] Mental and physical fitness in this context relates to the specific requirements of the role and is likely to include the ability to access and egress vehicles safely, sufficient mobility and eyesight to enable a high degree of situational awareness, the learning ability and potential to become competent operators, and the ability to perform related activities such as the securing and loading/unloading of materials and attachments.

understand whether they have the necessary knowledge, skills, and other attributes necessary to perform the role, or for the employer to assess suitability.

Systems also need to be in place at ground level to ensure that line managers and supervisors responsible for the day to day resourcing of activities know and understand the knowledge, skills, capabilities and relevant physical capabilities of the staff and the requirements of the roles or activities they are required to perform.

Defining Requirements

The primary mechanism for defining requirements in the recruitment process is the person specification. This provides a structured process for defining the essential, desirable, and ideal attributes. Used properly, it can provide an effective defence against Equality Act claims.

The seven point plan is structured to help employers to specify requirements and categorises the knowledge, skills, experience, and other attributes defined in health and safety law into the points below:

- Knowledge
- Qualifications and Training
- Experience
- Skills and Abilities
- Behavioural Requirements
- Specific Demands
- Specific Requirements

Used properly, the person specification serves two purposes, firstly it helps to identify the most suitable candidate for the position, and secondly, it identifies the gaps between what was required, and what the successful candidate holds, providing a gap to be filled through information, instruction and training.

Recruitment

The ease with which an organisation is able to recruit is a function of the extent to which the labour supply meets the skills demands of the organisation, and the relative attractiveness of the employer to the potential candidate.

Recent research[168] has highlighted the importance of factors such as organisational values, working practices, perceptions of the organisation, and the organisation's goals and strategy contribute to attractiveness.

It is important to remember that the labour market is becoming increasingly employer savvy, with access to social media on organisations, including worker and society opinions. Even big name 'brand' employers like Apple and Amazon have received negative criticism.

The same research highlights a desire to invest more time and effort in candidate quality, but in practice, few organisations have achieved their goal, and if organisations cannot ensure that they are hiring the most suitable candidates (with the necessary knowledge, skills, and experience) to fill the role, the 'saving' will be a false economy.

Selection Techniques

Hiring the best available candidates for positions often means removing over 90% of applicants before they are seen – typically with seconds spent on evaluating CVs. This can create a result that the best CVs beat the best candidates. Whilst there is some help for candidates seeking work, this can sometimes concentrate on over-promotion rather than a focus on individual strengths and capabilities.

Employers have a duty to hire the most competent and capable person for the job. This requires careful consideration of suitability based on knowledge, skills, experience, attitude, capabilities, and other traits.

Often factors like academic achievement, training, and experience, which are all common selection methods provide minimal value in predicting future job performance[169]. Evidence suggests that the most effective measures of performance relate to cognitive ability and personality. The same research also highlights the importance of conscientiousness and emotional stability as positive indicators of future performance across most roles, and identifies the importance of factors like extraversion and openness in sales and management, and unsurprisingly the importance of innovation in creative roles. Different roles will require different traits.

Organisations use a variety of techniques including interviews, selection tests (in about half of organisations), and reference taking (in under a quarter) as a part of their selection process.

The CIPD survey has shown that employers are moving away from competency based interviews with a return to the more traditional CV led interview approach. This can make comparisons very difficult and make an assessment of cognitive ability and personality difficult.

Selection tests can be used to test a very wide range of characteristics, from verbal and numeric reasoning, mechanical and reading comprehension, through situational judgement, technical competence tests, and personality questionnaires.

Evidence suggests a fall in the use of specific skill tests, personality questionnaires, aptitude questionnaires and assessment centres, but a slight increase in general ability tests and on-line testing.

Validity

Validity is critical in terms of both equality legislation and employer belief. Face and Faith Validity do not provide justification to meet the requirements of the Equality Act, but do provide confidence to gain obtain organisation support.

> Validity: *'the extent to which a test measures what it claims to measure - the extent to which it is possible to make appropriate inferences from the test scores'*, British Psychological Society

The move back to CV led interviews reflects a move back to less structured interviews which are less predictive in calculating future performance, and with a fall in psychometric test use overall, the current trends appear to be moving backwards.

Assessing and Checking Applications

It is estimated that about one third of CVs may portray a better view of qualifications than are realistic. Many organisations verify qualifications and it pays to validate these claims where the qualification is important for the role, for example with a candidate that has a medical, engineering, or similar qualification.

Some NHS trusts have had particularly bad experiences, including the imprisonment of a former Chief Executive for fraud by misrepresentation. Although this is a criminal offence, it appears that it is risk that candidates are willing to take to secure an appointment.

Whilst some organisations may take the view that the candidate had not enjoyed the career history that they have without the required qualification, that is no guarantee, and many organisations will not check educational qualification validity[ff].

The CIPD survey found that less than a quarter of respondents undertook references as a part of the recruitment process. Even if they are only used to verify previous employment dates, they provide a level of assurance to the organisation that they are hiring someone who worked where he or she said they worked.

Offers of Employment

Ensuring that employees receive all the information necessary for them to make the right decision about whether to accept the position is an important part of the employment process and ensures employees get off to the right start[gg]. Providing information about the organisation's vision, mission, and values, helps condition new employees to the new organisation before they arrive and sets the tone for future conduct.

[ff] The Higher Education Degree Datacheck service (for example) costs £10 per enquiry.

[gg] Employers have two months to supply a written statement of terms of employment.

This is often the time when organisations supply many and detailed policies and procedures in the expectation that employees are going to read the detailed statements prior to arrival and have a good understanding of what they can and cannot do. It is perhaps better at that time to concentrate on sharing the goals, values and relevant terms, and allowing the induction to address the remainder.

Follow up

Understanding the knowledge, skills, and experience of workers to perform certain tasks is a critical factor in defining the extent to which supervision, training, instruction and information is required. Competence, capability, knowledge, skills, or experience defines whether a person should be undertaking a task, for example when planning lifts or carrying out manual handling. Using untrained personnel to perform work without adequate supervision is a failure to manage health and safety at work, a statutory duty.

Good recruitment practices can identify the knowledge, skills and experience gaps at the start of employment and identify what information, instructions and training is needed so that the new starter can work safely. Arranging a pre-start medical provides important base line information to support monitoring activities during an employee's career and can identify specific issues that need to be addressed prior to commencement of work.

Where work involves driving or dangerous equipment, it is not unusual for employers to include drug and alcohol tests as a part of the pre-start medical. Employment is sometimes conditional on successful completion of that element of the medical process. Employers should be aware that positive tests may be linked to a protected characteristics. In Wales, Multiple Sclerosis sufferers can be prescribed Sativex, a cannabis-based medicine and Doctors across the UK can prescribe a variety of opioids for chronic pain linked to many conditions.

Ensuring that employees are informed of any adverse medical findings, and that supervisors and line managers receive appropriate information to enable them to effectively plan and organise work is an important next step.

Some tasks, such as the use of Display Screen Equipment requires workplace assessments to take place as soon as possible, and ideally before commencement of employment, whilst work activities such as Manual Handling should be undertaken only by those that have received training.

References

[163] https://www.gov.uk/government/publications/zero-hours-contracts-guidance-for-employers/zero-hours-contracts-guidance-for-employers

[164] Buncefield: Why did it happen? The underlying causes of the explosion and fire at the Buncefield oil storage depot, Hemel Hempstead, Hertfordshire on 11 December 2005, HSE, 2011

[165] Fatigue: the insidious risk to health and safety, Julie Bell, HSL, 2015

[166] CIPD Resourcing and Talent Planning Survey 2015

[167] Recidivist risk takers who work at height Victoria Haines, David Hitchcock, Zaheer Osman, Edward Elton Ergonomics and Safety Research Institute Loughborough University, HSE, 2004

[168] CIPD Resourcing and Talent Planning Survey 2015

[169] Choosing the right tools to find the right people, The Psychologist, J Hirsh, September 2009

VULNERABLE WORKERS

Almost every employee will be vulnerable at some point during their working life. Recognising that fact from the outset can improve the effectiveness of resourcing and recruitment, and reduce risk to the organisation by ensuring plans recognise the dangers associated with those processes.

There are significant benefits to be gained from increasing diversity at work. According to ACAS, diversity can hold the key to fostering new ways of thinking, reaching out to a wider range of customers and growing your business[170].

Employers are recruiting from a more diverse employment base, and increasingly using more flexible working arrangements, introducing short term or temporary workers, that create additional challenges. There is a duty on organisations to adapt work to the individual, and this means recognising the individual characteristics of employees and ensuring that the organisation, its managers and supervisors, and the employee understand how work may affect them and the specific measures that they need to take.

Recognising that certain activities form a part of a job may preclude some people from undertaking the work (for example, because they are too young to hold a driving licence, or because they suffer from medical conditions that may prevent them from performing particular types of work).

In reality there are few jobs that cannot be undertaken by 'vulnerable' workers provided they have the necessary knowledge, skills, experience and capabilities to perform the work. As we will see later, all new starters are vulnerable when they are first recruited. The more likely scenario is that certain precautions may need to be taken to protect the health and safety of workers that, by virtue of their circumstances, may be more vulnerable than others.

The main types of vulnerable workers identified by the HSE are:

- Younger and older workers
- Workers of a particular race, for example migrant workers and workers that do not have English as a first language
- Workers of particular religions or beliefs
- Disabled workers
- Expectant and New Mothers
- New starters
- Temporary or Agency Workers

Age

Age creates different challenges for employers. Age is a protected characteristic under the Equality Act. As such, discrimination, harassment, or victimisation is unlawful. It is also worth bearing in mind that individuals, both young and old, can have a wide variation of individual capabilities, including health, fitness, strength and maturity.

Young Persons

The legal system recognises that young people may lack experience, awareness and maturity at work, and so could be more at risk. As a consequence there are specific regulations relating to young persons (those under 18) and children (those still at school).

Specifically, under the Management of Health & Safety at Work Regulations (MHSWR), employers have an absolute duty to ensure that young persons are protected at work. To that end employers cannot employ a young person for work which is beyond their physical or psychological capacity; which may involve harmful exposure to dangerous chemicals, radiation, extremes of cold or heat, noise or vibration; or otherwise involving a risk of accident which it may reasonably be assumed would not be recognised or avoided by young people owing to their insufficient attention to safety or lack of experience or training.

Where it is necessary for training, young persons (who are not children) may be exposed to those risks, but only when they are supervised by a competent person and the risks have been reduced to the lowest reasonably practicable level. This has particular implications for organisations operating, or contemplating, apprenticeship schemes and their supervision requirements.

Competence and maturity are not simply a matter of age, and training in itself will not ensure competence. A risk assessment will establish whether a young person can be exposed to risk, and if so, what level of supervision is necessary. Specific factors to consider would be whether there are any specific high risks, opportunities to act irresponsibly or take short cuts, which could put young people or others at risk.

There is no requirement to carry out a separate risk assessment specifically for a young person, as long as the existing assessment already considers the specific factors for young people. Furthermore, there is no requirement to re-assess the risk each time an employer takes on a new young person, provided they have no additional requirements.

Employers that have not previously employed a young person should review their risk assessments to ensure they take into account specific factors for young people before they start work.

The HSE provides some specific guidance on what to consider prior to hiring a young person, and these are summarised below:

- The fit-out/layout of the workplace and site where they will work;
- The nature of any physical, biological and chemical agents they will be exposed to, for how long and to what extent;
- What types of work equipment will be used and how this will be handled;
- How the work and processes involved are organised;
- The level of health and safety training given to young people.

Students and trainees (including children) on work experience from schools, colleges and universities are regarded as employees, and should be accorded the same health, safety and welfare protection. Employers must inform the parents/guardians of any child of the key findings of their risk assessment and the control measures taken, before the child starts work or work experience.

> *Radiation exposure is a risk that takes on a higher significance in law when work involves young people. In this case, where the employer's control measures are not sufficient to prevent a significant risk to young people, they should undertake the work only if: (a) it is necessary for their training; (b) they are supervised by a competent person; and (c) the risk is reduced to the lowest level that is reasonably practicable. Under the provisions of IRR99, young people cannot be designated as classified persons (persons with higher levels of exposure) and are subject to dose limits that are substantially lower than those for adult employees.*

Older Workers

According to the HSE, whilst young persons may lack experience, awareness and maturity at work, older workers may have reduced physical capability, may tire more quickly, and may take longer to recover from musculoskeletal disorders[171]. This is often compensated by experience and maturity, and an increased sense of risk awareness.

Disabled Workers

Employers have a duty under the Equality Act 2010 to make reasonable adjustments for disabled workers. The Equality Act identifies three circumstances where interventions may be necessary.

Employers should undertake a risk assessment to determine what adjustments are required in relation to the three circumstances below:

- Changing provisions, criterions or practices;
- Removing, altering, or providing features to overcome physical barriers;
- Providing extra equipment (auxiliary aids).

A reasonable adjustment in this circumstance would be one that removes a substantial disadvantage in comparison with persons who are not disabled.

A disabled person is not required to pay any of the costs to comply with the duty although some funding may be available to employers through the Government's 'Access to Work' Scheme[172].

The Workplace (Health, Safety and Welfare) Regulations 1992 and the associated Approved Code of Practice (ACOP) for Workplace Health, Safety and Welfare establish a requirement for workplaces to meet the health, safety and welfare needs of each member of the workforce and requires workplaces to be 'suitable' for everyone, including people with disabilities.

As a consequence, an employer may need to make some changes to their facilities to take account of the disabled person's needs. This could include:

- Consideration of doors, passageways, stairs, floors, surfaces, traffic routes, and emergency exits used by people with disabilities. Some disabled people who can walk find it easier to negotiate a flight of stairs rather than a ramp, and for those people handrails for support may be a more effective solution.
- Workstations including seating for disabled persons. Workers using wheelchairs may need to have workstation access widened and the height of their workstation modified.
- Rest areas equipped with suitable seating, which is adequate for the number of disabled persons, and their particular disabilities, whilst at work.
- Showers, washbasins, toilets, and facilities suitable for use by disabled persons which may take the form of specially designed cubicles in separate-sex toilet washrooms or a self-contained unisex toilet. For disabled people who can walk, doors to compartments should be outward-opening.

Migrant workers

Race is a protected characteristic under the Equality Act 2010. As such, discrimination, harassment, or victimisation is unlawful. Migrant workers may present particular challenges to employers. These are:

- Language and communication
- Competence
- Culture
- Confusion

Language and Communication

Many migrant workers have a good understanding of English, but not all. The requirement on the employer is to ensure that information is provided in a manner which is comprehensible to those that need it.

Where method statements, operating procedures, or job descriptions are written in English, consideration should be given as to whether it is reasonably practicable to modify or simplify the wording, translate them, or whether the use of images, signs, or other practical solutions may be a reasonable alternative that may also benefit English speaking employees.

There may be more significant communication issues arising from hand gestures or the use of technical jargon, which may not translate easily. The use of generic internet based translators is not reliable because important safety messages may be lost.

It is tempting to assume that people from a broadly similar ethnic background are likely to be able to communicate more easily with each other. This is not always the case, as for example, there are 122 different languages spoken in India.

Competence

It is not always easy to compare qualifications between the UK and other nations. Qualifications may have different syllabi, be at different levels, and may be awarded for competence in practices which are not used or considered appropriate in the UK. Furthermore, there is evidence that some people wishing to work in the UK may have obtained qualifications fraudulently or through ID theft.

There are several mechanisms for evaluating the qualification, but the most effective test is likely to be through a formal assessment of knowledge, skills and experience, perhaps through a practical examination or discussion. Good practice at the recruitment stage is to be consistent in approach across all candidates and this is a good way to assess actual competencies in the role.

Cultural Attitudes

Much has been written on international behaviours and attitudes (see for example Hofstede, Globe). These include attitudes to management, team working, and uncertainty. Attitudes can manifest in the way that employees feel able to raise concerns, care for their colleagues, and ask questions at work.

The fact that these behaviours can be so profoundly different provides the greatest contribution to diverse organisations, whilst simultaneously creating difficult challenges to supervisors and managers that do not have experience of, or training in, working with culturally diverse teams and individuals.

New recruits who have only recently joined the company and may need to work, either as a condition of their visa, or to earn money, may not be keen or willing to ask for help or clarification which can create additional risk.

Confusion

The combination of different languages, working methods, and cultures may combine to produce an environment in which the employee does not know how to work correctly or feel able to ask questions.

The confusion that can arise from differences in communication, competence, and culture may create uncertainty, indecision, or disorientation, all of which have the potential to cause harm. This places additional requirements on managers and supervisors to check understanding.

The HSE have produced a useful guide that explores the communication, competence, cultural, and confusion concepts in more detail[173].

Religion and Belief

Some religions have specific codes relating to the wearing of clothing, the growing of facial hair, and rules relating to the observance of prayer. These can affect the ability to wear personal protective equipment, the timing of breaks, etc. In some cases, there are specific protections in law, for example the wearing of turbans at work. Religion is a protected characteristic under the Equality Act 2010. As such, discrimination, harassment, or victimisation is unlawful.

The Wearing of Turbans

The Employment Act 1989 (as amended) exempts turban wearing Sikhs from any requirement to wear head protection whilst at work. On the face of it, this unusual and rare requirement appears to place a factor above the first duty of the Health and Safety at Work etc. Act, i.e. the provision and maintenance of plant and systems of work that are safe and without risks to health.

However, employers still have a duty to consider the risk of a head injury arising from the work being carried out, and to establish suitable and sufficient control measures on the basis of the defined Principles of Prevention. In practice these should include controls that are sufficient to minimise the risks so that it is not necessary for turban-wearing Sikhs to wear head protection in addition to the protection afforded by their turbans.

Where these controls are not sufficient, consideration should be given to the residual risks and the effect of head protection for those Sikhs voluntarily prepared to wear it, and/or their re-deployment to other work areas if they are not willing to wear head protection and the residual risk cannot be sufficiently reduced. This legislation has recently been extended beyond construction sites to all places of work.

The Wearing of Veils

Countries like France and Belgium have placed bans on the wearing of veils in public. The European Court of Human Rights has upheld the right of France to pass a law that bans the wearing of the burka or niqab in public. The Netherlands and Turkey have introduced laws that ban the wearing of veils in some parts of their society, for example in government buildings.

In the UK, the case of a Muslim classroom assistant hit the headlines in 2006/07, when an Employment Appeal Tribunal upheld an earlier decision that the dismissal of an employee for wearing a veil during lessons was not discriminatory[174].

This judgement was based primarily on the importance of face to face communication or eye contact which would occur in professions such as health, education, and social care. The way that the school handled the matter amounted to victimisation and caused injury to feelings, leading to the award of damages in favour of the applicant.

The Wearing of Beards

Many religions including Sikhism, Islam, sects of Judaism and Orthodox Christianity encourage or require their men to have a beard[175]. The wearing of beards can have an impact on food safety and can substantially hamper the effectiveness of respiratory protective equipment by preventing a seal.

In both cases, these can be easily addressed. In food preparation, the provision of beard nets or snoods has become commonplace, and with a trend in the UK for more men to wear beards for reasons of personal choice, these have become commonplace.

Similarly, the wearing of tight facemasks which may be unsuitable for long periods (over an hour) in any event, may be changed to powered respirators, or loose fitting face-pieces such as hoods or helmets which do not rely on a tight seal.

Jewellery of Religious Significance

The European Court of Human Rights ruled in a landmark case that a desire to manifest a religious belief, in this case by the wearing of a cross, is a fundamental human right, and an individual who wishes to communicate that belief to others should be able to do so[176].

It is important for organisations to consider all of the unique circumstances relating to the wearing of jewellery. Jewellery can be a contributory factor in accidents at work – neckwear, watches and rings can come into contact with moving machinery, get caught or stuck against objects, and cause or harbour infectious diseases.

Sensible consideration of the right to manifest a religious belief should be recognised but the nature of work may comprise risks beyond damage to company reputation, and it may be more appropriate for workers to communicate their belief through alternative means, for example a lapel pin.

Prayer Breaks and Days for Religious Observance

Where possible time to observe religious duties should be accommodated by organisations. This might include an appropriate place for prayer at work (a quiet area), and will often align with the timing of morning and afternoon breaks where appropriate. There is no requirement for employees to receive payment for this time although if breaks are normally paid, and time for religious observance takes place in normal break times, this would be a reasonable expectation. If there are no breaks that align with prayers, arrangements should be agreed between the worker and the employer, perhaps with a requirement for time to be worked back at the start or end of the day.

Similarly, employees wishing to take time off on religious days should normally be permitted to take annual leave, or flexi time (if arrangements permit it). Where this is not possible, consideration should be given to unpaid special leave which might be considered a reasonable adjustment. Organisations that employ a high proportion of employees of a particular religious belief may agree to switch holy days with public holidays in the UK.

Other religious events, such as Ramadan, which requires Muslims to fast during the hours of daylight for a lunar month, can have an impact on performance at work. If there is a risk that performance may be hampered, this should be managed through sensible and reasonable adjustments. Particular arrangements should be considered for employees who are working on shifts.

> The Equality Act 2010 places a duty on employers not to discriminate indirectly, i.e. *by applying a provision, criterion or practice to others, that puts those people that share a protected characteristic at a particular disadvantage when compared to others, and it cannot be shown to be a proportionate means of achieving a legitimate aim.*

Communication and co-operation with employees in relation to how their religious needs can be accommodated without jeopardising the health, safety or welfare employees, their work colleagues, and others will ensure safe ways of working that are respectful of employee faiths.

Expectant and New Mothers

There are particular circumstances in which the potential for harm is increased because the worker is an expectant or new mother (i.e. employees who are pregnant, have given birth within the last six months or are breastfeeding)[177].

Specific considerations should be given to:

- **Nature of Work** – lifting/carrying heavy loads, standing or sitting for long periods, work-related stress, workstations/posture, or long working hours.
- **Workplace Exposures** – particularly infectious diseases, toxic chemicals, lead, or radioactive materials.

Employers are required to take action where the nature of work or exposures may cause harm to an expectant mother, or their child. Employers may:

1. Temporarily adjust working conditions and/or hours of work,
2. Offer suitable alternative work (at the same rate of pay) if available, or
3. Suspend the employee from work on paid leave for as long as is necessary.

Employers must ensure that female employees are informed about the possible risks and the importance of informing their employer (in writing) as soon as they are aware of their pregnancy.

Employers have additional duties to minimise radiation exposure to extremely low levels to expectant, new or breast feeding mothers because of the way that radioactive sources are preferentially taken up by the foetus and placenta and are concentrated in breast milk.

Similarly some infections[178], if they are contracted in pregnancy, can affect the health of the mother and baby. In some cases the baby may suffer serious harm which may result in permanent disability or death.

If any significant risks have been identified, employers must take appropriate action as soon as they are notified (in writing) that an employee is a new or expectant mother to ensure that she is not further exposed. Good practice may be to encourage employees seeking to have a family to share this information at an earlier stage.

New Starters

According to the HSE, workers are as likely to have an accident in the first six months at a workplace as during the rest of their working life[179]. On the one hand, this may be down to a lack of familiarity with the industry, organisation, workplace or role, but it is as likely to be as a consequence of a nervousness about raising concerns or an eagerness to impress others.

Workers may not recognise hazards, understand or be aware of unwritten rules for the use of equipment, be unfamiliar with the site, and, particularly if they see others doing so, may ignore warning signs or rules, without understanding what the consequences of their actions may be. Employers should align the recruitment process as closely as possible with the job to be undertaken in order to establish the applicant's abilities, knowledge, skills, and experience in relation to the role, taking into account reasonable adjustments where necessary.

Specific new starter interventions, for example display screen assessments, initial health surveillance activities, and recent toolbox talks can help to demonstrate a positive safety culture. Inductions must provide the necessary information, instructions and training, in a manner which is comprehensible to the audience. It may be useful to include visual, non-verbal methods such as pictures, signs, videos and practical activities such as a walk-around to cover specific hazards and emergency procedures.

Encouraging new starters to raise concerns from an early stage, and letting them see others, particularly their peers and more senior personnel, raising concerns and taking action in relation to hazards is a positive way to encourage new starters to ask questions.

Additional control measures may be suitable for large sites or where there is an increased risk of injury. Some organisations use different coloured hard hats to differentiate between new starters, more experienced personnel, and supervisors. Managers and supervisors need to understand the problems that can be caused by a lack of familiarity and experience at the site.

Particular care should be taken to ensure that new starters understand the way things happen at the site. Previous experience may have been gained at sites that had a poorer attitude to safety, or used different mechanisms to raise concerns.

Temporary and Agency Workers

If the organisation uses temporary or agency workers, care should be taken to ensure their competence before they start work. The same health and safety standards that apply to permanent employees are likely to apply to agency workers and contractors. New temporary workers, and those that have not been on site for some time, are likely to need site familiarisation and specific job training, as well as supervision and monitoring.

Temporary and agency workers may work across many sites and may not know, or remember, the correct way to raise a concern or ask a question. Providing inductions and refresher training, supported by regular demonstrations of commitment to safety, such as toolbox talks, are an important way to ensure that temporary or agency workers are reminded of the importance of raising concerns and taking action. There are two main challenges that arise from the use of temporary or agency workers.

- The first challenge relates to the adoption of working practices and the safety culture within the organisation. Employees on short term contracts may perceive their period in work as being short and as such, may not be inclined to raise safety concerns that are unlikely to affect them, or because of the precariousness of their employment contract may be nervous to raise a concern.

- The second challenge is procedural. Under the Conduct of Employment Agencies and Employment Businesses Regulations 2003 agencies, and businesses that use workers supplied by them, must exchange the information they both need to ensure the safety of workers.

There is a specific need between the employer and the agency to communicate and co-operate in relation to who will be responsible for what, and to ensure that information is relayed to the employee.

This includes:

- Who is responsible for the risk assessment, method statement or safe system of work?
- How will any particular risks or hazards associated with individual workers be communicated to the employer (for example language or learning difficulties)?
- Who is responsible for ensuring the workers have the necessary information, instructions and training?
- Who is responsible for checking that workers have the necessary knowledge, skills, or qualifications, and how is that assessed?
- Who will provide the necessary PPE and/or health surveillance?
- Who is responsible for reporting relevant accidents to the HSE?

Contractors

Contractors present many of the same challenges as temporary and agency workers, with the additional difficulty that contractors may have additional reporting lines at work. Contractors are used by many organisations for maintenance, repairs, installation, construction, demolition and a variety of other activities that often include significant risks. Organisations engaging contractors to work at their premises, have a responsibility to safeguard their health and safety. Accidents can happen because the hazards of their job have not been properly identified and effective controls have not been put in place, or because contractors are not familiar with the health and safety rules on site.

Interfaces between the organisation and the contractor, or between different contractors, may not be clear and can be a significant cause of workplace incidents.

The HSE have published a guide[hh] to working with Contractors which sets out the five steps to working safely with Contractors[180]. The five steps are:

- Plan the work effectively, identify the hazards, assess the risks and agree the control measures (and accountabilities) with the contractor. If they have greater expertise, invite the contractor to undertake the risk assessment and prepare a method statement, but review their documentation to ensure that their proposal will work effectively on your site.

- Choose a contractor based on the safety and technical requirements of the task. Ask questions and view evidence to ensure that the selected contractor is capable to perform the task safely.

- Ensure the contractors know the site rules, that they record their arrival and departure, and liaise with a named site contact. If work is dependent on the site performing prior activities, ensure those activities have been completed before work is permitted to commence[ii].

- Keep a check to ensure that the work is going as planned and that defined control measures are in place. The amount of checking should be proportionate to the level of risk and volume of work being undertaken.

- Review the work on completion. Learn any lessons about work planning, contractor and organisational performance, and their impact on the final outcome.

The same health and safety standards that apply to permanent employees also apply to agency workers and contractors. Organisations should have systems in place to establish the competence of contractors arriving on site before they commence work, and to establish what job and familiarisation training, supervision and monitoring is necessary. Organisations must supply their contractor(s) with any appropriate health and safety information about the workplace. Safety arrangements should be agreed before work commences, and contractors should be fully aware of any penalties they will incur, if they fail to follow them.

Organisations that have workers from different contractors sometimes incentivise contractor organisations to work safely or raise concerns. This can be linked to contractor scoring processes used in contract re-negotiation or agreements on rates.

[hh] Note that the HSE Guidance on Contractors does not reflect the Construction (Design and Management) Regulations 2015

[ii] Sometimes, permit to work processes are used to control risks, particularly if they include entry to confined spaces, hot work, or work on electrical systems. Ensure contractors understand these systems prior to arrival and commencement of work.

In many cases, where contractors are deployed, organisations are required to fulfil duties set down in the Construction (Design and Management) Regulations. In those Regulations the definition of Construction is particularly wide (see Construction).

Workers under the influence

Alcohol

According to a report published by the Office for National Statistics at the start of 2015, approximately 15% of people in the UK regularly engage in binge drinking[181]. Drinking the night before can mean employees are still under the influence of alcohol the following day.

Many organisations have arrangements in place to support employees that suffer from alcohol related problems, but all employers should consider the implications of employees reporting for work under the influence of alcohol, and operating machinery that could put their safety, or the safety of others at risk.

Drugs

People take medication for a variety of different reasons. In some cases, these are supplied on prescription by a medical practitioner, but that is not always the case. Illegal drug consumption remains a significant concern for employers. Drugs can have a significant impact on work activities, particularly involving equipment or vehicles and employers should consider the risks to employees and others.

Anti-Depressants

In the UK, an average of 9% of British adults[182] are on prescribed anti-depressant medication. There is significant regional variation, and between one in five and one in twenty British adults are on prescribed anti-depressant medication dependant on the county in which they live. This number is significant for most employers. The side effects of medication to treat depression can include lack of concentration, confusion, dizziness, nausea, tiredness, lethargy, and a lack of motivation.

Painkillers

GPs issued more than 60 million prescriptions for painkillers in 2012. In the same year, up to 2 million people took painkillers prescribed for someone else. Pain killing medication can cause lack of concentration and a disregard for risk.

Legal Highs and Caffeine Dependence

There has been an increase in the numbers of people taking legal highs, high caffeine based and other legal stimulants which can put pressure on the heart, increase risk taking behaviour, and cause death.

Illegal Drugs

According to 2015 Home Office data[183], 1 in 12 persons aged 16-59 took an illicit drug (1 in 5 of 16-24 year olds) last year. In the 16-59 age group, men taking drugs (11.9%) was more than double that of women (5.4%).

Drug use across the working population has remained largely stable over the last couple of years, although there has been an increase amongst those aged 16-24. Cannabis was the most common drug, the second most popular drug for adults was cocaine, then ecstasy. For those aged 16-24, ecstasy was more popular than cocaine.

Drug use[184] is associated with symptoms including sickness, vomiting and headaches; sleepiness and lethargy; memory problems; confusion, anxiety and paranoia; depression; and agitation and aggression;

Factoring these medicines against the number of people driving at work, operating machinery, or making decisions affecting others provides significant cause for concern for most employers. Some employers have responded by introducing drug and alcohol policies which may include pre-start assessments, regular or random testing, and the support to employees who admit they have a problem.

References

[170] The benefits of having a diverse workforce, Workplace snippet, ACAS, 2012

[171] Ageing and work-related musculoskeletal disorders, A review of the recent literature, Health & Safety Laboratory, HSE, 2010

[172] https://www.gov.uk/access-to-work/how-to-claim

[173] http://www.hse.gov.uk/migrantworkers/employer/protecting.pdf

[174] Azmi v Kirklees Metropolitan Borough Council [2007] IRLR 434 (EAT)

[175] http://www.huffingtonpost.com/2014/10/08/religious-beards_n_5947438.html

[176] Eweida v British Airways plc [2010] EWCA Civ 80

[177] New and expectant mothers who work A brief guide to your health and safety, HSE, 2013

[178] Infection risks to new and expectant mothers in the workplace A guide for employers, Advisory Committee on Dangerous Pathogens, HSE Books, 2005

[179] http://www.hse.gov.uk/vulnerable-workers/new-to-the-job.htm

[180] Managing Contractors, A guide for employers, Second Edition, HSE, 2011

[181] Adult Drinking Habits in the UK, ONS, 13 February 2015

[182] Prozac Nation claim as anti-depressant use soars, NHS News, July 2013

[183] Drug Misuse: Findings from the 2014/15 Crime Survey for England and Wales, Statistical Bulletin 03/15, Edited by: Deborah Lader, July 2015

[184] http://www.nhs.uk/livewell/drugs/pages/cannabis-facts.aspx

COMPETENCE & CAPABILITY

Introduction

Training and Development is often seen as the domain of HR. The HR function commonly identifies training needs, controls the budget, and facilitates delivery. Health and Safety legislation defines an organisation's legal duties in relation to information, instructions and training.

All organisations have duties to provide information, instructions and training to their employees through legislation including the:

- Health and Safety at Work etc. Act;
- Management of Health and Safety at Work Regulations,
- Workplace (Health, Safety and Welfare) Regulations;
- Provision and Use of Work Equipment Regulations and
- Regulatory Reform (Fire Safety) Order.

The duties recognise the type of organisation, its activities, its workforce and its risk profile will define organisational needs.

Larger organisations may gain competitive advantage by providing employees with a greater depth of knowledge in a specialist field; whilst smaller organisations may require more flexible personnel with broader, more general knowledge and the ability to adapt that knowledge to different situations.

Specific duties arise from activities such as manual handling, display screen equipment, noise, chemicals, etc. Each of these, and many other risks have their own legislation. All of which set out specific requirements for information, instruction and training.

Lastly, the nature of the workforce will also have a significant impact on the training requirements of the organisation. For example:

- Organisations with high attrition rates are likely to have different training requirements to those with more established personnel.
- Organisations in quickly developing industries need to invest more in continuous professional development to keep up to date with technical progress.
- Organisations employing vulnerable workers need to ensure that training programmes and methods fulfil the requirements of their audience.

A strategic approach to training and development ensures that investment in training is balanced against the potential benefits (improved performance or reduced risks).

The primary focus of the health and safety legislation relating to training is that all workers have the necessary knowledge, skills, experience and abilities to meet the needs of the organisation safely and effectively, and without harm to themselves or others.

The legislation sets out Information, Instruction and Training activities necessary to achieve required levels of knowledge, skills, experience and, in some cases, the behaviours the organisation expects, generally starting with induction.

HR can use their knowledge and experience to determine the most effective and most important training investments, and assess the effectiveness of any training interventions deployed.

Good learning and development practices help organisations and workers at all levels to understand their own capabilities and limitations, a key element of competence.

Strategic Learning and Development

The Human Resources function is normally the repository for budgets, resourcing (administration, acquisition and sometimes delivery), communication and reporting on effectiveness. HR are more likely to have an indication of organisational plans, hold performance and development review data, and where undertaken, hold employee survey data, all of which can be used to determine a strategic focus for learning and development. This information and knowledge places HR in a position to analyse training needs, justify or approve interventions, and develop or source training across a range of activities including:

- Formal courses – internal or external;
- Short interventions;
- Coaching or Mentoring;
- Classroom or IT based learning methodologies;
- Work activities (e.g. participation in cross-functional work teams); or
- A 'blended' combination of the above.

HR Practitioners are seen as the learning and development specialists, and understand the importance of learning, development, training and education. All can contribute to improved organisational performance and reduced risk. The challenge is in the determination of field, and many of the following concepts are recognised far more widely than across HR or organisations:

Learning – the process by which a person acquires and develops knowledge, skills, capabilities, behaviours and attitudes;

Development – the growth or realisation of a person's ability

Training – the systematic application of formal processes to impart knowledge and help people to acquire the skills necessary for them to perform their jobs

Education – the development of knowledge, values and understanding for life.

HR Practitioners generally understand concepts like goal theory and expectation theory which define why people learn, and have a good understanding of different learning theories and learning styles.

Many will have experience of continuous professional development to support individual and organisational learning, and ensure all stay up to date with technical advances.

Organisational Knowledge

It is important that organisations retain knowledge of current and past organisational knowledge. Lessons from incidents at work combine with reviews of other measures of performance help to define organisational learning requirements. According to Armstrong[185] knowledge management is about getting the knowledge from those that have it to those who need it in order to improve organisational effectiveness.

Organisations have developed a variety of systems and processes to capture lessons learned and computerised systems provide mechanisms to access this information. One of the greatest challenges facing this type of system can be the culture and willingness to recognise, admit and share failings that caused harm or cost. Ensuring the culture is in place to encourage this sharing, these systems can be very effective.

HR can support learning organisations through:

- A positive attitude to learning, starting with senior management
- An open culture, based on commitment and trust
- Effective organisation design, promoting networks and team working
- Mechanisms that value, attract and retain contributing employees
- Motivation and reward systems for information sharers
- Formal and informal events and activities to share knowledge
- 'Capture and share' IT systems for communicating information

HR can also draw on knowledge and experience of the organisation through involvement in:

- Systematic problem solving
- Learning from past experience including incident investigation
- Workplace observation
- Recruitment and control of contractors processes
- Professional networking to learning from others
- Performance management and disciplinary processes
- Transfer of knowledge processes and

- Change management and Continuous improvement processes (e.g. Kaizen).

Sharing this information with employees that are new to the organisation as soon as is practicable can have a fundamental impact on organisational performance and can quite literally, save lives.

Induction

Inductions should take place when someone joins a new organisation, starts a new role, or when the existing organisation, technology, equipment, or systems change.

The induction should commence where the selection and appointment process concludes. It is unlikely that the selection process will find a candidate with all the requisite industry, site, and professional knowledge, skills and abilities to perform the role immediately. The induction process should fill that gap.

> *If employees are joining the organisation on contract, they may not have been subject to a formal selection process by the employer so particular care should be taken to establish their capabilities.*

This process may include an analysis of the new starter's capabilities, including:

- Numeracy and literacy levels (including grasp of English)
- General health (and baseline particularly in relation to workplace hazards)
- Relevant work experience and relevant cultural experience
- Physical capability to do job elements (if this was not fully addressed during the recruitment process)
- Familiarity with the work being done and the working environment.

Typically organisations have a great deal of information to impart to new starters at the beginning of their time on site, ranging from employment terms (hours of work, holidays, requests for time off, etc.); organisational and reporting structures showing who is responsible for management oversight and supervision; site awareness (and location of facilities); etc.

Inductions provide an important opportunity for organisations to welcome new starters (whether they are contractors, workers, or employees) to their organisation, get new starters to sign up to their corporate goals, values and principles, and provide important information, instructions and training to smooth their transition into the new organisation, location, department, and team.

Workers are as likely to have an accident in the first six months at a workplace as during the whole of the rest of their working life. This data is presented in the table below.

Accident Rate by Length of Service	Reportable[jj]	All Injuries
Less than six months service	3,316	9,861
Six to twelve months service	1,023	3,821
One to five years service	1,084	3,092
More than five years service	973	2,829

Research[186] indicates there are four main causes for the frequency of injury in the first six months of employment. These are:

New employees are as likely to have an accident in their first six months as the rest of their working life

- a lack of industry experience,
- a lack of knowledge about how to work at a particular site,
- a reluctance to ask questions, and
- a desire to impress.

Where new starters are additionally vulnerable for other reasons, the figures are even more startling. An analysis of fatal accidents to migrant workers in the construction sector reinforces this evidence…

8 of 16 migrant worker deaths in Construction happened within 10 days of arrival on site

…It found that four out of sixteen fatal accidents happened on the first day on site, another four occurred during the first ten days on site. Of those that died, only two had been in the UK for more than a year. Five were known to have limited experience of the UK construction industry.

Inductions will commonly consist of a combination of training, information, and instructions described above, and will normally include a practical and theory information to enable workers to understand what they should do, how they should do it, and why they should do it that way.

Inductions will normally include physical visits to the site; photographs site specific information; images and video (where appropriate) and explanations of signs and symbols used to help employees, visitors and contractors to understand (particularly where participants may have language or learning difficulties).

A key element of all induction training is to ensure that workers have understood the information, instruction and training they have received, and are acting on it, especially during the vital first days/weeks at work. Remember to make sure workers

---

[jj] Data based on 3 Day Reportable incidents.

know how and with whom they can raise any concerns about their health and safety and that they know about any emergency arrangements or procedures.

Until recently (October 2015), there was an Approved Code of Practice (ACOP) which defined expectations of an induction programme. Although this was specifically designed for contractors on a construction site, it provides a good indication of what should be included. The ACOP required information on[187]:

- Senior management commitment to health and safety;
- Organisational purpose (or project outline);
- Management, supervision and any other key personnel (structures);
- Site-specific risks that the person may be exposed to;
- Control measures including site rules, systems, routes, security arrangements, restricted areas to protect them;
- Arrangements for personal protective equipment, including what is needed, where to find it and how to use it,
- Arrangements for housekeeping and materials storage,
- Facilities available, including welfare facilities,
- Emergency procedures, including fire and first aid;
- Arrangements for reporting accidents and other incidents;
- Details of any planned training;
- Arrangements for consulting and involving workers in health and safety, including the identity and role of any trade union or employee safety representatives and committees; and
- Information about the individual's responsibilities for health and safety.

Supervision of new starters

New starters often need increased levels of supervision whilst they familiarise themselves with the site, the equipment, their responsibilities and the working methods on site.

During this period, it is important that supervisors understand the risks associated with new starters and provide a supportive environment which ensures work is undertaken correctly and short cuts or risks are not taken. These risks can be significantly greater and different to the day to day risks associated with activities when undertaken by knowledgeable and experienced personnel.

Refreshers

As well as providing inductions when change initially occurs, routine refresher training reminds employees of what they need to do, how they need to work; and a reminder of the risks that the organisation and the people working within it may be exposed to, as well as the control measures put in place to protect them.

Although health and safety Regulations and guidance require refreshers, they do not define frequency. This should be based on the amount of knowledge needed, how often it is used, and how serious bad practices might be.

Information, Instruction and Training

Sitting at the bottom of the Hierarchy of Control and the Principles of Prevention, information, instruction and training is seldom enough on its own to protect employees from harm, but it links with so many other control measures that it is a common outcome of risk assessments.

Information, instruction and training are common themes across health and safety law. They appear in the Health and Safety at Work Act, Regulations, Approved Codes of Practice, and other guidance supplied by the HSE.

Although information, instruction, and training are differentiated in the legislation, there are many common themes. Information, instructions and training must:

- Be provided by all employers, and to all workers.
- Be provided where specific hazards exist.
- Reflect the risks and the capabilities of the worker.
- Be provided in a manner that reflects its nature. Complex, long, detailed or high risk should be communicated in writing, whilst simpler smaller tasks may be explained verbally.
- Be provided in a timely manner, as soon as reasonably practicable.
- Be delivered in a manner that is comprehended by those receiving it.
- Be subject to validation, checking or assessment to ensure that the communication was effective.

Information, instruction and training duties arise for all employees from Regulations such as:

- Management of Health and Safety at Work
- Employers' Liability (Compulsory Insurance)
- Health & Safety (First Aid)
- Health & Safety (Safety Signs and Signals)
- Health & Safety Information for Employees
- Provision and Use of Work Equipment

In some cases, information, instructions and training applies specifically to organisations that recognise worker representatives for safety purposes:

- Health and Safety (Consultation with Employees)
- Safety Representatives and Safety Committees

Additionally, specific hazards which have their own Regulations place duties on employers to inform, instruct and train employees, for example:

- Health and Safety (Display Screen Equipment)
- Manual Handling Operations
- Personal Protective Equipment at Work
- Control of Noise/Vibration; Pressure Systems Safety
- Work in Compressed Air
- Control of Substances Hazardous to Health
- Control of Asbestos/Lead; Ionising Radiations
- Dangerous Substances and Explosive Atmospheres
- Genetically Modified Organisms (Contained Use)
- Construction (Design and Management)
- Borehole Sites and Operations; Mines and Quarries
- Merchant Shipping and Fishing Vessels; Railways and Other Guided Transport (Safety); Dangerous Substances in Harbour Areas
- Nuclear Installations, Offshore Installations

(This list is not exhaustive)

Information

There is a statutory duty on employers to provide employees with information on the risks to their health and safety; fire risks; and risks arising from shared buildings; along with the control measures established to prevent, reduce the risk, or mitigate the effects of a harmful occurrence, including the emergency procedures, in place to protect them from harm.

This includes any activities they need to perform to ensure that their safety or health is not compromised. It should also include clear information on employees' own duties to protect the health and safety of themselves and others, to support the organisation in the fulfilment of its duties, and the requirement not to interfere with anything provided for their safety.

As a part of this message, clear guidance should be provided on the rewards associated with working safely and the sanctions that will be applied if those duties are breached. Information can be provided in a variety of forms including notices, written procedures, signage, or verbally.

Instructions

Workers should be provided with clear instructions on how to perform tasks safely. In the case of work equipment, instructions may be based on manufacturer's guidance, but may be altered by the nature of work environment, the way that the equipment is used, or by the person performing the task.

Training

Training consists of formal interventions provided to ensure that employees have the knowledge, skills and capabilities to work safely; and informal interventions, such as site visits and sharing experiences to improve a workers risk perception and situational awareness. The HSE require organisations to measure training, in terms of attendance monitoring, and in terms of its impact, for example through safety performance.

Health & Safety Requirements

Health and safety legislation sets down competence requirements for those undertaking work (typically setting down the knowledge and skills requirements), as well as the information, instruction and training expectations on employers. A common theme is the duty on employers to ensure that all workers are aware and understand:

- The hazards they are exposed to, or potentially exposed to at work,
- The risks those hazards might produce,
- Details of any precautions and other controls that the organisation has taken to keep them from harm, and
- The details of any relevant controls or precautions that they need to take.

Employers should keep suitable records to identify who was trained when, and the content. A programme should be established to ensure that new employees are identified and trained, and all personnel receive regular refreshers.

When workers are given appropriate training, it is important to ensure that supervisors and other more senior staff are also aware of the good practices that have been taught so that they can lead by example, encourage the workforce to use the appropriate techniques, and spot incorrect practices.

Careful consideration should be given to persons that may have language difficulties, perhaps because English is not their first language, or because workers may have learning difficulties.

For employees with little or no understanding of English, or those who cannot read English, employers may need to make special arrangements. These could include providing translation, using interpreters, or replacing written notes with clearly understood symbols or diagrams.

Employers have a duty to make reasonable adjustments to meet the needs of disabled persons, but sometimes, reasonable adjustments can improve the overall standard of learning for all participants.

Employers also need to take account of the needs of people other than employees who may be present on site, such as contractors, members of the public, etc. While it may not always be practical to provide formal training in these circumstances, employers should consider what information or instructions may be necessary, for example, pictorial signs for infrequent visitors or for those for whom English is not their first language.

Workplaces

The Workplace (Health, Safety and Welfare) Regulations 1992 (as amended) and the supporting ACOP sets out specific competence requirements for those engaged in building inspection and maintenance; workplace or equipment maintenance, and for those planning, supervising or carrying out work at height.

The ACOP also sets out information and competence requirements for those modifying, extending or converting premises. The Regulations place particular duties on employers to give adequate information, instruction and training on hazardous workplace features such as tanks, pits and silos.

Emergency/Fire Safety

The Regulatory Reform (Fire Safety) Order requires organisations to provide employees with comprehensible and relevant information on identified risks, preventative and protective measures, emergency procedures, and the personnel with specific responsibilities in the event of an emergency.

This information must include details of specific work hazards and hazard identification arrangements, the details of any specific hazards that might arise in the event of an incident, accident, or emergency; warnings or communication systems used in the event of an incident, or in the event of operating conditions which could trigger an incident; including warnings to ensure that workers can get to a place of safety before an explosion occurs; and the details of emergency exits and escape facilities.

Employees with specific duties in the event of a fire, explosion, or other emergency must be competent, and must have received adequate training taking into account the size of and the activities performed in the premises. In this context, competence is described as 'sufficient training and experience or knowledge and other qualities to enable him properly to implement the measures referred'

The Regulations require employers to ensure that employees are provided with adequate safety training:

- at the time when they are first employed; and
- on their being exposed to new or increased risks because of
  - o Their being transferred or given a change of responsibilities within the responsible person's undertaking;

- o The introduction of new work equipment into, or a change respecting work equipment already in use within, the responsible person's undertaking;
- o The introduction of new technology into the responsible person's undertaking; or
- o The introduction of a new system of work into, or a change respecting a system of work already in use within, the responsible person's undertaking.

The training must:

- Include suitable and sufficient instruction and training on the precautions and actions to be taken by the employee in order to safeguard himself and other relevant persons on the premises;
- Be repeated periodically where appropriate;
- Be adapted to take account of any new or changed risks to the safety of the employees concerned;
- Be provided in a manner appropriate to the risk identified by the risk assessment; and
- Take place during working hours.

Manual Handling

The HSE have invested extensively in guidance for manual handling training because of the number of employees suffering manual handling injuries and musculoskeletal disorders.

There is specific guidance about what manual handling training should include and this is detailed below:

- *Manual handling risk factors and how injuries can occur;*
- *How to carry out safe manual handling, including good handling technique:*
  - *Think before handling/lifting;*
  - *Keep the load close to the waist;*
  - *Adopt a stable position;*
  - *Ensure a good hold on the load;*
  - *Moderate flexion (slight bending) of the back, hips and knees at the start of the lift;*
  - *Don't flex the back any further while lifting;*
  - *Avoid twisting the back or leaning sideways especially while the back is bent;*
  - *Keep the head up when handling;*
  - *Move smoothly;*
  - *Don't lift or handle more than can be easily managed;*
  - *Put down, then adjust.*

- *Appropriate systems of work for the individual's task and environment;*
- *Use of mechanical aids (training in use, maintenance, and reporting faults);*
- *Employees' duties to take reasonable care for their own safety and for the safety of others and to co-operate with their employers;*
- *Practical work to identify and put right anything the trainee is not doing safely.*

Employees should be trained to recognise loads whose weight, shape, features, and the circumstances in which handling might cause injury, such as methods for estimating weight on the basis of volume, or where that is no guide, alternative techniques for assessing the load, such as rocking from side to side.

Training should ensure that unfamiliar loads are treated with caution. For example, it should not be assumed that closed containers are actually empty. They should be tested first, for example by trying to raise one end, applying force gradually until either too much strain is felt, in which case the task should be reconsidered, or it is apparent that the task is within the handler's capability.

Display Screen Equipment

Information and Training

Employers have a duty to ensure that Display Screen Equipment operators and users receive adequate health and safety information relating to their workstations, and the measures taken by the employer to protect health and safety at work. These measures should include arrangements relating to daily work routines, eye tests, and details of any available training provided.

Employers have a duty to provide information and training to users when they become or display screen equipment user, or when their workstation, or the organisation of their workstation, is substantially modified.

Provision and Use of Work Equipment

Work planners must have the necessary knowledge, skills and experience to plan the work, giving due regard to factors such as the task (for example strenuous work), the environment (for example extremes of heat and cold), the individual or team and the organisation of work, such as working time, periodic breaks, and resourcing. Where work is contracted out, consideration should be given to the capability of the organisation to undertake the work.

Employees should not be authorised to use equipment until they have received the necessary information, instructions and training, have been assessed, and authorised to undertake the activity.

PUWER places a duty on employers to ensure that all persons who use, or supervise and manage those that use work equipment have available to them adequate health and safety information, and where appropriate, written instructions pertaining to the use of the equipment.

Information and instructions for these purposes include:

- The conditions and methods by which the work equipment may be used,
- Foreseeable abnormal situations and the action to be taken, and
- Conclusions to be drawn from experience in using the equipment.

The ACOP provides particular guidance on the importance of providing information to temporary workers.

Careful consideration should be given to whether the information should be provided verbally or in written form. The level of skill of the workers undertaking the task, their experience and training, the level of supervision, and the complexity and length of the activity should all be considered when establishing the most effective way to communicate information and instructions.

The information should be readily comprehensible to those that need to refer to it and should be presented in a manner which is easy to understand – in this context, consideration should also be given to the first language of those undertaking the work, as well as any employees that may have language or learning difficulties. Illustrations can be helpful to improve understanding.

The ACOP also provides guidance on training in the context of work equipment: *'every employer shall ensure that:*

> *' all persons who use work equipment have received adequate training for purposes of health and safety, including training in the methods which may be adopted when using the work equipment, any risks which such use may entail and precautions to be taken…*

> *'any of his employees who supervises or manages the use of work equipment has received adequate training for purposes of health and safety, including training in the methods which may be adopted when using the work equipment, any risks which such use may entail and precautions to be taken.'*

The ACOP provides additional guidance on what adequate training means.

> Employers should *'evaluate existing competence levels against the full range of work equipment that they may use; evaluate the competence required to manage or supervise the work;* and *train employees to make up any shortfall between their competence and that required to carry out the work with due regard to health and safety.'*

Training is likely to be greatest after recruitment, but also following changes to working methods, materials or equipment.

Maintenance Work

Maintenance work should only be undertaken by those who are competent to do the work. In most cases, maintenance will be performed in-house by suitably trained and competent staff. These employees may have completed apprenticeships in engineering or similar disciplines and should have a good theoretical knowledge of the engineering principles of their work, combined with a good understanding of the equipment, environment and tasks undertaken on the site.

In other cases, for example for simple equipment with limited requirements for maintenance, work may be performed by operators who have received training. In these cases, it is important that operators understand their capabilities, their limitations, and the extent of authority they have to undertake maintenance on their equipment.

In some cases, organisations may take the view that equipment should only be maintained by the manufacturer or by specialist contractors, although under these circumstances, there remain substantial duties on the duty holder to ensure their safety.

Isolation

It is important that employees working on or around work equipment understand the importance of isolation. All personnel involved in the isolation of plant and equipment should be competent to carry out their responsibilities. They should understand the purpose, principles and practices of isolation procedures and safety rules – for their own role, and for others involved in the operation of isolations systems; and be aware of the site's major accident hazards, i.e. the potential consequences of any release of energy or substances.

Isolation systems should include the establishment of roles to plan isolations; authorise isolations, vary isolations, install and remove isolations, and work on the plant. Staff undertaking maintenance may need to undertake significant on-the-job risk assessment (essentially considering what could go wrong and how to avoid injury), as the situation may develop and change in ways that could not be foreseen at the outset.

The HSE identify a series of specific competencies required for isolating plant and its associated activities. This should be reviewed against your organisation's requirements:

Competencies for Isolation Activities (HSE)

Hazards	• An awareness of the hazards represented by the plant. • A detailed understanding of the hazards on the plant and from adjacent plant.
Documents	• Understand the P&IDs, loop diagrams, cause and effect diagrams and power supplies applicable to the isolation.
Permit to work	• Understand the permit system and isolation certificates. • Know the procedures for issuing PTW and for identifying what isolations are required. • Certified as a permit issuer.
Isolation procedures	• Good working knowledge of isolation and risk assessment procedures for plant. • Understand the importance of following procedures. • Know how to check what isolations are in place and that they are the correct isolations required. • Know the procedures for installing/removing isolations. • Know the procedures for draining, venting, purging and flushing. • Know how to test and confirm correct installation of isolations. • Know how to record isolations on an isolation certificate. • Be able to assess the risks from non-standard isolations.

Lifting Operations and Lifting Equipment

A register of lifting equipment requiring routine inspection should be prepared by someone with the appropriate competence to do so. This should specify the parts of the lifting equipment to be routinely examined and tested. The register should specify appropriate intervals taking into account the condition of the equipment, its operating environment and use (frequency and loads).

It should be maintained and kept safe to prevent loss or modification by an authorised person, and should be updated from time to time to reflect changes in equipment and updated inspection records. Specific information should be produced following inspection by a competent person and this should be retained in a manner that can be provided to an Inspector on request.

The LOLER ACOP defines competence as 'such appropriate practical and theoretical knowledge and experience of the lifting equipment to be thoroughly examined as will enable them to detect defects or weaknesses and to assess their importance in relation to the safety and continued use of the lifting equipment'.

The ACOP also provides guidance as to the independence and authority of the competent person such that 'the competent person must be sufficiently independent and impartial to allow objective decisions to be made. This does not mean that competent persons must necessarily be employed from an external company.

If employers have the necessary competence to undertake inspections, they can perform them. However, if they do, they must ensure that their 'in-house' examiners have the genuine authority and independence to ensure that examinations are properly carried out and that the necessary recommendations arising from them are made without fear or favour.'

Whilst LOLER does not preclude the use of the person or organisation that maintains the equipment from carrying out the inspection, it does make it clear that this should not 'normally' be the case, otherwise the inspector would be responsible for assessing his own work. More information can be found in the HSE document: Thorough examination of lifting equipment - A simple guide for employers[188].

The ACOP places specific competence requirements on those responsible for planning, supervising and undertaking the lifting operation.

The ACOP requires that the person planning the operation should 'have adequate practical and theoretical knowledge and experience of planning lifting operations. The ACOP also provides a definition of competence as 'the skills, knowledge and experience to make the relevant assessment of the requirements of the lifting equipment being used and the type of task being carried out'.

The person planning the lift should also give consideration to the personnel available to undertake the lift and their knowledge, skills and experience. This is a critical element in the determination of responsibility allocation and the extent of written procedures required to support the lift.

The ACOP requires employees engaged in lifting operations to have received training and instructions so that they are able to perform pre-use checks on equipment to ensure that the equipment is free from faults or damage prior to the commencement of work, at the start of each working day, or at the beginning of every shift.

Pressure Systems

Competence under the Pressure Systems Safety Regulations refers to an organisation rather than an employee (unless the employee is self-employed). In general terms, the competent person must Carry out examinations in accordance with the Written Scheme of Examination (WSE) including:

- Review the WSE and confirm it is suitable
- Produce a written report for each examination
- Notify user/owner of repairs required
- Identify action in case of imminent danger
- Agree postponements of examination, where appropriate
- Draw up or certify written schemes of examination

The user of hired or leased equipment should make sure that the WSE is in place and that the certificate of examination is also current.

Where the competent person is employed by the organisation responsible for the equipment (the employer or dutyholder), they should be independent from the operating functions of the organisation, and they must have sufficient authority to stop the use of the pressure equipment should the need arise.

The ACOP requires competent persons (organisations) to be able to demonstrate:

- Staff with practical and theoretical knowledge and experience of the relevant systems;
- Access to specialist services;
- Effective support and professional expertise within their organisation;
- Proper standards of professional probity.

The level of qualification and experience is linked to the nature and use of the pressurised system but requires staff to be trained to incorporated or chartered engineer level with adequate relevant experience and knowledge of the law, codes of practice, examination and inspection techniques, and understanding of the effects of operation for the system.

Noise / Vibration

Information, instruction and training must be provided to employees when noise levels are at or above the lower exposure action limit, although in some cases it may be prudent to do so even when the lower limit is not reached.

The regulations require the following information to be provided:

- The nature of risks from exposure to noise;
- The organisational and technical measures taken in order to comply with the duty to eliminate or control exposure to noise or vibration in the workplace;
- The exposure limit values and upper and lower exposure action values;
- The significant findings of the risk assessment, including any measurements taken, with an explanation of those findings;
- The availability and provision of personal hearing protectors and their correct use;
- Why and how to detect and report signs of hearing damage/injury;
- The entitlement to appropriate health surveillance and its purposes;
- Safe working practices to minimise exposure to noise/vibration; and
- The collective results of any health surveillance undertaken in a form calculated to prevent those results from being identified as relating to a particular person

The HSE provide further guidance and recommend the provision of the following additional information:

- The likely noise/vibration exposure and the risks it creates;
- What the organisation is doing to control risks and exposures;
- Where and how people can obtain personal protective equipment;
- How to report defects in personal protective equipment;
- The employee's duties under the Noise/Vibration Regulations;
- What health surveillance employees will be provided with and how you are going to provide it;
- What symptoms employees should look out for, to whom and how they should report them.

The content should be reviewed in the event of significant changes in the type of work or working methods used.

The employer should also ensure that any person who carries out work in connection with the employer's duties has suitable and sufficient information, instruction and training.

The HSE have published a guide for employees that helps them to understand the problems associated with noise exposure, how to identify whether they are exposed to noise, and the duties of employers and employees[kk].

Research[189] into employer's failings to comply with the Regulations has identified the following key areas for consideration when undertaking a review of your internal processes:

- Insufficient awareness
- Training and re-training to ensure employees continue to recognise the risks of noise and protect themselves properly and
- Poor quality noise surveys that did not allow individual noise exposures to be estimated, and a lack of clear quality assurance practices and plans for continuous improvement.

Having an identified person with overall responsibility for the noise or vibration hazard, with sufficient authority to ensure that quality assurance and action plans are implemented, is considered to be fundamental to successful compliance.

Further research[190] indicates that the extent to which noise concerns are taken seriously is a function of three 'drivers' – these are:

- The knowledge and awareness of managers, particularly given the long latency nature of the potential health consequences;

[kk] http://www.hse.gov.uk/pubns/indg363.pdf

- The reactive nature of organisational cultures which tend to manifest in a reliance on personal hearing protection; and
- The size of the organisation, with larger companies perceived to have a higher level of time and money to invest in health and safety measures generally.

This highlights the importance of ensuring that managers at different levels of the organisation are aware of the long term risks associated with noise and vibration related hazards.

Driving in the Workplace

Employees should be authorised to drive vehicles in the same way that they should be authorised to operate or use other work equipment on site. The HSE has published guidance in the form of the Approved Code of Practice for Rider-operated lift trucks: Operator training and safe use[191] which requires operators to undergo basic training and testing unless they are under suitable supervision. The ACOP which can be applied to almost any type of workplace transport activity sets out details on a variety of topics. The ACOP guides employers to retain records of the recruitment and training processes.

Induction, information, instruction and other training should be provided to enable operators to fully and safely operate vehicles and attachments at work, including:

- The layout of workplace routes.
- How and where to report faults and hazards, incidents and accidents.
- How to use the vehicle and equipment safely.
- Specific risks and the control measures to reduce their likelihood or severity, for example speed limits, speed bumps, arrangements for loading and unloading areas, etc.
- Any requirements for personal protective equipment, or fall arrest systems.
- The organisational structure, level of supervision, and penalties for failing to follow working instructions.
- The details of any emergency procedures.

Driver assessment and refresher training should be provided at appropriate intervals to ensure that good habits are maintained and knowledge is not lost. Specific additional training should be provided when there are changes to activities, working methods, equipment, or following an incident or accident.

Supervisors should have sufficient training to be able to spot safe and unsafe practices. They do not need to be competent operators but should have a good understanding of the risks involved and how to operate safely to reduce them.

Employers should select instructors carefully (whether they are employed within the organisation or come from an external training or instructor company). Instructors should be able to demonstrate that they have a valid certificate of training, an insurance certificate (covering public liability), and proof that they are competent to train on the vehicles used on site. In the event that training companies use different vehicles to undertake basic training, it is important that familiarisation or conversion training is provided to ensure that operators are competent to operate the specific vehicles that they will be operating when at work.

Employers should give specific consideration to the different requirements of employees, contractors, and visitors (including delivery drivers). Pedestrians should receive specific information relating to the safe routes, and the risks associated with working on a site with vehicles should be incorporated into induction training and regular refreshers. This is particularly significant where vehicles are used (such as front loading shovels) where driver visibility can be partially obscured, or the size of parked vehicles can introduce new blind spots.

Construction

The Construction (Design and Management) regulations make specific reference to Pre-Construction Information (including information in the construction Health & Safety File) which must be provided as soon as is practicable to every designer and contractor appointed, or being considered for appointment, to the project.

The Regulations set down duties to those engaged in a project to provide comprehensible information or instruction, promptly (as soon as is practicable) and in a convenient form.

Designers and the Principal Designer have particular duties to provide information about hazards and ensure that it is captured in the Health & Safety File. The Principal Designer must also ensure that all information is provided to the Principal Contractor to support the development of the Construction Phase Plan. The Principal Contractor must ensure that information is supplied to the Principal Designer so that it can be captured in the Health & Safety File.

Workers and their representatives are entitled to take copies of the information held by the Principal Contractor, which relates to the health, safety and welfare of employees on site, unless the information might compromise national security, contravene a prohibition, relates clearly and specifically to a person (unless that person has consented to a disclosure), or the information may cause substantial injury to an undertaking, or has been gathered for the purposes of bring, prosecuting or defending legal proceedings.

Contractors must provide each worker under their control with appropriate supervision, information and instructions so that work can be carried out, so far as reasonably practicable, without risks to health and safety. The information must include a suitable site induction, procedures to be followed in the event of serious and imminent risk to safety or health, information relating to site risks, and information, relating to another contractor's undertaking, or otherwise, about which the worker ought to be aware.

A designer (including a principal designer) or contractor (including a principal contractor) appointed to work on a project must have the skills, knowledge and experience, and, if they are an organisation, the organisational capability, necessary to fulfil the role that they are appointed to undertake, in a manner that secures the health and safety of any person affected by the project.

A designer or contractor must not accept an appointment to a project unless they fulfil the conditions above. A person who is responsible for appointing a designer or contractor to carry out work on a project must take reasonable steps to satisfy themselves that the designer or contractor fulfils the conditions above.

A contractor must not employ or appoint a person to work on a construction site unless that person has, or is in the process of obtaining, the necessary skills, knowledge, training and experience to carry out the tasks allocated to that person in a manner that secures the health and safety of any person working on the construction site.

Specific work relating to excavations, cofferdams or caissons is conditional upon work being carried out by competent persons under the Construction (Design and Management) Regulations. In some cases, other 'competencies' may be required, for example those relating to work equipment, workplaces, lifting operations or lifting equipment.

A separate report exploring catastrophic events within construction[192] recommended specific training to include:

- A greater awareness of the importance of corporate risk management including the use of independent reviews,
- The effective management of temporary works, communication and interface management,
- Improved competence in construction design and management,
- Knowledge, skills and experience in safety risk management, and
- Better awareness of lessons learned from previous projects.

Control of Substances Hazardous to Health

Every employer who undertakes work which is liable to expose a person to a substance hazardous to health must provide suitable and sufficient information, instruction and training which reflects the nature of the work being undertaken and the level, type and duration of exposure.

The information should include:

- Details of the substances including their names, risks, and any limits;
- Specific information in relation to particular biological agents or materials, access to data sheets and specific legislative provisions relating to the chemicals;
- Significant risk assessment findings including details of precautions and actions to be taken by employees;
- The results of any monitoring and anonymised health surveillance information.

The nature of the information shall be such that workers will be able to clearly identify the contents of containers and pipes that may be hazardous to health. In certain cases involving biological hazards, written instructions must be provided on how to handle the substance.

Information on arrangements relating to accident, incidents, or emergencies; health surveillance; and the provision of facilities should be provided to employees.

Instruction and training on how and when to use control measures, defined methods of work, the safe use of protective equipment (including cleaning, storage and disposal), and emergency procedures should be suitable and sufficient.

In this context, good training provides the theory and reasoning behind decisions and is not restricted to what employees should do and how they should do it.

Chemical Classifications

The Approved Classification and Labelling Guide (Sixth edition) Chemicals (Hazard Information and Packaging for Supply) Regulations 2009 (CHIP 4) Approved Guide[193] provides guidance on the labelling of chemicals with particular characteristics. These include:

- Explosives
- Oxidising and corrosive substances
- Extremely Flammable, Highly Flammable, and Flammable substances
- Very Toxic, Toxic and Harmful substances
- Irritant and sensitising substances
- Carcinogenic and mutagenic substances
- Substances toxic to fertility, effecting fertility or lactation
- Special cases including gas cylinders, metals, alloys, gaseous preparations and organic peroxides

Employees should receive information, instruction and training in the safe use of substances which should include the provision of information on substance characteristics, storage, handling, use, and emergency arrangements. Specific phrases should be used for substances and preparations to ensure they are used safely. These are listed on the next page:

Keep locked up	Do not breathe dust
Keep out of the reach of children	Avoid contact with skin
Keep in a cool place	Avoid contact with eyes
Keep away from living quarters	Do not empty into drains
Keep container tightly closed	Never add water to this product
Keep container dry	Wear suitable protective clothing
Keep container in a well-ventilated place	Wear suitable gloves
Do not keep the container sealed	Wear eye/face protection
Keep away from heat	In case of fire and/or explosion do not
Handle and open container with care	breathe fumes
When using do not eat, drink, smoke	Keep only in the original container
	Use only in well-ventilated areas

- Keep contents under ... (appropriate liquid to be specified)
- Keep under ... (inert gas to be specified by the manufacturer)
- Keep away from food, drink and animal feeding stuffs/...combustible material/...sources of ignition/...(incompatible materials to be indicated)
- Do not breathe gas/fumes/ vapour/spray (appropriate wording)
- Take precautionary measures against static discharges
- In case of contact with eyes, rinse immediately with plenty of water and seek medical advice
- Take off immediately all contaminated clothing
- After contact with skin, wash immediately with plenty of...
- This material and its container must be disposed of in a safe way
- In case of insufficient ventilation wear suitable respiratory equipment
- To clean the floor and all objects contaminated by this material use ... (to be specified by the manufacturer)
- During fumigation/spraying wear suitable respiratory equipment
- In case of fire use ... (indicate in the space the precise type of fire-fighting equipment). If water increases the risk add: Never use water
- In case of accident or if you feel unwell seek medical advice immediately (show the label where possible)
- If swallowed, seek medical advice immediately and show this container or label
- Keep at temperature not exceeding ...°C
- Keep wetted with ... (appropriate material)
- Do not mix with ... (to be specified by the manufacturer)
- Not recommended for interior use on large surface areas
- Avoid exposure – Obtain special instructions before use
- Dispose of this material and its container to hazardous or special waste collection point
- Use appropriate containment to avoid environmental contamination
- Refer to manufacturer/ supplier for information on recovery/ recycling
- This material and its container must be disposed of as hazardous waste
- Avoid release to the environment. Refer to special instructions/SDS
- If swallowed, do not induce vomiting: seek medical advice immediately and show this container or label/... rinse mouth with water (only if the person is conscious)
- In case of accident by inhalation: remove casualty to fresh air and keep at rest

Biological Hazards

Employees need to understand the nature of the biological-hazards to which they are exposed and the effective treatment. All employees should be aware of the procedures for recording and reporting the incident.

Some employees should be aware of what to do in the event of an emergency affecting a fellow worker, contractor or visitor.

First Aiders should take particular precautions including covering any open wounds. They should also wear disposable gloves, and if splashing is possible, wear eye, nose and mouth protection and a disposable apron.

Where there is a requirement for mouth to mouth resuscitation, face shields should be provided and first aiders trained in their use. First aiders should always wash any parts of their body that may have come into contact with the patient or contaminated surfaces after treating the patient.

Ionising Radiation

The provision of information, instruction and training must be sufficient to ensure that employees are aware of the main risks, including the risk of accidental exposures, and the control measures provided to prevent or reduce those risks. Where appropriate, key staff should have adequate information about how and when to consult the Radiation Protection Advisor or other experts such as approved dosimetry services or the appointed doctor.

Every employer has a duty to ensure that employees who work with ionising radiation are given appropriate training in radiation protection and receive such information and instruction as is suitable and sufficient for them to know –

- The risks to health created by exposure to ionising radiation;
- The precautions which should be taken; and
- The importance of complying with the medical, technical and administrative requirements of these Regulations.

Training should be appropriate to the nature of the work and the needs of the individual. Individuals should be aware of when they need to seek help and where they should find it. The approved code of practice advises employers to consult their Radiation Protection Advisers when planning who needs what information, instruction and training.

Because of the particular risks to female employees, information, instruction and training should be provided on the risks from radiation to the foetus or nursing child.

Managers, supervisors and employees all need to receive information to ensure that they develop and maintain a commitment to reducing exposure wherever reasonably practicable. Employers also need to ensure that employees are competent to follow a defined safe system of work or wear personal protective equipment properly to avoid or reduce exposure.

Employers must also ensure that adequate information is given to other persons who are directly concerned with the work with ionising radiation carried on by the employer to ensure their health and safety so far as is reasonably practicable.

Employees performing particular tasks associated with the regulations, such as Radiation Protection Supervisors, those making entries in passbooks for outside workers, or those monitoring levels in controlled or supervised areas must also be competent to perform those functions.

Dangerous Substances

Where a dangerous substance is present at the workplace, the DSEAR Regulations require employers to provide sufficient information, instruction and training to employees on the appropriate precautions and actions necessary in order for employees to safeguard themselves and others in the workplace.

The information, instruction and training provided should be appropriate to the level of understanding and experience of employees. It should be provided in a form which takes account of any language difficulties or disabilities. Information can be provided in whatever form is most suitable in the circumstances, as long as it can be understood by everyone.

The ACOP provides additional guidance on what some of these duties mean, and how they should be achieved. Dangerous substances and explosive atmospheres present significant risks and employers rely on the full and proper adoption of necessary control measures and compliance with appropriate operating procedures and written or verbal instructions.

Information, instruction and training can be provided using a range of different techniques and media. Employers should select the most appropriate solution for their own circumstances taking into account employees, contractors, delivery drivers and other visitors that may attend the site. These include:

- Class or group tuition;
- Individual tuition;
- Written instructions including leaflets, courses etc.;
- Refresher training, toolbox talks etc.
- Notices explaining hazards (e.g. warning notices, no smoking signs etc.)
- Copies of emergency and evacuation procedures

Employers should provide information to workers on the substance(s) including the name(s) and the risk(s) the substance(s) present, provide access to any relevant safety data sheets and any legislative provisions which concern the hazardous properties of the substance. The employer should also provide employees with the significant findings of the risk assessment.

The ACOP additionally requires employers to provide information to employees and others (to the extent that it is required by the nature and extent of the risk) on the following:

- How and where the dangerous substance is used;
- The control and mitigation measures adopted, including methods of work, the reasons behind them, and how to use them properly;
- Training and instruction in the use and application of control measures and equipment taking into account manufacturers recommendations and instructions and should include the reasoning (theory) behind the practice.
- Procedures for dealing with incidents, accidents and emergencies.
- Any further information, particularly following a review of a risk assessment that culminates in changes to the way that work is undertaken, including why the change has been made and how the changes will affect the way that employees perform the work in future.

Employers should provide employees with sufficient training to ensure that the control measures and systems of work are fully implemented and operating procedures are correctly followed. Sufficiency in this context is defined by reference to the degree of complexity of the hazards, risks, processes and controls.

Significant findings of the risk assessment help to explain what the risks are, how the control and mitigation measures are designed to protect their safety, and help employees to understand and use the safeguards that employers introduce.

Electricity

The HSE guidance highlights the importance of training to ensure competence. Even the most highly qualified and capable people may not be competent to carry out specific types of work without suitable training.

Competent workers will be self-disciplined and aware that reckless behaviour with electricity can lead to injury and death. Those in control of the work should:

- Assess the degree of competence of individual workers against the specific type of work to be done;
- Provide clear instructions, information and adequate training for employees on: the risks they may face; the measures in place to control the risks, emphasising the safe system of work to be used; and how to follow emergency procedures;
- Arrange for those being trained or those newly trained to be accompanied and supervised.

People doing the work should be aware of their own limitations to perform that work and the constraints as to how they carry out the work. This includes recognising when it is unsafe to continue with the work and knowing how to deal with any contingencies that may arise.

Major Hazards

Employees must receive suitable and sufficient information and instructions on the conditions and methods of use of equipment, any foreseeable abnormal conditions and the actions to be taken in the event that they arise.

Training should be provided in accordance with appropriately defined standards and should specifically include an awareness of the applicable regulations, the activity being undertaken and any foreseeable risks that may arise from it, as well as safe systems of work and other control measures to be used to reduce risk, and the actions that should be taken in the event of an emergency.

The training should provide both the necessary content to perform the role, and sufficient theoretical knowledge as to enable the employee to understand why work should be performed in a particular manner.

The training should provide the employee with the necessary knowledge, skills, and experience to fill any gaps in his previous knowledge and should include a period of familiarity with the process, plant and equipment. Refresher training should be provided to ensure that bad habits do not creep in or work steps forgotten.

All training should be provided by competent instructors and should use the most appropriate techniques which may include a combination of group and individual learning.

As described earlier, within process safety, competence is defined as:

> 'an ability to undertake responsibilities and perform activities to a relevant standard'.

'Major hazard organisations require competent staff who have the necessary skills, knowledge and experience to undertake critical tasks in such a way as to prevent a major accident or minimise the consequences to people and the environment should one occur'[194] – in this context, competence is defined in a manner consistent with other regulations.

The guidance makes specific reference to human factor issues to the extent that they should be addressed with the same rigour as technical and engineering measures. The importance of human factors led to an extension of the traditional definition of competence and the need for an additional definition for 'competence management'.

Work at Height

Every employer shall ensure that no person engages in any activity, including organisation, planning and supervision, in relation to work at height or work equipment for use in such work unless he is competent to do so or, if being trained, is being supervised by a competent person.

Where the risks of falling as a consequence of working at height have not been removed entirely, employers shall provide such additional training and instruction or take other additional suitable and sufficient measures to prevent, so far as is reasonably practicable, any person falling a distance liable to cause personal injury.

This training shall include training in the use of work equipment or fall arrest devices to protect the employee from falling. The organisation shall ensure a sufficient number of available persons have received adequate training specific to the safeguard, including rescue procedures.

Where work at height involves the assembly, dismantling or significant alteration of scaffolding, this work must be supervised by a competent person, and be undertaken only by persons who have received appropriate and specific training in the operations envisaged, and which addresses the specific risks such work entails.

Although competence and training are seen as key factors in ensuing work at height safety, a report[195] evaluating the effectiveness of the new regulations (which included a requirement to ensure employees were adequately trained before working at height), indicated that only 52% of trade union representatives thought training was provided to people who worked at height. This figure was much lower than the level reported by managers, but 30% of employees indicated that their companies needed to take further measures to make work at height safer, especially training.

Confined space

Workers must have adequate training and experience in the particular work involved to be competent to work safely in a confined space.

Training standards must be appropriate to the task, and to the individual's roles and responsibilities, so that work can be carried out safely. Where the risk assessment indicates that properly trained individuals can work for periods without supervision, you should check that they are competent to follow the established safe system of work and have been provided with adequate information and instruction about the work to be done.

Specific training for work in confined spaces will depend on an individual's previous experience and the type of work they will be doing. This training will need to cover:

- an awareness of the Confined Spaces Regulations and in particular the need to avoid entry to a confined space, unless it is not reasonably practicable to do so;
- an understanding of the work to be undertaken, the hazards, and the necessary precautions;
- an understanding of safe systems of work, with particular reference to 'permits-to-work' where appropriate;
- How emergencies arise, the need to follow prepared emergency arrangements, and the dangers of not doing so. More detail on emergency training is provided below.

Emergency Procedures

The regulations are clear on the importance of emergency procedures: *'no person at work shall enter or carry out work in a confined space unless there have been prepared in respect of that confined space suitable and sufficient arrangements for the rescue of persons in the event of an emergency, whether or not arising out of a specified risk.'*

Organisations must make suitable arrangements for emergency rescue which will depend on the nature of the confined space, the risks identified and the likely nature of an emergency rescue. Organisations should not rely on the public emergency services.

Organisations should consider accidents arising from a specified risk, and any other accident in which a person needs to be recovered from a confined space, for example incapacitation following a fall. To be suitable and sufficient the arrangements for rescue and resuscitation should cover:

Rescue and resuscitation equipment;	Control of plant;
Raising the alarm and rescue;	First aid;
Safeguarding the rescuers;	Public emergency services; and
Fire safety;	Training.

Training for emergencies is likely to include some or all of the following:

- *The likely causes of an emergency;*
- *The use of rescue equipment, e.g. breathing apparatus and lifelines;*
- *The check procedures to be followed when donning and using apparatus;*
- *Checking of correct functioning and/or testing of emergency equipment;*
- *Identifying defects and dealing with malfunctions and failures of equipment during use;*
- *Works, site or other local emergency procedures including the initiation of an emergency response;*
- *Instruction on how to shut down relevant process plant as appropriate;*

- *Resuscitation procedures and, where appropriate, the correct use of relevant ancillary equipment and any resuscitation equipment provided;*
- *Emergency first aid and the use of the first-aid equipment provided;*
- *Use of firefighting equipment;*
- *Liaison with local emergency services in the event of an incident, providing relevant information about conditions and risks, and providing appropriate space and facilities to enable the emergency services to carry out their tasks; and*
- *Rescue techniques including regular and periodic rehearsals/exercises. This could include the use of a full-weight dummy. Training should be realistic and not just drill based, and should relate to practice and familiarity with equipment.*

There are publicly available qualifications in confined space work accredited by City and Guilds, IOSH, and others, but these may not address the particular rescue, first aid or fire-fighting equipment in use, the nature of the work environment in which the activity will take place, local arrangements for shutting down plant, or local arrangements with local emergency services. As such, a recognised qualification should be seen as a part of the overall training requirement, but not the training requirement itself.

Leaders, Managers, and Supervisors

The leaders of the organisation have specific requirements. They need to understand:

- Their legal obligations, particularly in relation to the Health and Safety at Work etc. Act and the Management of Health and Safety at Work Regulations.
- Guidance on Leading Health and Safety at Work.
- The activities undertaken and the risks they pose to the organisation;
- Organisational processes.

Managers and Supervisors need to be provided with an understanding of what their employees do, and how they are expected to do it, so that they can effectively monitor behaviours. These need to be closely aligned with hierarchical structures.

Managers and Supervisors also need to receive regular training to ensure that they are up to date with current thinking in their industry and are able to respond to technical advances.

The primary purpose of supervision should be the assurance that control measures and systems of work have been fully implemented and that operating procedures are being followed. As such, managers and supervisors must have the necessary knowledge of working methods, risks and control measures to be able to spot safe and unsafe practices and deal with those effectively.

Supervisors should have a good understanding of the workers under their control to the extent that they can identify what training, information and instructions they need to perform the role.

All workers should engage in continuous professional development to ensure that they are aware of the latest thinking for their industry and discipline. This is a key component of the principles of prevention.

Competence

According to the CIPD[196], the terms 'competency' and 'competencies' focus on the personal attributes or inputs of an individual. They can be defined as the behaviours (and technical attributes where appropriate) that individuals must have, or must acquire, to perform effectively at work.

'Competence' and 'competences' are broader concepts that encompass demonstrable performance outputs as well as behaviour inputs, and may relate to a system or set of minimum standards required for effective performance at work.

The HSE[197] has a slightly different view of Competence, and somewhat unhelpfully, uses the term in a variety of settings and contexts interchangeably. According to the HSE, employers need to make sure that all managers, supervisors and employees are competent to do their work properly. This means processes must be in place to ensure that:

- New recruits (including managers) have the relevant knowledge and experience to be able to do their jobs safely.
- Existing employees are competent, and receive such information, instruction and training as to remain competent, particularly where changes in equipment, processes or technology occur.

Competence, to a greater or lesser extent, depends upon the context in which the work is performed. In environments where risks are greater (such as the major hazard industries), competence is defined more robustly.

> **Competence** - *the ability to undertake responsibilities and perform activities to a relevant standard, as necessary to ensure process safety and prevent major accidents. In this context, competence is a combination of knowledge, skills and experience and requires a willingness and reliability that work activities will be undertaken in accordance with agreed standards, rules and procedures.* (COMAH)

Competence Management/Competency Frameworks

According to the HSE, 'Competence Management' consists of the arrangements to control, in a logical and integrated manner, the cycle of activities within the organisation that will assure and develop competent performance. The aim is to ensure that individuals are clear about the performance that is expected of them, that they have received appropriate training, development and assessment, and that they maintain, or develop, their competence over time.

Key to this process is the concept of the 'Competence Standard' or standard of competence, which is defined as the standard of work expected to satisfy a number of requirements, including business objectives as well as process safety, environmental protection, and health and safety requirements. The context, environment and culture are particularly relevant during an individual's development programme, before their first competence assessment, and when seeking to address any subsequent sub-standard performance.

This is reproduced below under the terms of the open government licence.

DEFINE COMPETENCE MANAGEMENT SYSTEM	• *Identify activities and assess risks* • *Select standards*
DESIGN THE COMPETENCE MANAGEMENT SYSTEM	• *Develop procedures and methods* • *Decide how to meet the standards* • *Establish requirements for training, development and assessment* • *Maintain managers competencies*
IMPLEMENT THE COMPETENCE MANAGEMENT SYSTEM	• *Select and recruit staff* • *Train, develop and assess staff* • *Control activities undertaken*
MAINTAIN AND DEVELOP COMPETENCE	• *Monitor and re-assess staff performance* • *Update the competence of individuals* • *Manage sub-standard performance* • *Keep records*
VERIFY/AUDIT THE COMPETENCE MANAGEMENT SYSTEM	• *Verify and audit the CMS* • *Review and feed back*

The model is intended to be cyclical to the extent that the verification, audit and review processes should trigger a revised set of requirements for a Competence Management System and so the process re-commences.

This differs from a 'Competency Framework', which according to the CIPD is a structure that sets out and defines each individual competency required by individuals working in an organisation or part of an organisation.

Selected 'competencies' were used in Selection (by 85% of respondents), Learning and Development (82%), Performance Management (74%) and Reward (30%)[198]. The top 7 most common behavioural competencies used are:

Team orientation – 86%	Results orientation – 59%
Communications – 73%	Problem solving – 57%
People management – 67%	Planning and organising – 51%
Customer focus – 65%	

Other competencies include Technical Skills, Leadership, Business Awareness, Decision Making, Change Orientation, Developing Others, Influence and Persuasion, Initiative, Interpersonal Skills, Strategic Orientation, Creativity, Information Management, Quality Focus, Self-Confidence/Assertiveness, Self-Development, and Management.

In many ways, the CIPD Competency Framework reflects the 'behavioural' and 'human factors' approach from the HSE and others, and particularly the role that behaviours contribute to events at work. In a similar vein, managers and supervisors are being orientated towards coaching and supporting workers and promoting a positive safety culture as a part of their roles and responsibilities.

Competence (Competency) management as a wider process which will typically include a variety of standard and non-standard HR processes, such as:

- Performance management and review processes;
- Incident investigation and workplace observation processes;
- Change management processes;
- Sub-standard performance / disciplinary processes; and
- Recruitment and control of contractors processes.

Training Effectiveness

Training evaluation is a critical but often overlooked part of the training function. Factors like poor line manager expectations, budgetary prioritisation on volume over quality, poor recognition of value amongst those responsible for training delivery, and a senior management focus on cost over value, can all undermine training effectiveness.

Many HR practitioners use the Kirkpatrick model to evaluate training[199] and establish the effectiveness the training, the learning achieved, the resultant behaviour and the impact of that change on organisational results.

Kirkpatrick is not without its detractors, and it is important to recognise that the model is imperfect because it does not consider external factors on delegate and organisational performance, but it provides a view on training effectiveness.

One of the best examples of assessing training effectiveness can be found in the Assessment of Competence Systems across COMAH sites between 2012 and 2015. Their work amounts to best practice competence management review and audit, and provides a method for practical and pragmatic assessment of competence systems.

The assessment consisted of two parts: (i) a review of basic operational competence, and (ii) a thorough and more systemic audit of competence. The content of these two elements – the review and audit – are described below.

Assessing Competence Management System Effectiveness

A Review of Basic Operational Competence

The first stage consisted of walk-throughs or talk-throughs[II] of critical task. Success was measured based on the following performance criteria:

- Designated competence standards exist for key tasks;
- The person performing the task meets a designated competence standard;
- The person fully understands the task to be undertaken and its significance in controlling risk;
- Activities follow a documented procedure (where one exists);
- Plant and process design facilitates the task being undertaken in accordance with the documented procedure;
- The person has been provided with sufficient resources (including time) to undertake the task; and
- The person performs effective checks to determine that the key task is undertaken to the correct standard.

A Thorough and Systemic Audit of Competence

The second stage consisted of a more thorough review of competence on site and was intended for sites that had shown a weakness in the first approach, or where other evidence indicated that the first stage would not be necessary to indicate system weaknesses.

[II] Walk-throughs involve practical evidence at the point of work. Talk-throughs happen remotely and are not evidenced at the job site, but may use plant diagrams to provide a point of reference.

This process started with an analysis of the following information:

- Job descriptions and competence matrices (if available);
- Evidence of training needs analysis;
- Records of audit/review of the competence management system;
- Examples of training materials;
- Documents relating to validation and evaluation of training; and
- Evidence that incident findings and/or "near miss data" are incorporated.

It was followed up with a series of interviews with:

- Experienced frontline staff;
- Trainees, new recruits and/or employees new to the role;
- Supervisors, Middle/Senior Managers;
- Engineers responsible for design and/or changes to design;
- Those responsible for developing procedures and systems of work;
- Training Managers, Trainers, Assessors; and
- Safety Representatives/Employee Representatives.

Lessons to be learned from the Review and Audit Model

The guidance reflects the importance of:

- The periodic assessment of all levels, including Directors, in terms of their training needs.
- Managers need to understand the tasks of those that report to them.
- Instructor Training – to a standard where they cannot be faulted by line management or trainees.
- The use of measured and structured on-the-job training linked to major accident hazards.
- Training under realistic conditions taking into account the pressure and seriousness of potential outcomes.
- The use of knowledge-based systems (why we do things), then rule-based systems (how), then skill-based systems (what, when), which all have a place in a competence system.
- The use of logs to record training, attainments, and reports by relevant personnel.
- Monitoring and measurement of performance on the job using independent scoring by two or more trained[mm] supervisory personnel with close knowledge of the individual's performance on carefully defined rating scales for general and specific attributes known to contribute to skilled performance.

[mm] Formal training for supervisors and assessors in order to ensure consistency.

- Assessments to clearly indicate whether employees are competent or not yet competent, and where employees are not yet competent, whether they should be suitable for more training and development or are not suitable for the activity.
- Evaluating whether existing competence systems, such as NVQs, fully address the major accident hazard focus.
- Recruitment and selection decisions based on suitability for the activity.

Talent Management

When The War for Talent[200] was published in 2001, it highlighted the benefits of organisations that adopted the five principles below:

- Creating a talent oriented mind-set;
- Developing superior employee value propositions;
- Retooling the recruitment strategy;
- Developing people effectively and progressively; and
- Differentiating and retaining the most talented personnel.

Unfortunately, the last point has caused criticism of HR departments that have lost sight of the other four goals, and have engaged in talent management practices that have concentrated training spend on a minority at the expense of the wider organisation (and demoralising many employees as a consequence). This has undermined a wider recognition of the contribution and role of team working, process or system failings, and encouraged risk taking behaviour associated with recognition and reward. In extreme cases, talent management has provided development to the most able, whilst neglecting those with greatest need.

In defence of HR, organisations face significant risks by personnel in key positions, either through the decisions they make and the impact those decisions can have on the organisation, or through the loss of key personnel. This lack of a holistic view has created programmes that are poorly aligned with other corporate or HR programmes[201]. What seems to have been lost in the process is the:

'A Talent oriented mind-set'

A belief that talent is a [the] source of competitive advantage which should be provided by all leaders and managers to all employees to create a positive impact for every part of the organisation, and as basis on which all organisations can build and grow.

'Superior employee value propositions'

A set of value propositions which are equitable based on the talent that every employee contributes.

The War for Talent recognised the difference in importance expressed by individuals and proposed that 'value propositions' should be assigned to work activities, organisational brand, personal development, reward, and work-life balance.

'Retooling the recruitment strategy'

The War for Talent recognised that deploying traditional approaches to recruitment, based on the filling of vacancies with suitable candidates, as and when they arose, fails to recognise the unique nature of people and their skills. The paper proposed a new approach to recruitment that is not based on traditional hierarchies or vacancies, but:

- Identifies new labour markets,
- Recognises the uniqueness of each organisational unit and their challenges,
- Recognises the value of the employer brand,
- Allows for some creativity in approach, and
- Flexibility in traditional grading structures.

'Developing people effectively'

Which includes a recognition that in order for development to be successful, it needs to be established in the organisational culture, with less reliance on training and a greater recognition of the role of job experiences, coaching and mentoring, albeit in a manner which is structured and valued as a part of a wider recognition of the importance of talent in the organisation.

More recent surveys by the CIPD have shed some light on the basis of a talent management policy built on developing future senior management; developing high potential employees; supporting achievement of strategic goals; attracting, recruiting and retaining key personnel; and meeting future skills requirements.[202]

Without effective talent management, internal resourcing cannot be relied upon to fulfil organisational needs through career development opportunities (career maps), or build 'bench-strength' (the talent pipeline or internal talent pool) to support succession planning objectives or attract/retain key workers.

A key element of personal fulfilment and self-worth comes from the belief that individuals can grow and develop in their current role and have an opportunity to progress in their personal development.

Understanding Capability and Competence

All employers have a duty when entrusting tasks to employees, to take account of their capabilities. In some cases, these is prescribed in law.

> *For example, the Fire Safety (Employees' Capabilities) (England) Regulations 2010 and the Fire Safety (Employees' Capabilities) (Wales) Regulations 2012, require: 'Every employer must, in entrusting tasks to employees, take into account their capabilities as regards health and safety, so far as those capabilities relate to fire.* [203]

This same duty applies equally to competence, for example, the brief guide to working at height[204], competence at different levels is described in some detail:

> *'You should make sure that people with sufficient skills, knowledge and experience are employed to perform the task, or, if they are being trained, that they work under the supervision of somebody competent to do it.*
>
> *In the case of low-risk, short duration tasks (short duration means tasks that take less than 30 minutes) involving ladders, competence requirements may be no more than making sure employees receive instruction on how to use the equipment safely (e.g. how to tie a ladder properly) and appropriate training. Training often takes place on the job, it does not always take place in a classroom.*
>
> *When a more technical level of competence is required, for example drawing up a plan for assembling a complex scaffold, existing training and certification schemes drawn up by trade associations and industry is one way to help demonstrate competence.'*

HR practitioners spend a lot of time dealing with employee issues because establishing whether a matter is one of capability or one of competence, rightly or wrongly, often determines the procedure that should be followed in addressing the concern.

Legislation, Approved Codes of Practice, and Guidance provide good indicators of acceptable behaviour or standards of performance, and in some cases advocate sanctions to be applied when failings occur.

For example, employees working with chemicals have clearly defined duties that they are expected to follow when at work. Specifically, under the Control of Substances Hazardous to Health Regulations, employees should:

- use control measures in the way that they were intended;
- follow defined methods of work;
- wear PPE and RPE in accordance with employers instructions;
- store PPE when not is use;

- Remove PPE and other equipment that could cause contamination when eating, drinking or smoking;
- Maintain a high standard of personal hygiene;
- Report defects or concerns promptly to an appointed person.

Where employees do not follow instructions, the HSE can be similarly prescriptive. Their published guidance[205] relating to the Control of Noise at Work advises organisations to:

> *'keep a record and introduce a system to enable people to report deficiencies to a person with responsibility and authority for remedial action... Where an employee is not using hearing protection properly you should ask them why, and either resolve the difficulty or give and record a verbal warning...Where people persistently fail to use protectors properly you should follow normal disciplinary procedures'.*

In this context, a disciplinary investigation is likely to be sufficient if it is possible to demonstrate that:

- The employee was aware of the importance of wearing personal protective equipment (PPE),
- Had received sufficient information, instruction and training,
- Was able to obtain his PPE,
- Employees had been given an opportunity to raise concerns about the use of the PPE, those issues had been considered, and subsequent actions reported back to employees and/or their representatives.

It is important to note that the mere act of not wearing hearing protection in this case, of itself, is unlikely to warrant disciplinary action if the organisation does not have effective systems and controls in place to ensure that nothing prevents the wearing of PPE.

Capability

The HSE interpret capability differently to the HR community. The HSE identify capability as being the wider elements of a person's knowledge, skills, abilities and attributes that enable him or her to perform a task. This can cause some confusion.

Health

Capability related actions commonly occur as a consequence of persistent lateness or absence which may well have been caused or exacerbated by work. Properly investigating and understanding the causes of absence can have an impact beyond any individual and enable an organisation to identify and address the root causes of the absence/timekeeping issues.

The most common causes of work related illness are musculoskeletal disorders caused by manual handling, repetitive movements, or tiring positions; psychosocial conditions such as stress, anxiety and depression; or to a lesser but still significant degree, exposures to substances at work. These have all been detailed elsewhere in the book.

Applying the same logic to the investigation as that described in the Noise example above, will help organisations to identify circumstances within their control. Identifying these illnesses and the contribution made by the organisation to the illness (where one exists) can help to protect other members of the workforce. Early identification, through routine health surveillance, encouraging reporting of concerns, or through effective return to work processes can enable an organisation to introduce changes before matters reach a significant stage.

Employers may identify a greater sense of duty to care for employees that have been harmed at work. Where an employer has little choice but to terminate employment for capability reasons, the manner of that termination and the support provided by the employer in the lead up to that time is likely to have an impact on the culture of the organisation because of the significance of the departure to the team.

Other Capability Reasons

Despite the best efforts of the employee and the employer, sometimes it is not possible for an employee to reach the standard required to perform the role. In some cases, the nature of the work requires a component that the individual does not possess and is not capable of possessing, whether through a lack of competence or a physical characteristic which is an absolute job requirement.

The Equality Act sets out specific rights for employees with protected characteristics and this is supported by other legislation, such as the Workplace (Health, Safety and Welfare) Regulations that require employers to make reasonable adjustments in the form of:

- Changing provisions, criterions or practices;
- Removing, altering, or providing features to overcome physical barriers;
- Providing extra equipment (auxiliary aids).

Unless reasonable adjustments are considered under the three criteria described above, that decision will almost certainly be unfair and unlawful.

Specific duties, such as those described in the Noise and Vibration Regulations, require organisations to consider moving an employee who has suffered harm as a consequence of his environment to an area of work where that exposure does not exist.

Competence

Where the HSE differ from the HR community in relation to capability (including competence), they interpret Competence in a more similar light – Competence is generally regarded as possessing the necessary knowledge, skills, and experience to perform a role. Where necessary this is supplemented through the receiving of information, instructions, and training (and sometimes supervision).

A clear element of competence in this context is the understanding of the role holder of what is expected:

- What work they are required to perform;
- What standard the work should achieve;
- How the work should be completed.

If employees fail to reach the right standard, further information, instructions and training should be provided. If, despite this, employees still fail to reach the right standard, a process of targeted improvements should be undertaken, either to bring the employee to the right standard or to exit the individual from the organisation.

The nature of the work undertaken is likely to have a significant impact on the way that process will work, and the degree of supervision and other support that may be necessary during the interim, transitionary, step.

Qualifications/Statutory Contraventions

In some cases, organisations require employees to hold particular qualifications to perform work (for example gas installation). Employees are sometimes hired with a provision that a qualification will be obtained during a period of training for the role. If employees are unable to achieve the qualification, or if they lied about holding a qualification to gain an appointment, and this subsequently came alight when the certificates were checked, the employer may have no choice but to terminate employment.

This may be particularly relevant where the law requires an employee to meet a particular requirement, for example to hold a driving licence, or where work involves particular activities from which an employee or Director is barred as a consequence of legal process. This could include, for example a Director who is disqualified or an employee whose name has been added to the sex offenders register. In some cases, the employer may be able to consider alternative employment, but this would depend very much on the individual circumstances of each case.

Conduct

The HSE expect employers to apply a reasonable level of control over their employees. Partly, this is through a recognition that managers have a right to manage, but more significantly it is in recognition of a philosophy that those who create the risks should manage the risk – a theme which appears consistently throughout the Health & Safety at Work and the Management of Health & Safety at Work Regulations.

Behaviour is covered within the context of wider employee engagement and human factors in the next chapter. Where conduct is unacceptable, employers have a duty to act. So called horseplay can be dangerous and lead to serious injuries. Discrimination (despite being felt by 6%) of the workforce remains prevalent in many organisations where 'banter' is seen as a way to make the days pass faster. These environments are often the ticking time bombs waiting for a moment to turn nasty. More importantly, their reliance on other factors suggests that the nature of work may not be sufficiently fulfilling to work on their own.

As with the noise example provided earlier, it is important to carefully investigate and understand the root causes of poor behaviour. Stamping out the root causes is likely to be more effective in the long run than dealing with individual transgressions if there is a more significant cause involved.

Managing Events – Capability and Competence

Capability like competence is a necessary prerequisite for work to be undertaken effectively and safely. These can be in the form of contractual or legal requirements that the holder must meet, physical or psychosocial conditions that may prevent an employee from working in a particular work environment or from performing a particular work activity without putting his health or safety, or that of others at risk.

> *In rare cases, it can be caused by serious illness, either with the job holder, or with someone for whom they are the primary carer. Macmillan provide an Essential Work and Cancer toolkit for employers on the basis that 'right now, or sometime soon, you are going to have to deal with cancer in the workplace'. This is available from www.macmillan.org.uk/atwork*

Managing Sickness Absence

The HSE are keen to help employers and employees to reduce sickness absence for many of the reasons described above, and encourage employers to actively support the rehabilitation and return to work processes[206]. The HSE identify several steps that employers can take to facilitate a return to work, to end a period of absence and contribute to the rehabilitation – called 'readjustment'. These are:

- Understanding the employer's role
- Managing return to work
- Recording sickness absence

- Keeping in contact
- Planning and undertaking workplace adjustments
- Making use of professional or other advice or treatment
- Agreeing and reviewing a return to work plan
- Co-ordinating the return to work process
- Developing a policy on return to work and putting it into practice.

Understanding the employer's role

Although there is no absolute duty to help every ill employee to return to work, there are specific duties set down in the Equality Act, the Workplace (Health, Safety and Welfare) Regulations, the Employment Rights Act, and the Health and Safety at Work Act.

The HSE identify good practice, and suggest that employers start with a review of Getting started on those practices, particularly taking a fresh look at the ways in which:

- You work with trade union and other employee representatives on help for ill, injured or disabled workers;
- You check and record sickness absence;
- Your managers are trained to deal with sickness absence and disability;
- You involve absent employees in planning their return to work;
- Wage arrangements and conditions of work can help or hinder return;
- You plan reasonable adjustments for disabled workers;
- You control any risks to employees from work activities;
- Work is managed to prevent poor health being made worse by work.

The Fit-Note

The Department for Work and Pensions has produced a Guide for Employers and Line Managers called 'Getting the most out of the Fit Note'[207]. According to the authors, *'using the fit note to its full potential helps you reduce your sickness absence costs (for example sick pay, staff cover and lost productivity), and minimises the disruption caused by employees being off sick unnecessarily'*. The guide is based on four principles:

- Appropriate work is usually good for people's physical and mental health.
- This is also the case for people who have a health condition - work can support their recovery and help them maintain their wellbeing.
- In most cases, people do not need to be 100% fit to return to work. This may not mean doing their normal job.
- People with health conditions may have limits on what they can do at work, but these will not always mean they cannot do any work.

Managing return to work

This comprises a series of six elements:

- Recording absence – to identify those whose return may be delayed without intervention; to better understand the underlying causes; to plan cover for absence; to identify trends or patterns; and to benchmark performance against others.
- Keeping in contact – there is no definitive right frequency for contact, everything should be decided on the individual circumstances, but the HSE Guidance contains a series of 'Dos and Do nots'
- Planning and undertaking controls and adjustments
- Making use of advice and treatment
- Agreeing a return to work plan, and
- Co-ordinating the return to work process.

Good practice[208] also identifies the benefits of collecting telephone reporting data at the commencement of an absence, automated interventions when trigger points arise, and regular reporting so that managers understand the significance of the problem. These techniques can further enhanced[209] by effective absence management policies, monitoring, cause analysis, absence management, and well-being initiatives.

The government launched the Fit for Work programme in 2015, targeted primarily at small to medium enterprises so that they can refer employees that have been absent due to sickness for four weeks or more, for a review which culminates in a 'Fit for Work – Return to Work Plan'.

The return to work interview

The purpose of the return to work interview is to confirm the circumstances of the sickness absence, and to ensure that any remaining health concerns are properly addressed before work re-commences. It can be an opportunity to discuss any necessary adjustments that may need to be put in place on a temporary or permanent basis. Evidence indicates that the return to work interview can also provide positive encouragement and re-assurance to an employee when conducted well, but can become threatening if not managed well[210].

Accidents at work

In some cases, capability can be affected because of an event at work. That may be because of an accident, or through an adverse reaction to an event, or through a gradual build-up of exposure that has caused serious harm. The HSE has published guidance[211] on investigating accidents at work. Their four stage plan: gathering evidence, analysing the information, identifying risk control measures and developing and implementing an action plan. The focus of this exercise is to ensure that others do not suffer the same fate.

Good practice recommends incident investigations consider the following information:

- Where and when did the event happen?
- Who was injured or otherwise involved?
- How did the event occur?
- What activities were being undertaken at the time?
- Was there anything unusual or different about the circumstances?
- Were there safe working procedures and were they being followed?
- What injuries or ill health effects were caused?
- If there was an injury, how did it occur and what caused it?
- Was the risk known, and if so why wasn't it controlled?
- Did the organisation and arrangement of work influence the event?
- Was maintenance and cleaning sufficient?
- Were the people involved competent and suitable?
- Did the workplace layout influence the adverse event?
- Did the nature and shape of materials influence the event?
- Did difficulties using plant or equipment contribute to the event?
- Was the safety equipment sufficient?
- Did other conditions influence the adverse event?
- What were the immediate, underlying and root causes?
- What was the role of human factors?
- What risk control measures are needed/recommended?
- Do similar risks exist elsewhere, if so where?
- Have similar adverse events happened before?
- Which risk control measures should be implemented in the short/long term?
- Which risk assessments/working procedures need to be reviewed/updated?
- Are there any trends or common causes that need investigating?

References

[185] Handbook of Human Resource Management Practice, Ibid.

[186] http://www.hse.gov.uk/vulnerable-workers/new-to-the-job.htm

[187] Managing Health & Safety in Construction: Construction (Design and Management) Regulations 2007 Approved Code of Practice L144, HSE Books, 2007

[188] Thorough examination of lifting equipment - A simple guide for employers, HSE, 2008

[189] Epidemiological evidence for the effectiveness of the noise at work regulations, Prepared by the Institute of Sound and Vibration Research, the Medical Research Council's Institute of Hearing Research and the MRC Hearing & Communication Group, HSE, 2008

[190] Influencing duty-holders behaviour regarding the management of noise risks Nikki Bell and Jennifer Webster, Health & Safety Laboratories, HSE, 2011

[191] Rider-operated lift trucks Operator training and safe use, Approved Code of Practice and guidance, HSE, 2013

[192] Preventing Catastrophic Events in Construction, CIRIA and Loughborough University, HSE, 2011

[193] Approved Classification and Labelling Guide (Sixth edition) Chemicals (Hazard Information and Packaging for Supply) Regulations 2009 (CHIP 4) Approved Guide, HSE, 2009

[194] COMAH Competent Authority Inspection of Competence Management Systems at COMAH Establishments (Operational Delivery Guide), published by the Competent Authority, 2011

[195] First evaluation of the impact of the work at height regulations: First Evaluation of the removal of the 'two metre rule' Prepared by System Concepts Limited for the Health and Safety Executive, 2007

[196] Competence and Competency frameworks, CIPD Factsheet, retrieved November 2015

[197] www.hse.gov.uk/competence

[198] Competency and Emotional Intelligence (2006/7) Raising Performance through Competencies: Annual Benchmarking Survey, London

[199] Evaluating Training Programs The Four Levels, Donald Kirkpatrick and James Kirkpatrick, March 2006

[200] The War for Talent, Ed Michaels, Helen Handfield-Jones, Beth Axelrod, Harvard Business School, 2001

[201] Talent Management Survey, CIPD, 2007

[202] Talent Management Policies Survey, CIPD, 2013

[203] http://www.legislation.gov.uk/uksi/2010/471/regulation/2/made

[204] Working at height A brief guide, HSE, 2014

[205] The Control of Noise at Work Regulations 2005, Guidance on Regulations, HSE, 2005

[206] Managing sickness absence and return to work, An employers and managers guide, HSE, 2004 as amended to include the Fit Note

[207] Getting the most out of the Fit Note, Department for Work and Pensions, September 2015

[208] A pilot study into improving sickness absence recording in National Health Service acute trusts, Simon Hill, Dr Gerard Woodruff, Dr Peter Verow, HSE, 2007

[209] Managing sickness absence in the police service, IES, Published by the HSE, 2007

[210] Attendance management in the Fire and Rescue Service, National Centre for Social Research, HSE, 2008

[211] Investigating accidents and incidents A workbook for employers, unions, safety representatives and safety professionals, HSE, 2004

PERFORMANCE & REWARD

Performance and Reward are two hotly debated areas within the field of HR, and rightly so as they can have a significant impact (positive or negative) on the organisation. Over the last decade there has been a drive to more closely link reward through performance assessment with corporate objectives and, simultaneously an increase in the link between the working methods and the values and principles held by the organisation.

A fair appraisal?

In recent times, large organisations including IT giants like Microsoft and Dell have ditched the appraisal process[212]. Even Deloitte[213], a global leader in consultancy services (notably in HR) scrapped their annual appraisal process. For these organisations, making such a significant decision will not have been taken lightly, but with evidence suggesting that less than 10% see added value and more than half think it is a waste of time, something had to change.

There has to be some consideration of where it went wrong for a process that on the face of it at least, ought to be so effective. In some cases, failings are linked with the design of the process. Microsoft ditched their process because of a perception that it actually drove the wrong kind of behaviour, the wrong outcomes and a high degree of internal competition.

Despite these changes, little has really been done to address the failings in delivery which cause the complaints, poor morale, and lack of impact. Elements of the process such as the frequency, the format, the preparedness and engagement of line managers, and the pre-conceptions of those being reviewed, can all lead to a process which is painful for all concerned. These views are captured by Duncan Brown[214]:

> *'the problems* [of performance management] *are... not of ambition or intent, but rather of practice and delivery. Low rates of coverage, and even more frequently low quality conversations and non-existent follow up are commonplace, in the wake of uncommitted directors, incompetent line managers, uncomprehending employees, and hectoring HR with their still complex and bureaucratic HR processes.'*

The fact remains that linking employee activity with organisational direction is a key element of both organisational and individual 'performance' and given that far too few employees really know what the organisation is trying to achieve, alignment appears a long way off.

Any kind of performance measuring process has to have as its starting point a recognition that from the top down employees know:

- What the organisation is trying to achieve,
- How it intends to achieve it,
- The role that their department, and their role is expected to perform, and
- How that will help the organisation to achieve its goals.

Some organisations have criticised the performance appraisal process for stifling some of the factors that really matter to them, such as innovation and creativity[215] but this is more likely a function of the process than a reason to remove the appraisal process altogether. Despite this, according to a leading consultancy[216], as many as two thirds of large employers are considering ditching the performance appraisal altogether.

Performance appraisals can be an important method of reminding employees what is expected and how they are expected to achieve it. In that sense it builds role clarity, a lack of which is closely linked with psychosocial illnesses such as stress and anxiety.

Performance appraisals can also provide a check and balance process to ensure that employees are doing what is expected of them, and equally, how they are achieving it. Good performance appraisal processes, when linked with other systems and processes support organisational culture development.

Getting performance appraisal processes on track will require new ways of thinking. Recognising the changing nature of work, the importance of positive psychology (particularly in relation to constructive feedback, employee recognition, and corporate culture), and the role that every member of the organisation has to play in the process, can provide a basis for change.

Devising systems that reflect the existing organisation culture but contribute towards the desired behaviours and activities of the organisation, supported with high levels of employee engagement at all levels, will be necessary to produce a system that can produce positive organisational change. Current thinking appears to be that less formal, more regular reviews of performance feeding into an annual review of reward are more effective.

One of the common themes throughout the book has been the importance of job quality factors: security, autonomy, variety, equity, recognition, and strength of relationships. Performance Appraisals can contribute on every level:

- Security – through the sense of sustainability that achieving goals produces;
- Autonomy – through the knowledge that providing a clear direction to employees enables an organisation to increase autonomy with less fear of the consequences;

- Variety – through an approach that recognises that employees can perform different tasks that contribute to organisational success, and that wider knowledge promotes business performance;

- Equity – through that recognise and reward employees based on the value they contribute to overall business performance;

- Recognition – through understanding the part every individual plays in delivering organisational performance; and

- Strength of relationships – built as a series of support structures designed to help the organisation to achieve its goals in the manner that it believes is right.

Goal Setting

Clear goals, measured, monitored, reviewed, and reported upon regularly underpin health, safety and wider corporate risk systems in the same way that they establish the effectiveness of any other organisational system.

Monitoring performance against these goals is key to the management of health, safety and corporate risk. The extent to which risk is incorporated effectively into the decision making process can have a profound impact on the way that an organisation plans, organises, controls, monitors and reviews activities, which in turn can have an impact on whether adequate resources are assigned to and through an activity.

At a simplistic level, reward mechanisms such as bonuses that reflect short term profitability can impact spending on consumable safety items that can increase health and safety performance, whilst capital investment targets could influence management performance in relation to addressing the more effective forms of addressing risks at work such as elimination, isolation or substitution.

As well as looking at what was done, there is increasingly a focus on how it was done – leading more and more performance management systems to consider factors like attitudes and behaviours. These might include factors like risk taking and compliance, supporting and encouraging behaviours, and a visible, active commitment to the principles, standards, and values of the organisation.

This approach balances the transformational behaviours with the transactional behaviours of the more senior members of the management team.

Appraisals are less common amongst operational personnel, but operational and technical personnel are becoming increasingly subject to formal and regular assessment. All employees have duties to protect the safety of themselves and others, to co-operate with their employer, and to use what is provided in accordance with the training that they have received. The appraisal provides an opportunity to assess that.

Where a failing in respect of a statutory duty occurs, employees can find themselves implicated, as well as the organisation, particularly if it can be evidenced that the event occurred as a consequence of their action or inaction.

The Link with Learning

Performance can be hampered by a variety of factors, such as the impact of sudden and unexpected events, the impact of persistent external factors outside of the control of the job holder, or a lack of clear understanding about what was expected or how that should be delivered.

Great performance achieved in the wrong manner does not provide an organisation with a sense of sustainability. Investigating and understanding how some hurdles have been overcome ensures that problems solved today are not building up a debt of liability which will strike the organisation in future.

Similarly, poor performance is not necessarily a bad outcome. It may be a function of other circumstances. Unless these circumstances are investigated and understood, they are likely to sustain poor performance. Addressing these challenges provides an opportunity for organisational and individual performance to improve, and to provide an opportunity for the organisation to learn from events.

When things go wrong, immediate, underlying and root cause analysis provides organisations with the opportunity to establish failings at an individual and organisational level that contributed to event(s) and correct the circumstances, behaviours, and systems that contributed to the failure.

In the most extreme cases, identifying incidents that have occurred through the consent, connivance or neglect of a senior manager can have an impact both on the organisation, and the senior manager concerned. Ensuring Senior Managers understand the risks inherent in the role should go a long way to preventing this from happening, but when it does, understanding the scale of this risk can help organisations to plan and prepare for the potential consequences, and to identify steps that need to be taken to prevent similar incidents from happening again.

Reward

Effective reward requires a complex balancing act between a vast and significant array of competing forces.

When the Economic Environment shows periods of low or high inflation, organisations are pressured to respond by aligning their practices with the economic model to remain competitive in a macro-economic climate.

Organisational performance can significantly influence an organisations ability to pay the high pay rises enjoyed by other organisations competing in the same labour market, putting pressure on an organisation to find other ways to retain their workforce.

Meeting legal duties relating to equality can limit an organisations ability to recognise and reward particular individuals within the workplace, not least because of a need to address historic inequalities.

Achieving a sense of fairness and equity between employees who are likely to have profoundly different views about the importance of their role and the contribution they make to the organisation.

Balancing flexibility to meet difficult needs with the ability to demonstrate rigidity and robustness to fulfil legal obligations.

Satisfying the simultaneous needs of shareholders to keep costs down, whilst achieving a high level of retention particularly amongst key workers.

Balancing the recognition of both contribution and effort in a fair and equitable way, particularly when external forces have reduced exceptional effort to marginal contribution.

Creating an attractive employee value proposition for new starters without undermining existing employee terms, and keeping costs under control.

According to Ghoshal and Bartlett, 1995[217], reward should add value to people, not just attach value to people. In practice, reward does this, knowingly or unknowingly by reflecting the goals and values of the organisation. Logic suggests that organisations are more likely to attract and retain the type of people that they reward.

Many organisations regularly review approaches to reward, citing total reward programmes, new performance pay, new evaluation methodologies, pay structures or systems. The down side to this approach is that they can end up with excessive administrative burdens at a time when most organisations are looking to reduce the cost of back office functions.

Put simply, pay should be competitive and internally equitable, reflecting the values that an organisation holds dear. It is likely to comprise of:

- Basic pay (salary or rate);
- Additional pay based on organisational values such as skills, service, performance, etc.);
- Non-pay benefits; and perhaps most importantly of all;
- The non-financial benefits of work such as self-worth, personal fulfilment, self-development and growth.

According to Benefits Research[218] in 2013, the main factor shaping the benefits offer from employers was employee engagement. Following the earlier recession and concern over employees seeking work elsewhere, that should not have come as a surprise. There is however a danger to applying such short term thinking to reward and benefits solutions as once these are contractual benefits they are difficult to remove.

The Reward Framework

The reward framework has transformed over recent years and now contains a rich patchwork of rewards and benefits across an array of themes which include:

- Pay, Bonus and Reward;
- Employee Share Ownership;
- Pensions and other Financial Support;
- Employee Health and Wellbeing;
- Group Risk Initiatives;
- Flexible Benefits;
- Childcare, Bikes-For-Work, and other Voluntary Benefit Schemes; and
- Company Cars.

Pay, Bonus and Reward

Reward is often seen as an important measure of equity and recognition within organisations, often negatively as a causer of low motivation amongst those that feel they are not adequately rewarded for the contribution that they make, either individually or in comparison with others.

Although pay is described as a 'hygiene' factor and not a 'motivator', it is surprising the extent to which it has the ability to promote negative feelings across the workforce.

Equality

In simple terms, there is a requirement across organisations to ensure that work of equal value is paid equally. A report[219] prepared by the National Institute of Economic and Social Research for the Equality and Human Rights Commission in 2009 found evidence of:

- A gender pay gap;
- A sexual orientation pay gap (based on very limited evidence, this is the one group where the minority may earn more);
- An ethnic minority pay gap;
- A religion or belief pay gap (negative for Muslims, positive for Jews);
- A disability pay gap; and
- An age pay gap (with younger and older workers earning less than median age workers).

Other Negative Factors

These vary from the 'job and finish' practices on construction sites that lead to rushed jobs, to the banker's bonuses stories of the last decade.

Bankers Bonuses

In fact, the UK Government initially sought to block the European legislation limiting banker's bonuses but subsequently withdrew their challenge from the European Court. The position now is that bonuses cannot exceed 100% of basic salary, subject to two provisions:

- Shareholders may approve a bonus of up to 200% and not the 100%; and
- Up to 25% of the bonus target can be converted to a long term reward at a 2:1 ratio.

The effect of the second caveat is that banker's bonus can be structured 2:3 long term v short term gain. This approach has not been without its critics. Employers in the banking sector have raised concerns over breaching employees terms, and there has been some introduction of 'allowances' which are defined as a part of basic pay, but which can be terminated (seemingly therefore not as fixed as they might be painted).

The increased use of Bonus

Between 2012 and 2013, there was a significant increase in bonus provision to employees. More than three quarters of respondents to the survey provided a bonus to their employees. This is significant because bonuses influence behaviour.

Bonuses are often used by an organisation to link employee performance with organisational performance, firstly to incentivise better organisational performance, but also to build a sense of fairness, equity and recognition amongst the organisation.

When the organisation performs well, the organisation has cash and can afford a higher wage bill, when the organisation performs poorly, its wage bill diminishes accordingly.

The Nature of Bonus

There is a wide variety in the types of bonus paid to employees. For example:

- **Executives** are more likely to receive longer term and share scheme based rewards, often controlled independently through Corporate Governance and Remuneration Committees;
- **Professional and Technical Staff** are more likely to receive additional pay in relation to their skills, flexibility or capabilities;
- **Sales Personnel** are more likely to receive bonuses linked to personal sales performance; and
- **Manual Workers** are more likely to receive piece work or payment by results.

The perils of relying on bonus

Unfortunately most bonuses are calculated on the basis of short term measures such as Turnover, Profit, Stock levels, and Costs. Rewarding achievement of short term achievements creates a culture where employees concentrate on short term financial impact, often at the price of longer term non-financial factors.

Bonus schemes impact performance – callers to an American call centre were typically transferred five times until the bonus scheme formula was changed from average call time to resolution rate.

Rewards that focus on keeping costs down, spending under budget, or maximising profits may result in activities that are under-resourced or undertaken without the necessary operational or safety equipment, or with equipment that does not conform to the correct standard.

Where work is not performed to the correct standard; balancing the need for honest and open information sharing can be difficult because of fear of sanction, but this is necessary if a real understanding of the standards is to be achieved.

When VW were faced with a multi-billion risk, they invited employees to come forward with information relating to the causes without fear of reprisal.

Addressing the balance

The way that an organisation rewards its workers should reflect what matters. There is some movement towards linking reward with adherence to organisational standards, values and principles. In an environment where pay is seen as a particularly gender biased value, many organisations have been nervous about introducing what is often seen by many as a largely subjective factor.

Employee Share Ownership

In 2013, the UK Government introduced the concept of 'Employee Shareholders' through the Growth and Infrastructure Act 2013. To date, there is little evidence that organisations have chosen to adopt the new concept. Approximately 350 organisations have adopted employee shareholders, and a little over 7,000 employees have accepted part-ownership for a forfeiture of their rights to request training, undertake flexible working, or protections against unfair dismissal or redundancy. In practice, most organisations appear to have adopted the belief that if employees want to have a share in an organisation, they would be better owning the whole company and work as a self-employed person.

Despite this, other more traditional forms of employee share ownership have remained popular, although rare and in 2013, 1% of respondents to the Employee Benefits survey indicated that they had provided opportunities for employees to obtain shares through a company share option plan.

As well as providing options that are tax efficient, employees often appreciate the sense of part ownership that share option plans provide. Shares offered through Share Incentive Schemes, Save as You Earn Schemes, Company Share Option Plans, and Enterprise Management Initiatives all benefit from tax efficiencies[220].

Pensions

At the end of 2015, all employers with more than 30 employees will have gone through the process of auto-enrolment unless they already had a comparable solution in place. Over the next 18 months, almost every remaining organisation will go through the process. This will put some pressure on organisations that offer pension provision as the volume of effort will be substantially disproportionate to the process of the past.

Towards the end of 2015, approximately 70,000 employers and 21 million employers had gone through the process of auto-enrolment, with approximately half of workers (9.4m) already in schemes by the staging date, a quarter joining an auto-enrolment pension (5.5m), and a further quarter (5.3m) unaccounted for.

With employees reporting fears over their ability to retire, and employers generally failing to obtain or provide quality financial advice, the opportunity to address this concern provides a good opportunity for employers to increase the perception of value that they give to employees through a cheap, if not free, advice service. It is no wonder that organisations like MetLife are actively engaging in the CIPD conference, presenting to employers on the 7 deadly trends.

Although some employers are providing education to their employees on retirement planning, investment and pension advice, financial calculators and modellers, etc., there remains a lack of basic information for employees.

Employee Health & Wellbeing

At least in part due to a growing number of stress and mental health problems in work, there has been a growth in the adoption of employee assistance programmes providing 24 hour, 7 day support and counselling services to employees.

At the same time, there has been an increase in the introduction of corporate medical plans, health cash and dental plans, eye care, occupational health and health screening, and private medical insurance.

In some cases, this has been driven by compliance with statutory duty or obligation (for example the requirements of the Display Screen Equipment Regulations) and to ensure adequate defence of potential future personal injury claims.

To a lesser extent, and in a minority of organisations, there has been a realisation that investment in employee health can improve performance (with notable organisations investing in nutritional guidance and support for shift workers).

Other organisations have seen the benefits that health and wellbeing, stress management, and wellness programmes can provide to build the resilience of their employees and help to keep them in work.

The Health & Safety legislation establishes a requirement that if health surveillance can be used, then it should be used. It recognises that health surveillance does not identify every medical condition, and that in many cases, the first signs of symptoms occur sometime after the damage has already been caused, but where it can be used to identify a consequence, health surveillance is a statutory duty.

Group Risk Initiatives

Employers can use their size to obtain organisation wide benefits to staff such as group life assurance and death in service benefits, critical illness, group income protection, and personal accident insurance and rehabilitation services.

Employers are able to take out key worker or unexpected event insurance to mitigate losses.

Other Benefits

Based on the Employee Benefits research, more than 4 in 5 respondents highlighted the reason for providing benefits to staff for the purposes of recruitment, retention, or to support employee health and wellbeing. Two thirds of respondents introduced benefits because they believed the particular benefits aligned with the corporate brand.

Around a half of respondents offered benefits because they wanted to improve work life balance, whilst a third of respondents said they wanted to stimulate particular employee behaviour, they provided a financial benefit to the organisation, or were required as part of a statutory duty. One in four introduced benefits because they believed it would have a positive impact on sickness absence.

The top six factors shaping benefit strategies were:

- Employee engagement;
- Pensions Auto-enrolment;
- Desire for flexibility;
- Desire to reduce or control costs;
- Alignment with business strategy; and
- Contribution to a high performance culture.

There are an array of benefits which when viewed in the context of the organisational strategy, goals, and values, provides a substantial menu for an organisation considering providing benefits that reflect the corporate brand or reflect the needs of target recruits.

Childcare, Bikes-For-Work, and other Benefits

There are a variety of childcare options for employers. Typically these include:

- A workplace childcare facility;
- Reimbursement for employees that pay for childcare themselves;
- Direct contract with a childcare commercial nursery or childminder
- The provision of employee childcare vouchers

The government has extended the existing childcare voucher scheme until 2017, which means that employees can still benefit from the existing arrangement to receive childcare vouchers free from tax (within limits) and national insurance from their employer. This has been, and continues to be a very popular benefit for employees with young children.

Because of the way that the childcare vouchers can only be used with professional, reputable and organised childcare organisations, this benefit also helps to provide employers with the knowledge that their employees are leaving their children safely in the care of an organisation that should not cause undue worry or concern, and so contribute to an improved employee state of mind whilst at work.

In many cities around the country, the bike for work scheme has been a popular way for employers to provide bikes for their employees in a tax efficient manner to help them to get to and from work.

Flexible Benefits

One trend that continues to grow significantly is the extent to which employers offer flexible benefits, either in relation to some of the examples already described (for example increased pensions through salary sacrifice) or share option schemes.

They are particularly popular in relation to some of the options below, where employees adopt to take advantage of opportunities provided by the employer in return for deductions to their salary (either before or after tax depending on the nature of the flexible option).

Other Selected Benefits

The following benefits were all reported in the Employee Benefits Survey 2013, either as a part of a core or flexible benefit programme.

- Extra Holidays (Long Service/Salary Sacrifice arrangement)
- Long Term Incentive Plan
- Private Medical Insurance (including Dental)
  (Personal/Spouse/Dependents)
- Health/Hospital Cash Plan (Personal/Spouse/Dependents)
- Life Assurance/Death in Service Benefits (Personal/Spouse)

- Health Screening (Beyond statutory health surveillance)
- Personal Accident Insurance (Personal/Spouse/Family)
- Critical Illness Cover (Personal/Spouse)
- Income Protection/Permanent Health Insurance
- Financial Advice/Education
- Travel Insurance
- Car Parking
- Fuel for private use (Company Car drivers)
- Breakdown Cover (Company Car/Non-Company Car Drivers)
- Season Ticket Loan
- Luncheon Vouchers
- Gym Memberships
- Student Grants/Student Loan Repayments
- Non-vocational training
- Optical care or vouchers
- Counselling or Employee assistance programmes
- Mortgage Subsidies or other Employer Subsidised Loans

Many employers have also found that they have been able to obtain discounted products, incentives, and services across a variety of organisations to bring offers to their employees that might not otherwise have been available. These range from reduced gym memberships or free trials, half price nights out at cinemas or restaurants, and discounts at shops on-line and on the high street.

Many organisations offer some of these benefits, although it is not always clear whether these were implemented as part of a strategic attempt to meet corporate objectives, retain personnel, or increase employer attractiveness to potential employees with the right knowledge, skills and experience. In fact, employers are often criticised for failing to publish the number and variety of benefits they offer.

Company Cars

The popularity of the company car remains. Approximately half of all new car registrations in 2014 were for company cars, although as they account for only one in 12 of all cars on the road, it is evident that they do not remain as company cars for long. Although these figures are down from a high of one in 10 cars in 1997, it is up by half a percentage on its lowest point (in 2010).

According to the Department for Transport[221], new registrations are returning to their pre-recession levels, approximately 3 million per year.

The government operates a number of practices which are unique in Europe[222], for example charging tax on the actual cost of personal fuel used by company car drivers, allowing UK firms to fully depreciate the cost of environmentally free cars in the first year, and adopting a taxation regime based largely on CO2 values. According to the HMRC this has had the effect of replacing less environmentally friendly over less environmentally friendly cars, rather than reducing the actual number of registered company cars. Although many organisations provide company cars, other organisations have adopted car allowance or similar processes to increase employee choice.

Driving on the Public Highway

At the present time, the HSE does not record accidents arising as a consequence of driving for work on the public highway. According to the UK Department of Transport, in 2014, there were:

- 1,775 road deaths
- 22,807 serious injuries, and
- 169,895 slight injuries.

The trend over the last 15 years has been downward but has plateaued over the last three years and has showed a slight increase year on year in 2014.

Approximately 5% of all incidents occur on Motorways. Of the remainder half of all fatalities and three quarters of minor injuries occur in non-built up areas.

> *The Department of Transport estimate that over a quarter of all road traffic incidents involve someone who is driving as a part of their work[223].*

The HSE has produced guidance to help employers with employees that drive as a part of their normal work activities which is intended to reduce injuries, the risk of work related ill-health, reduce stress and improve moral. This guidance, in line with the latest thinking from the HSE is set out in the Plan, Do, Check, Act approach which is the basis of their new guidance on Managing Health and Safety.

There is no individual piece of legislation that applies to driving for work. Instead, there are a variety of regulations that apply to drivers (such as Road Traffic Act), and to the organisation such as the Management of Health and Safety at Work Regulations 1999 (MHSWR).

When considering risks, the Transport Research Laboratory have provided useful research[224] on incident frequencies. Their findings (in order of frequency) were:

- Collisions between vehicles and property.
- Collisions between vehicles.
- People getting hurt whilst getting on or off of vehicles, or being hurt as a consequence of loading or unloading the vehicle.
- Objects falling from vehicles,
- People struck by a vehicle,

- Vehicles overturning,
- People falling from moving vehicles,
- Vehicle malfunctions causing accidents or injuries,
- People being run over by vehicles, or
- Being hit by something falling from a vehicle.

There is some evidence that individual factors such as age, gender, education, personality, attitudes and behaviours are correlated with driving incidents[225]. Research suggests benefits can be gained from the inclusion of psychometric testing in relation to personality, aggression, thoroughness in decision making, driving confidence, attitudes, and risk perception in recruitment and selection processes.

The HSE has published a work-related road safety checklist and this is summarised below:

Safe Journey	• Do you consider safe routes, eliminate or reduce long journeys and plan routes in consultation with drivers taking into account rest breaks, toilets and washing facilities? • Do schedules consider driver fatigue, periods of peak traffic flow? Do you make allowances for new starters and young workers? • Do you take into account weather conditions etc. when planning journeys? • Do you consider the impact of the weather – e.g. snow, high winds, heavy rain,
Safe driver	• Are skills to do the job safely defined, are employees assessed? • Do you check driving licence validity on recruitment and subsequently? • Are you communicating the work-related road safety policy to drivers? • Do you use written procedures and procedure training for drivers? **Are your drivers properly trained?** • Do you provide general induction training for drivers? • Do you arrange for drivers to be trained (giving priority to those at highest risk) to enable them to carry out their duties safely? • Do you assess training needs periodically, including refresher training? **Do you ensure drivers have clear instructions about how to be safe?** • Do you need to provide a handbook for drivers on road safety? • Do drivers know how to carry out routine safety checks? • Do drivers know how to correctly adjust safety equipment? • Do drivers know what to do if their vehicle breaks down? • Do drivers know not to drive under the influence of drink or drugs? • Do drivers know the rules and risks of using mobile phone equipment? • Are drivers aware of the height of their vehicle, laden and empty? • Do you provide suitable crash helmets and protective clothing? **Are your drivers sufficiently fit and healthy to drive safely?** • Do drivers of HGV/PSVs have the appropriate medical certificate? • Do drivers meet eyesight and other health requirements? • Do drivers understand the impact of medication on their judgement? • Are drivers aware of tiredness and what to do if they start to feel sleepy? • Do you encourage drivers to report health concerns?

Safe vehicle	**Are vehicles fit for the purpose for which they are used?** • Do you assess suitability /public safety when buying vehicles? • Do you make sure your vehicles have driver aids and safety devices? • What rules do you apply for the use of privately owned vehicles? • Are drivers and passengers adequately protected in an incident? • Do you ensure vehicles do not exceed their maximum load weight? • Do you have arrangements for carrying/securing goods and equipment? **Are vehicles maintained in a safe and fit condition?** • Do you ensure routine inspections are undertaken • Are consumables replaced as necessary? • Is maintenance carried out to manufacturers' recommendations? • What procedures are there for reporting defects and are they remedied promptly and to an acceptable standard? • Do you have a clear policy that unsafe vehicles should not be driven? **Are you sure that drivers' health and safety, is not being put at risk?** • Do you consider ergonomic factors/provide guidance on good posture?

The HSE offers specific guidance for those organisations involved in the movement of goods[226] and the movement of dangerous goods[227]. These are not discussed further in this section but the references pinpoint sources of further information.

Medical Suspension

No consideration of reward would be complete without a consideration of the rights on medical suspension. The Employment Rights Act 1996 protects individuals from suffering detriment or dismissal in certain circumstances relating to health and safety issues and provides rights for workers on medical suspension. Regulations concerning work involving **ionising radiation, lead**, and some other **chemicals** set down specific additional circumstances in which employers may be required to suspend an employee on medical grounds.

During this period, an employee is entitled to be paid for up to 26 weeks as long as he remains with his employer, and is not provided with work.

There are certain limitations, he or she must have been employed for at least a month and fit to work (not absent due to disease or disablement).

If an employee unreasonably refuses to perform suitable alternative work, or does not comply with reasonable requirements to make him or herself available, the employee is not entitled to remuneration.

In some cases, medical suspension with pay may arise out of a risk assessment, for example in relation to an expectant mother and a workplace risk of exposure to chicken pox, if temporary alternative accommodations cannot be made.

Equal Pay

Employers have a duty under the Equality Act to provide equal pay for work of Equal Value. This extends beyond rights to pay and includes benefits. The

Employment Rights Act and Equality Act set out specific rights 'not to suffer a detriment' as a consequence of a protected characteristic (Equality Act) or as a consequence in participation or non-participation in specified activities.

References

[212] Are Annual Appraisals losing impact? Lucie Mitchell, HR Magazine, November 2014

[213] Reinventing Performance Management, Marcus Buckingham and Ashley Goodall, Harvard Business Review, April 2015

[214] Handbook of Human Resource Management Practice, Ibid.

[215] Are Annual Appraisals losing impact? Ibid.

[216] More companies planning to ditch annual performance reviews and ratings, but will employees benefit? PwC research, July 2015

[217] Handbook of Human Resource Management Practice, Ibid.

[218] The Benefits Book, Employee Benefits, Centaur Publishing, 2013

[219] Pay gaps across the equality strands: a review, Hilary Metcalf, National Institute of Economic and Social Research, , 2009

[220] https://www.gov.uk/tax-employee-share-schemes/overview

[221] Licenced Vehicles 2014, Department for Transport, ONS, 2015

[222] Taxation Paper No 22, Company Car Taxation, Prepared by Copenhagen Economics for the European Union, 2010

[223] Driving at work: Managing work-related road safety, HSE, 2014

[224] Review of workplace control measures to reduce risks arising from the movement of vehicles, Prepared by Transport Research Laboratory (TRL) Ltd for HSE, 2002

[225] The contribution of individual factors to driving behaviour: Implications for managing work-related road safety, Rebecca Lancaster and Rachel Ward, Entec UK Limited for the HSE, 2002

[226] http://www.hse.gov.uk/movinggoods/index.htm

[227] http://www.hse.gov.uk/cdg/index.htm

ENGAGING EMPLOYEES

Introduction

The CIPD Profession Map recognises the importance of Employee Engagement and Employee Relations to successful organisational performance.

Adopting different approaches to employee engagement and employee relations can result in confused messages to the workforce, although they are occasionally necessary to ensure that employees receive the information that is important to them.

The HSE recognise the importance of involving employees in safety and Regulations apply to ensure that employees and/or their representatives are consulted about their safety. Furthermore, some of the more specific hazard based legislation identifies particular communications and consultations that need to take place to reduce the risk of harm.

Engagement

HR Practitioners are not new to the concept of employee engagement. In 2009 David MacLeod and Nita Clarke published their report to government: Engaging for Success: Enhancing performance through employee engagement[228] which sought to establish a definition and present a case for employee engagement.

What is Engagement?

The paper presented a definition from the Institute of Employment Studies amongst others that seemed to sum up a variety of thoughts on what engagement was.

> *A positive attitude held by the employee towards the organisation and its values. An engaged employee is aware of the business context, and works with colleagues to improve performance within the job for the benefit of the organisation. The organisation must work to develop and nurture engagement, which requires a two-way relationship between employee and employer. (IES)*

That report provided a variety of consultancy led and academic research on the impact of employee engagement on organisational performance and employee well-being, as measured through:

- Absenteeism
- Retention
- Increased discretionary effort
- Output Volume
- Quality
- Growth/Other Success Measures

Engaging for Success highlighted examples of what might happen in an organisation that sought to achieve 'Engagement'…

> *Organisations can achieve better performance and reduced costs through lower accident rates, higher productivity, fewer conflicts, more innovation, lower numbers leaving, and reduced sickness rates.*
>
> *An employee might feel pride and loyalty and be a great advocate for the company to clients (attitude), or go the extra mile to finish a piece of work (behaviour).'*

Unfortunately, some of the negative effects of poor approaches to engagement have created conflicts (through employee fear or frustration), reduced sickness rates (through increased presenteeisim), and employees willing to go the extra mile despite future ramifications that those actions may have on the organisation (such as the VW case).

Since 2009, employers have engaged in a range of employee engagement surveys and interventions to improve performance, some focussed more directly on employee satisfaction, others focussed on performance and productivity, and most somewhere in between. One of the best surveys to provide an indication of what is happening in the market place is the CIPD Employee Outlook Report[229].

In Autumn 2015, the CIPD reported that:

- About half of employees were satisfied with their jobs – although the figure was significantly lower for public sector employees.
- About 1/3rd of all employees described themselves as 'Engaged' – approximately 1 in 25 described themselves as disengaged.
- Employees believed that Senior Managers did not have a clear vision about where they were going and were not involving employees in the decisions that affected them.
- Almost half believed that they were not fairly well or fully informed of what was happening.

That report indicated that around 2/3rds of employees were satisfied or very satisfied with their jobs, but that only 2/5ths regarded themselves as 'engaged' with their employer. Approximately 1/4 of employees were looking for a job with a different employer.

Human Factors

These elements arise as a consequence of a combination of environmental, organisational and job factors, and human and individual characteristics, which influence behaviour at work. Where they combine in a way that affects health and safety, they are referred to as 'human factors'[230].

According to the HSE, careful consideration of human factors at work can reduce the number of accidents and cases of occupational ill-health. It can also pay dividends in terms of a more efficient and effective workforce[231].

Work systems and processes are unlikely to be effective if they consider these aspects in isolation. According to the HSE:

Organisation
The way in which the organisation structures and plans work, including working patterns, the level of supervision, job design, national context[nn], organisational culture, communications and leadership can have a significant influence on the way in which workers behave.
Tasks
The way in which the tasks are developed, the design of work stations, the volume of work, and the organisation of the work environment, should all be designed in such a way as to consider human limitations and strengths.
Person
Individual capabilities should be considered when assigning a person to a role. According to the HSE, this should include his/her competence, skills, personality, attitude, and risk perception, but should also include physical characteristics where the job demands it.

Events seldom occur as a consequence of a single factor or event in isolation. Human factors have played a significant part in some of the worst events that have occurred over the last forty years.

More commonly, incidents occur as a consequence of a number of events or circumstances that coincide in a moment. Human factors often contribute to these events, either through:

- an active failure – for example poor decision, lack of intervention, or
- a latent failure – poor design, ineffective training, supervision, role clarity.

[nn] The nature of national culture defines attitudes to power distance, individualism or collectivism, masculinity or femininity, uncertainty avoidance, long term orientation, and attitudes to indulgence and shapes behaviours at work. For more information, refer to Cultures and Organisations, Software of the Mind, Hofstede, Hofstede and Minkov, 2010.

The examples that follow (from the HSE guidance published under the open government licence) highlight the scale of damage that can be caused as a consequence of 'human' factors.

Incident	Human Factors
King's Cross Fire: 31 people died	*A discarded cigarette probably set fire to grease and rubbish underneath one of the escalators.* *Organisational changes had resulted in poor escalator cleaning. The fire took hold because of the wooden escalator, the failure of water fog equipment and inadequate fire and emergency training of staff. There was a culture which viewed fires as inevitable.*
Clapham Junction: 35 people died, 500 injured in triple train crash	*Immediate cause was a signal failure caused by a technician failing to isolate and remove a wire. Contributory causes included degradation of working practices, problems with training, testing quality and communications standards, poor supervision. Lessons not learnt from past incidents. No effective system for monitoring or limiting excessive working hours.*
Herald of Free Enterprise Ferry sank in shallow water off Zeebrugge killing 189.	*Immediate cause was the failure to close the bow doors before leaving port. No effective reporting system to check the bow doors. Formal inquiry reported that the company was 'infected with the disease of sloppiness'. Commercial pressures and friction between ship and shore management had led to safety lessons not being learnt.*

High Level Human Factors

The Energy Institute have identified 10 high level human factors issues[232] that, if addressed, will contribute to a safer and more effective organisation. These are:

- Managing organisational development and change (particularly during transition);
- Staffing arrangements and workload;
- Training and Competence;
- Fatigue (from shift work and overtime);
- Human factors in workplace and system design;
- Procedures;

- Organisational culture;
- Communications and interfaces;
- The integration of human factors into risk assessments, incident investigations, and safety management systems; and
- Managing human failure.

Other research[233] has identified the impact of other high level motivation and morale, alertness (aligned with fatigue), the availability of information and advice, the suitability of human resources (the people, not the function), external conditions, and stress.

These high level human factors issues can be examined across almost every industry and incident, although it is more valuable, after an event to look more closely at detailed human factor contributors to events.

Slips and Trips – Applying Human Factors

An investigation[234] of 62 slip and trip incidents (one of the most common types of accidents) across a variety of industry sectors found the following human factor causes:

- Lack of understanding of requirements of health and safety legislation to identify and control slip/trip risks
- Lack of awareness/Poor perception of slip/trip risks
- Failure to identify slip/trip risks
- Failure to report spillages, slip/trip risks etc. (employees and members of the public)
- Inadequate or lack of reaction to reported problems
- Lack of ownership/understanding of health and safety responsibilities
- Poor understanding of the importance of implementing existing health and safety measures to control slip/trip risks (e.g. effective maintenance / cleaning programmes)
- Failure to provide staff with health and safety training, including slip/trip risks
- Failure to monitor and investigate effectiveness of control measures
- Lack of staff supervision
- Lack of enforcement of health and safety rules
- Poor communication between staff
- Failure to adequately investigate slip/trip incidents and identify ways to prevent recurrence.

There has been recent criticism of dress codes recently, research on slips and trips from the Rossmore Group[235] described members of the public who chose to wear high heeled shoes within a certain environment as 'impaired'. Although their research related to members of the public, they did suggest that the 'factor could be influenced by management policies and procedures when applying the model for employees'.

Wearing Personal Protective Equipment

Research into what needed to be done to increase the extent to which employees wore personal protective equipment, found interventions including basic noise awareness training, provision of alternative types of hearing protection, and coaching of management in basic feedback and communication techniques for encouraging workers to modify their behaviour. The interventions were designed to be participative and involving. These were largely re-iterated by a report from the Institute of Employment Studies[236] which identified particular techniques that could be used to influence and address human factors at work. These were:

- Workplace inspections
- Face to face awareness events

> *These two were considered particularly effective alongside large scale print based approaches – in part because of their stand-alone effectiveness but also because of the effect of a multi-method campaign.*

- Targeted initiatives – for example a particular focus on themes
- Tools – for example manager/supervisor aids or employee aids (the London Olympics used branded clothing and other low cost items)
- Safety and Health Awareness Days
- Worker Involvement Techniques

The same report also identified the effectiveness of regulation (except for invisible risks such as mental health) and advances in techniques, highlighting the importance of keeping up to date with sectoral and functional advances.

The need to involve the workforce is key to the success of addressing human factors at work. As well as providing that benefit, there is also a legal duty on many employers to do this.

Consultation

Employers must consult with their employees, in good time, on health and safety matters, such as changes to working conditions, the introduction of new technology, or new equipment.

It is good practice and a statutory duty on employers to engage with employees to understand the work they perform, the risks they are exposed to, and the actions that can be taken to reduce their exposure and improve their effectiveness.

Providing communications downwards helps management to demonstrate their commitment to safety, whilst providing opportunities for upward communications enables employees to raise concerns.

Consultation involves employers not only giving information to employees, but also listening to them and taking account of what they say before making decisions about health and safety that may affect them. When these consultations take place early enough, they can contribute to financial savings because costly mistakes can be avoided. Issues employers should consult employees on include: risks arising from their work; proposals to manage and/or control these risks; the best ways of providing information and training.

Engaging with employees with a concern for their well-being contributes to feelings of satisfaction, commitment, engagement and motivation on a shared agenda, while worker involvement in decisions that affects them results in increased feelings of autonomy which is one of the six quality factors of a good job.

Walking the floor provides an opportunity for senior members of the organisation to visualise the content of board reports and better understand the significance of any stated concerns or requests for investment.

Employers should involve employees or their safety representatives when carrying out and reviewing risk assessments as it is a good way of helping to manage health and safety risk. Employees who are carrying out the work often have a better understanding of what the hazards are, and may notice things that are not obvious. They often have practical ideas on how to control the risks.

Statutory Duties

In workplaces where a trade union is recognised, this is undertaken through the union 'Health and Safety Representatives' (Safety Representatives and Safety Committees Regulations 1977). If there is no union present, employers have a duty to consult either with 'Elected Representatives' (Health and Safety (Consultation with Employees) Regulations 1996) or with employees directly. There is a joint Approved Code of Practice applicable to both sets of regulations[237].

Recognised Unions

Where a union is recognised and there is at least one employee, unions may appoint safety representatives without permission from an employer. The appointment shall continue until the union advises the employer, the employee resigns the role, or the employee ceases to be employed at the site (unless he transfers to another site within the organisation).

There is no prescribed formula for determining the numbers of trade union representatives that should be appointed, although the HSE provide some guidance based on factors such as organisation size, the number of different occupations, different workplaces, different shifts, and the type of work activity and its risks.

Safety Representatives should participate in consultations with a view to the making and maintenance of arrangements which will enable him and his employees to cooperate effectively in promoting and developing measures to ensure the health and safety at work of employees and in checking the effectiveness of such measures. They should additionally:

- Investigate potential hazards and dangerous occurrences at the workplace (whether or not they are drawn to his attention by employees he represents) and to examine the causes of accidents at the workplace;
- Investigate complaints by any employee he represents relating to that employee's health, safety or welfare at work;
- Make representations to the employer on matters arising out of paragraphs above;
- Make representations to the employer on general matters affecting the health, safety or welfare at work of employees at the workplace;
- Carry out workplace inspections, inspections following notifiable accidents, occurrences and diseases, and inspections of documents and provision of information;
- Represent employees he was appointed to represent in consultations at the workplace with inspectors of the Health and Safety Executive and of any other enforcing authority;
- Receive information from regulatory inspectors; and
- Attend meetings of safety committees where he attends in his capacity as a safety representative in connection with any of the above functions.

Duty to Consult

Employers have a duty to consult with Safety Representatives in good time with regard to:

- The introduction of any measure at the workplace which may substantially affect the health and safety of represented employees;
- Arrangements for appointing or, as the case may be, nominating competent persons under MHSWR;
- Any health and safety information he is required to provide by or under the relevant statutory provisions;
- the planning and organisation of any health and safety training he is required to provide by or under the relevant statutory provisions; and
- the health and safety consequences of the introduction (including the planning thereof) of new technologies into the workplace.

Provision of Facilities

Every employer has a duty to provide reasonable facilities and assistance that the Safety Representatives require for the purpose of carrying out their functions.

Workplace Inspections

Safety representatives are entitled to inspect the workplace or a part of it:

- If they have given the employer reasonable notice in writing of their intention to do so and have not inspected it, or that part of it, as the case may be, in the previous three months (although they may carry out more frequent inspections by agreement with the employer).
- Where there has been a substantial change in the conditions of work (whether because of the introduction of new machinery or otherwise) or new information has been published by the HSE relevant to the hazards of the workplace since the last inspection
- In the event of an over-three-day injury[oo], a reportable accident, dangerous occurrence, or notifiable disease. However, the examination must not interfere with any evidence or the testing of any machinery, plant, equipment or substance which could disturb or destroy the factual evidence before any inspector from the appropriate enforcing authority has had the opportunity to investigate the circumstances of the accident or occurrence as thoroughly as is necessary.

The duty to provide such facilities and assistance as the safety representatives may reasonably require such as facilities for independent investigation and private discussion with employees for the purpose of carrying out the inspection, but nothing in the regulations precludes the employer or his representative from being present in the workplace during the inspection. In fact, the HSE encourage joint inspections in their guidance.

Where inspections culminate in a written report, employers have a duty to respond with the actions taken, or the reasons why the specified action will not be taken, not be taken without the timeframe requested, or

Provided representatives have given an employer reasonable notice, they are entitled to inspect and take copies of any document relevant to the workplace or to represented employees which the employer is required to keep by virtue of a relevant statutory provision (related to health, safety or welfare), unless the:

- Document refers to the health record of an identifiable individual.
- Disclosure of which would be against the interests of national security;

[oo] Although RIDDOR reporting guidelines have changed, safety representatives still have the right to carry out an inspection following an over-three-day injury.

- Information could not be disclosed without contravening a prohibition imposed by or under an enactment; or
- Information relates specifically to an individual, unless he has consented to its being disclosed; or
- Disclosure would, for reasons other than its effect on health, safety or welfare at work, cause substantial injury to the employer's undertaking or, where the information was supplied to him by some other person, to the undertaking of that other person; or
- Information was obtained by the employer for the purpose of bringing, prosecuting or defending any legal proceedings.

Safety Representatives have the right to request an employer to establish a safety committee to keep measures taken to ensure health and safety at work under review (HASAWA74). In carrying out this function, health and safety committees should consider drawing up agreed objectives or terms of reference.

HSE Guidance suggests that committees should establish an objective and suggest *'the promotion of co-operation between employers and employees in instigating, developing and carrying out measures to ensure the employees' health and safety at work'*

The HSE suggests that committees:

- Study accident and notifiable disease statistics and trends, so that reports can be made to management on unsafe and unhealthy conditions and practices, together with recommendations for corrective action;
- Consider aggregated absence statistics and reasons for such absences on a similar basis;
- Examine management's safety audit reports;
- Consider reports and factual information provided by inspectors of the enforcing authority appointed under the 1974 Act;
- Consider reports which health and safety representatives submit following inspections;
- Assist in developing works safety rules and safe systems of work;
- Watch the effectiveness of the health and safety content of employee training;
- Watch the adequacy of safety and health communication and publicity in the workplace;
- Provide a link with the appropriate enforcing authority.

It is important to make the point that the HSE guidance recommends that the committee study accidents with a view to looking at facts in an impartial way, consider what precautions should be taken, and make more appropriate recommendations. The HSE guidance is that safety committees should not apportion blame.

It is also important to highlight the value of involving the safety committee in the consideration of new safety rules. The result is likely to be more effective, and more widely accepted by employees if they understand that the safety committee was consulted on the matter.

Safety Representatives may bring a complaint to an Employment Tribunal if they were not permitted to take time off to undertake inspections, or lost pay as a consequence (TULRA74).

Some points to consider

Trade Unions do not have to represent the interests of all workers. They can choose to represent their own members; workers in a particular category; or non-members, who are a part of a group for which a union is recognised.

No Recognised Unions/Partial Union Coverage?

Where there are employees who are not represented by safety representatives under the 1977 Regulations, the employer has a duty to consult those employees under the Health and Safety (Consultation with Employees) Regulations 1996, in good time on matters relating to their health and safety at work and, in particular, with regard to:

- The introduction of any measure at the workplace which may substantially affect the health and safety of those employees;
- His arrangements for appointing or, as the case may be, nominating competent persons in accordance with the Management of Health and Safety at Work Regulations 1992;
- Any health and safety information he is required to provide to those employees by or under the relevant statutory provisions;
- The planning and organisation of any health and safety training he is required to provide to those employees by or under the relevant statutory provisions; and
- The health and safety consequences for those employees of the introduction (including the planning thereof) of new technologies into the workplace.

In good time – means sufficient time for organisations to provide employees with information about their intentions, sufficient time for employees to express their views, and enough time for the organisation to consider their responses.

> *Consult those employees – means the employees directly, or such elected representatives of employee safety as are in place.*

When consulting with employees or representatives of employee safety, employers have a duty to make available such information, within the employer's knowledge as is necessary to enable representatives to participate fully and effectively in the consultation. This information is subject to the same limitations above, and is intended to be broad (so far as health, safety and welfare is concerned) but not to include information:

- Which refers to the health record of an identifiable individual.
- Disclosure of which would be against the interests of national security;
- Which could not be disclosed without contravening a prohibition imposed by or under an enactment; or
- Which relates specifically to an individual, unless he has consented to its being disclosed; or
- Disclosure would, for reasons other than its effect on health, safety or welfare at work, cause substantial injury to the employer's undertaking or, where the information was supplied to him by some other person, to the undertaking of that other person; or
- Which was obtained by the employer for the purpose of bringing, prosecuting or defending legal proceedings.

Representatives of Employee Safety have significantly reduced rights when compared to union health and safety representatives. Their rights are limited to:

- Making representations to the employer on potential hazards and dangerous occurrences at the workplace which affect, or could affect, the group of employees he represents;
- Making representations to the employer on general matters affecting the health and safety at work of the group of employees he represents and, in particular, on such matters as he is consulted about by the employee; and
- Representing the group of employees in consultations at the workplace with regulatory inspectors.

There is, however, nothing in the legislation that precludes employers from extending the involvement in safety by representatives of employee safety, either on a temporary, or permanent basis.

Representatives of Employee Safety have rights to:

- Training at the employer's expense, including travel and subsistence costs,
- Time off for candidates wishing to stand in elections for representatives of employee safety,
- Time off during normal working hours to fulfil their duties, including training and
- Facilities and assistance a representative of employee safety may reasonably require for the purpose of carrying out his functions.

Specific Duties to Consult

This list, which is not intended to be exhaustive, provides an indication of the types of work where duties to consult are defined. In practice, the statutory requirement –

when to consult – described above makes it clear that any organisation will have a duty to consult with employees and/or their representatives at certain times.

In some cases, it may not be even to consult only with safety representatives, or representatives of employee safety, the Dangerous Substances and Explosive Atmospheres ACOP also guides employers towards proper consultation with those who know precisely how the work is done, including identifying the implications of any short cuts, is crucial and helps to build a culture of health and safety awareness.

Consultation should take place in relation to:

- Manual Handling
- Provision and Use of Work Equipment
- Display Screen Equipment (DSE)
- Lifting Operations
- Control of Noise/Vibration
- Control of Substances Hazardous to Health, and including Asbestos/Lead
- Confined Spaces
- Control of Major Accident Hazards
- Construction
- Ionising Radiation
- Offshore Installations, Quarries, Railways, Mines

The HSE have published a useful and practical guide to employee involvement[238].

Duty to provide Information and Consultation

Where an employer employs over 50 staff, there is a duty on employers to inform their staff about:

- The recent and probable development of their activities and economic situation;
- The situation, structure and probable development of employment within the undertaking and on any anticipatory measures envisaged, in particular, where there is a threat to employment within the undertaking; and
- Decisions likely to lead to substantial changes in work organisation or in contractual relations, including redundancies and matters relating to a Transfer of Undertakings.

Factors influencing Employees

The Role of the Unions

Over the last three decades, union membership has significantly reduced from 13 million in 1979 to around 6.4 million at the end of 2014. Union membership today is marginally higher than 24% of all employees, a position which has not been seen since the start of the Second World War[239].

Older workers and female employees are more likely to be union members. Employees from ethnic minorities are less likely to be represented by a union in general, although Black or Black British workers are more likely to be in a union.

Although union membership in the public sector has declined, and there has been a slight increase in private sector union membership, public sector union membership (at 54%) remains far higher than private sector union membership (at 14%).

The top 5 sectors for union membership are:

- Education;
- Public Administration;
- Energy;
- Human Health and Social Work;
- Transportation and Storage.

Where union relations exist, there has been a general move from the pluralist and acrimonious relations, towards recognition of the value all participants can contribute towards a successful, sustainable and healthy organisation.

Traditionally unions have occupied a strong position in relation to working conditions and employment terms, and have played an important role in the protection of employee rights and protection at work. In the absence of this contribution, it is likely that organisations have been less constrained in the adoption of less acceptable conditions. It could be argued that the loss of effective union power has contributed, to some extent, to the level of industrial illness and injury prevalent today.

The Role of the Line Manager

According to the CIPD[240], up to a third of the UK workforce is likely to leave their employer in the next two years because of a poor relationship with their line manager. The report criticised managers' abilities to coach; communicate; support; recognise employee contribution; provide feedback; and evaluate performance.

Interestingly, employees identified that their manager did not have enough time in the day to manage the people responsibilities of the role. Managers criticised tools that were not easy to use, and criticised the lack of empowerment or knowledge provided by their organisation to enable them to manage people well.

Whilst it would be easy to identify training as being an obvious and necessary intervention to address these line manager failings, the evidence from line managers suggests that a wider review of organisation design including structures, systems and processes may be more appropriate.

Line Managers have a duty to perform particular activities in relation to safety:

- In their transformational role, demonstrating active commitment, worker involvement, assessment and review, and
- In their transactional role, assessing risks, applying the principles of prevention, organising for safety (planning, organising, controlling, monitoring and reviewing), and ensuring that the right people with the right training, capabilities, and information undertake the work.

The Role of Culture

The term "safety culture" emerged almost 30 years ago in the report into the Chernobyl disaster by the International Atomic Energy Agency (1986). It was another 7 years before a clear definition of safety culture was defined by the HSE[241]

> 'The safety culture of an organisation is the product of individual and group values, attitudes, perceptions, competencies, and patterns of behaviour that determine the commitment to, and the style and proficiency of, an organisation's health and safety management.

This was subsequently developed and broken down into three clear and independent elements:[242]

- The psychological element (what people feel)
- The behavioural element (what people do)
- The situational element (what is expected)

There are valuable lessons that can be learned from industries that have undertaken significant cultural change in relation to safety. Between 1997 and 2002, the railways suffered one of their worst periods for events and consequences. 13 events occurred, culminating in 59 deaths, and 1,000 injuries. This was particularly significant because this period followed the transition into private ownership between 1994 and 1997.

Following the Ladbroke Grove and Southall Rail incidents, the Railway Inspectorate (the Rail equivalent of the HSE) called for a review of safety culture across a railway industry[243]. Five indicators were chosen as having a particular influence on safety culture. These were:

- Leadership
- Two-way communications
- Employee involvement and motivation
- Learning culture
- Blame and accountability

Leadership

In what has become a common but all too often unlearned message over the last thirty years, Lord Cullen recommended *'the noise around performance must be tempered to ensure it does not swamp the noise around safety'*. This is equally transferable to all forms of corporate risk. In 1988, Lord Chief Justice Hidden, investigating the Clapham Rail Disaster criticised a safety system that *'lagged frighteningly behind the idealism of words'*.

Leadership commitment needs to be clear, well communicated, and evidenced in practices that demonstrate commitment across the organisation, for example in budgets, verbal and written communications, and training.

Two (Three) way communications

Communications need to ensure that:

- Top down communications effectively promulgate through the organisation that the message is understood by those receiving it, and that management concern for significant risks is clear.
- Bottom up communications need to be clear and undiluted by the time they reach the decision managers responsible. Feedback to those raising concerns needs to be clear and equally positive.
- Horizontal communications about work organisation and planning need to be structured and clear, and unambiguous.

Staff Involvement and Motivation

Motivation and involvement exists when the workforce are involved in decisions that affect them; have an opportunity to contribute to their own safety; to make suggestions and receive feedback on their ideas; receive information about changes that might have an effect on them.

The Learning Culture

Learning cultures capture opportunities to investigate from previous events, either within the organisation or outside; monitor, review and analyse trends; evaluate safety improvements and the effectiveness of change programmes; and undertake safety culture surveys at all levels of the organisation.

Accountability over blame

There is seldom a single cause of an incident. Often a combination of human error, poor supervision, ineffective systems and inadequate controls enable the convergence of a series of circumstances that culminate in an incident or event.

A quick leap to blame creates a culture where errors and incidents are covered up, employees are fearful or anxious about raising concerns, and organisations are unable to learn from previous mistakes.

Investigation that understands the wider causes of the event or incident, and the fair and appropriate identification of actions to prevent those circumstances from occurring again enables organisation to reduce future risk.

This does not mean that employees should not be sanctioned for their failings, but that those sanctions should be fair and just, and reflect all of the failings that contributed to the event, and not just those that rest with the operator.

Room for Engagement

HR Practitioners are familiar with the variety of engagement surveys that exist to measure factors like employee motivation and commitment. Some of these tools incorporate a degree of measurement against organisational practices considered to improve organisational performance as well as employee engagement.

Given the similarity of 'safety' culture to wider organisational culture and employee engagement, there is room for these surveys to incorporate an element of the safety surveys available, to obtain a measure, not just of how committed employees are, but how safe they are as well.

British Standard 76000 – Valuing People

In September 2015, the British Standards Institute published its first auditable, principles based standard. This 'Valuing People' standard (BS 76000) provides a framework for organizations to assess the extent to which they value people.

According to BSI, '*This principles-based management system standard is based on the premise that people are an organisation's biggest asset and should be treated as such – so the organisation gets the most out of them, and people get the most out of their working life.*'

The Central principles are:

- *The interests of staff and other stakeholders are integral to the best interests of an organization;*
- *The organization is part of wider society and has a responsibility to operate in a fair and socially responsible manner;*
- *Commitment to valuing people should come from the most senior leaders of an organization;*
- *The people who work for an organization have rights over and above those in law or regulation, and these rights and legal protections are respected by the organization.*

The standard was developed by a number of subject matter experts including representatives from employers, unions, BSI, the HSE and the CIPD, amongst others. Their work was then subjected to a 100-day public consultation.

According to BSI, this standard '*will help organizations of all sizes recognize the actual and potential value of their people and help develop a new and effective working partnership for sustainable success. It's relevant not only to HR professionals and large organizations with HR departments, but also to small businesses, those working with volunteers or temporary staff, recruitment agencies, and institutions that teach HR or governance – in fact all organizations.'*

References

[228] Engaging for Success: Enhancing Performance through employee engagement, a report to Government by David MacLeod and Nita Clarke, July 2009. Crown Copyright.

[229] Employee Outlook, Employee Vies on Working Life, CIPD and Halogen Software, Autumn 2015.

[230] http://www.hse.gov.uk/humanfactors/introduction.htm

[231] Reducing error and influencing behaviour, HSE, 2009

[232] https://www.energyinst.org/technical/human-and-organisational-factors/human-factors-top-ten

[233] Influences on safe/unsafe practices Farmers' perspectives Prepared by BOMEL Limited for the Health and Safety Executive 2009

[234] Identifying human factors associated with slip and trip accidents Prepared by System Concepts for the HSE, 2005

[235] Research into the behavioural aspects of slips and trip accidents and incidents Part 1: Literature review Prepared by Rossmore MCA Limited for the HSE, 2005

[236] What works in delivering improved health and safety A review of the existing evidence Prepared by the IES for the HSE, 2008

[237] Consulting workers on health and safety - Safety Representatives and Safety Committees Regulations 1977 (as amended) and Health and Safety (Consultation with Employees) Regulations 1996 (as amended) HSE Books ACOP, HSE, 2014

[238] Involving your workforce in health and safety Good practice for all workplaces, HSE, 2008

[239] Trade Union Membership 2014, ONS, June 2015

[240] One in five line managers 'ineffective', according to employees, Grace Lewis, CIPD, February 2015

[241] HSE's Advisory Committee on the Safety of Nuclear Installations, 1993

[242] Towards a Model of Safety Culture. Safety Science 36, Cooper, M.D., 2000.

[243] A review of safety culture and safety climate literature for the development of the safety culture inspection toolkit Prepared by Human Engineering for the HSE, 2005

SERVICE INFORMATION & DELIVERY

Introduction

By now, it should be clear that HR Practitioners can have a significant impact on health, safety and corporate risk. HR Practitioners play an important role in establishing what the organisation does, how it does it, and how well it aligns with its environment. Once the organisation is established and the structure is filled, how HR demonstrate leadership and management further shapes attitudes and behaviours across the organisation.

In this context, service, information and delivery are vital to the sustainability of the organisation:

- The range and type of services provided contribute to business performance;
- The information collected and shared with decision makers shapes the future of the organisation; and
- The quality and timeliness of delivery determines the extent to which future risks are being created and accepted within the organisation.

There is significant evidence that business performance can be enhanced by the adoption of the effective organisational behaviours. These behaviours, sometimes referred to as high performance work practices have been categorised across three areas. The areas are:[244]

- Human resource practices
- Reward and employee commitment practices
- High employee involvement practices

Human Resource practices

Effective Human Resource practices contribute to higher skill levels across the organisation which improve productivity or increase innovation, both of which contribute to organisational performance.

Common practices across the best performing organisations are:

- Work design to improve performance
- Reviewing vacancies against the organisation's strategy
- Workforce diversity
- Formal assessment tools for recruitment
- Structured 'induction' training
- An annual review of employees' training needs
- Training to perform multiple activities, tasks, and jobs
- Continuous skills development processes

- Mentoring
- Annual performance appraisal processes
- Formal feedback from a variety of sources
- The adoption of a structure or standard, such as quality assurance, business excellence, or a similar standard

Reward and employee commitment practices

By creating a link between the individual and the organisation which increases a sense of identity, equity, and belonging with the organisation, reward can more effectively align with performance and employees have a greater sense of belonging. Current thinking on performance pay based on values and longer term objectives are increasingly becoming a matter of statute.

Common practices across the best performing organisations are:

- Performance pay, profit-share, or share-options for all or some employees
- Flexible job descriptions
- Flexible working and family friendly policies
- Job rotation
- Non-pay benefits, and the extension of benefits to the wider family (e.g. health or other insurances)

High employee involvement practices

As well as contributing to improving working methods and the identification of new opportunities, these practices produce a greater level of trust and communication, increasing factors such as motivation, leadership and team work.

Common practices across the best performing organisations are:

- Sharing information on company performance and strategy
- Sharing business plans and targets
- Creating staff associations
- Internal surveys and suggestion schemes
- Quality circle, kaizen, and other involvement based improvement groups
- Self-managed or self-directed teams
- Cross-functional activities to improve organisational performance

These practices reflect approaches to organisation design and development, resourcing and recruitment, capability and competence, performance and reward, and employee engagement which have been consistent across the preceding chapters and highlight the link between good performance and risk management.

HR Practitioners have access to a wealth of information about their organisations. Making this useful, in the form of metrics that provide a meaningful value and a basis to identify good practice, concerns and trends is an important and necessary activity in the age of HR data.

Organisation Design

Organisation design (OD) which is often seen very much as an important role of HR, fundamentally determines the interaction between people and equipment. OD provides an opportunity to adapt work to the individual, especially in workplace design, work equipment selection, and the choice of working and production methods, with a view to alleviating monotonous work and work at a predetermined work-rate, reducing negative effects on health.

HR investment in these processes can support the creation of jobs with higher levels of autonomy and variety, which in turn create feelings of fulfilment and self-worth. These positively contribute to employee satisfaction, motivation and engagement which in turn increases employee retention and reduces absence.

OD provides an opportunity for employers to create comfortable working spaces with suitable operating temperatures, lighting and ventilation; suitable facilities for rest and welfare; and ergonomically designed work stations, so removing work in tiring or uncomfortable positions. There is evidence that people do not sit in uncomfortable positions for long.

In more hazardous environments, OD provides the opportunity to remove risks at source and to substitute hazardous environments, substances, equipment and activities with non-dangerous or less dangerous alternatives.

The role of job design in these environments is to find ways of working that do not expose employees to hazards. Where that cannot be avoided, jobs can be structured to minimise exposures through work planning, technology, or through rotation and variety to produce a lower exposure across a wider cross-section of employees.

Where work equipment is provided, effective OD ensures adequate provision for maintenance and inspection regimes (often jobs themselves or sub-contracted services); working arrangements to ensure a sufficiency of personnel to compensate for factors such as cover for holidays, training, sickness, and health screening.

OD costs should also include the necessary costs of:

- Recruitment (particularly at the skill level required to operate safely, effectively, and productively),
- Induction and lead time to effective contribution (wages and training costs),
- Additional costs arising from work activities and environments, such as personal protective equipment,
- Costs of any additional training or equipment, and
- Other costs such as or thorough inspections of equipment or DSE costs.

Beyond the physical organisation (workplace, equipment, etc.), governance systems and hierarchies should produce structures with a volume and capability of management and supervision with sufficient oversight, proportionate to all the risks, with reasonable spans of control, and is sufficient for the breadth and variety of working hours.

As with other employees, managers and supervisors will require knowledge, skills and experience to fulfil their roles, as well as the necessary information, instructions and training on internal equipment and processes (competence). Dependent on the nature of their exposures, they may similarly require health surveillance and personal protective equipment, particularly if they are required to ensure workers are required to wear PPE in their working environments.

Balancing the investment of HR in these activities has to be measured against the implications of that presence not being made. The impact on reputation, retention, sickness, and other factors make input at this stage critical, if HR is to be able to pursue anything other than a non-reactive role once the organisation is in place.

Numbers Employed

Changes in the nature of work, such as the use of agency, contract, temporary, part-time and zero-hours labour has created a challenge for many employers, but numbers employed are an important value, not least because of the way that numbers employed influence certain statutory requirements.

To provide a meaningful basis for factors such as productivity, many organisations rely on Full Time Equivalents (FTE) as a basis for measuring organisation size. However, with normal full time hours across organisations in the UK varying between 35 and 42 hours per week, there is a potential variation in comparisons of 20% even when comparing FTE data. As well as looking at total values, analysing ratios within those numbers can provide important data to identify risks. For example:

- Ratios of management and supervision to operational personnel will provide an indication of oversight and control.
- Percentage of workers exposed to risk (physical or psychosocial risks associated with work), homeworkers, lone workers, shift-workers, workers based on the road, etc.
- Workers that consistently work excessive hours – this figure is defined in law, but there is significant variation across countries. An organisation figure based on exposures may be more appropriate.
- Headcount in relation to volume of work (productivity), sales and profit.

Organisation Development

The need to keep organisations under review is continual if organisations are going to remain competitive, keep up to date with technical advances, and provide the expected return on investment and operating costs. HR have an important role to support review processes, encourage other leaders and managers, and provide support, knowledge and skills to identify and implement change.

Although organisation development can be largely based on changes to organisation design, for which all the points above apply, it often looks at elements like cultures, behaviours, and processes.

In this context, HR has a duty to ensure suitable controls are in place to protect the organisation from harm. This applies in equal measure to the change process itself (through effective management of change) and post change through the delivery of an effective organisation fit for purpose, and with sufficient safeguards to ensure safe operation.

For organisations employing more than 50 staff, the duty to share these plans through information and consultation processes means that dialogue with workers and their representatives should start in good time.

In any event, where there are likely to be changes to the way that work has been performed previously, perhaps through the use of new processes, technology or equipment. There are specific duties to consult with workers and their representatives, irrespective of whether unions are recognised.

This is particularly relevant where the new organisation has been established to develop a new product, access a new market, or access a new geography (either for supply or market). In these circumstances, the pressure to ensure the new structure is successful can carry a personal weight, inclining employees to be more willing to make a sacrifice, cut a corner, or take a risk, which requires an approach to risk management and oversight that ensures these risks are captured, calculated, and managed.

HR can play an important role in this process by providing an understanding of employee and organisational behaviour, and by establishing effective mechanisms and personnel to perform the required oversight and control functions.

Balancing the risk to the organisation without compromising innovation and creativity is an important balancing mechanism requiring a fine balance in organisational systems and processes which are proportionate to the potential for harm.

Organisation Costs

Costs of employment are useful in identifying areas of vulnerability for organisations and supporting business cases for change. In this context, the following factors can help to identify concerns:

- Net pay levels (minimum, maximum and mean)
- The cost of management and supervision to operational personnel
- Wages costs as a proportion of total business costs, and as a proportion of total revenue.
- The ratio between internal and external labour costs

The cost of wages, salaries and employee benefits can be anything from 18% to 52% of operating expenses[245], so small percentage changes to these figures can have a significant impact on overall financial performance.

Other metrics, such as the extent to which shifts satisfies the HSE Guidance on good shifts is a good way to identify opportunities to improve shift working practices.

In some industries, the HSE provides specific guidance on organisation monitoring regimes, particularly focussing on the contribution of leading indicators (the causes of events) rather than lagging indicators (their results).[246]

Costs of Safety

The nature of the working environment or activities performed can create additional costs which can be controlled through alternative interventions. These include:

- Accident costs
- Costs of PPE
- Medical assessments
- Cost of Employer's Liability Insurance (ELI)
- Cost and defensibility of ELI claims.

These costs can form a part of a business case to justify changes to working practices or capital equipment (e.g. segregating employees from noisy environments to replace the costs associated with noise protection).

Other costs of safety can be harder to identify but can include costs of reviews and audits, the costs of the actions to put right any findings (capital and expenditure), and the cost of administering that process.

Employers Liability

The HSE estimate a cost of £1,405m in costs of insurance related to employee compensation. It is important to bear in mind that whilst the organisation's hazard profile is likely to have a significant effect on actual premium, previous experience can produce far greater variations as insurers attempt to price insurance relative to their perception of client risk.

According to the Association of British Insurers[247] (ABI), Employers' Liability[PP] insurers paid out claims of £2.3 million per day in 2013. Despite this, the ABI declared a liability underwriting loss of £826 million, the largest loss for more than 30 years indicating that premiums are likely to follow a general upward trend.

Data[248] analysed from over 110,000 Employers' Liability claims submitted by UK unions on behalf of their members identified the hazards that lead to the highest volume of claims. The top four are:

- Slips, trips and falls;
- Manual handling;
- Noise and
- Stress.

The same report showed typical times for claims to be settled was between 27 and 42 months, this creates a long and protracted difficulty in the relationship between employers and employees. Furthermore, whilst settlement values may have ranged from £1 to £1,133,462, mean levels were typically between £1,000 and £5,000 which many claimants indicate do not reflect their true sense of loss.

Resourcing and Recruitment

Resourcing and recruitment require a careful balancing act between the need for skills acquisition and retention on the one hand, and the need for organisations to be agile and flexible on the other. Carrying vacancies can result in increased overtime, lack of skills, or insufficient supervision, which in turn can lead to incidents or accidents. In many cases, work must be undertaken by 'competent' persons.

Whilst techniques like person specifications can significantly improve recruitment process effectiveness, many organisations do not have job descriptions to support recruitment processes. Knowing the necessary knowledge, qualifications, training, experience, skills, abilities, and behavioural requirements for the post can significantly improve the likelihood of job holder success and retention.

The same can be said for other parts of the recruitment process. A return to the more traditional cv led, over competence based, interviewing techniques; a fall in the use of psychometric testing; less than one in four employers pursuing references; and a general failure to identify, specify and actively seek the right behaviours is reflective

---

[PP] The Employers' Liability (Compulsory Insurance) Act 1969 requires employers to have current Employers' Liability Insurance to a minimum value of £5m. Organisations can be fined £2,500 per day for every day they do not have valid insurance, and £1,000 for a failure to show the certificate to an HSE Inspector.

of many organisations that are keen to invest more time in recruitment, but do not have the ability to achieve the goal in practice. This has implications for the success of the recruitment process.

With as many as one in three CVs containing a level of dishonesty and candidates willing to risk imprisonment for higher returns, recruitment processes need to ensure that the wrong applicants do not slip through the net.

Perhaps the business case for investment in recruitment is becoming more apparent. With typical labour turnover targets of between 5 and 10%, current labour turnover at 14%; four fifths of employers saying competition for talent is on the increase; and three quarters reporting recruitment difficulties, something needs to happen to ensure that the right people are hired for the right job at the right time.

The recruitment process provides an opportunity to identify candidates with the greatest fit to the role, and to identify and capture the gaps that need to be addressed through subsequent information, instruction and training. If the process fails on either of these goals, organisation performance will suffer and the employee will find it harder to become a full and effective member of the organisation.

This is particularly the case with vulnerable workers, for whom a failure to manage the introduction to the organisation can have profound implications on the employee, the organisation, and the local community.

A variety of metrics (numeric and financial) can indicate the types of risks an organisation is exposed to.

The percentage of vulnerable workers that make up the numbers employed, including temporary, agency and contract workers, etc. will provide an indication of risk from resourcing and recruitment activity as well as from the organisation itself.

Understanding the demographics of the workforce, for example those over 65, can provide an indication of future recruitment needs – particularly in key worker roles, for jobs where there are known recruitment difficulties, where time to train is significant, or where there are complex succession arrangements that need to be put in place.

Non-employees as a proportion of total workers engaged at the site provides an indication of exposure to a variety of risks associated with contract, temporary, and agency workers.

Recruitment and retention factors – open vacancies, hires, leavers, can provide an indication that there may be a problem in a particular department, whereas time to fill vacancies, numbers applying for positions, and numbers withdrawing during the recruitment process (including those declining a formal job offer) can provide an indication that there are problems with perception of work.

Numbers of new starters leaving within one year may also be an indication of problems during recruitment, induction, working environment or the nature of the work activities. At the same time, average tenure may provide a good indication of the balance of the organisation.

It is worth considering that given the high levels of unpleasant exposures in work, employees may seek to leave to work in more pleasant, comfortable, and less hazardous environments.

Numbers of new arrivals and inductions amongst temporary or contractor personnel may indicate organisational vulnerability, particularly if management and supervision is insufficient or induction programmes do not adequately address knowledge gaps.

Factors like the ratio of overtime to normal working hours, the ratio of overtime cost to basic salary, and the total hours worked per person (planned versus actual) may be indicative of an organisation that is not adequately resourced to meet current demand or one that may be exposed to additional risks because of problems in the recruitment process.

Recruitment difficulties may indicate problems with organisation design (producing complex skills gaps) that may be hard to fill or may highlight problems of alignment to the local labour market that may need to be addressed. Recruitment source rates can be helpful in identifying the most effective channels to fill vacancies.

Understanding factors like how many employees have protected characteristics, and how many of those personnel are in management positions may be indicative of the success or failure of attempts to make the organisation more reflective of the customer base or local environment.

The number of employees working under flexible terms, or for whom reasonable adjustments have been made, may provide an indication of organisational culture, as would be the extent of requests made and granted.

The cost of losing an employee can be grossly under-calculated, but when used properly, can provide a strong business case for making adjustments. Typically, an organisation that loses an employee (that needs to be replaced) will incur costs of recruitment, costs of induction and other training, the administration processes involved in the leaver and starter processes, management time, loss of output during the vacancy, and a potential lack of quality during the transition between appointment and full competence.

Linking the cost of a leaver with factors like likelihood of loss, ease to replace, time to replace and impact of loss to the organisation, can provide a useful way of identifying who the key workers are. It is not always the most obvious roles.

Activities linked to health and safety, for example health surveillance for new starters, the provision of safety related training, and PPE must be provided in working time and at no cost to the employee. If any of these are provided off site, travel and subsistence costs must be met by the employer.

Factors like 'hiring manager satisfaction rate', average distance travelled, average test scores, percentages of new hires reaching 'satisfactory' at first appraisal, can also provide meaningful intelligence on the effectiveness of recruitment processes.

Competence and Capability

HR often control the budget for training and have the duty to ensure good returns from training investment. Organisations have a unique variety of training needs, and a variety of ways to spend the money across a variety of learning interventions including training, development, and education, which all serve to increase the breadth and depth of organisational learning.

These gaps are normally filled through a combination of formal courses, e-learning, coaching and mentoring programmes, work activities and their combinations.

The first experience that most employees gain of training is through the induction programme. As we have already seen, a good induction programme can save lives and substantially reduce risk. The design and content of an induction programme shapes future employee behaviour and performance.

Over time, learning interventions will provide employees (and other workers) with the necessary information, instructions and training to perform their roles competently. These may be based on a minimum defined knowledge or skills base, expected behaviours, the hazards and risks associated with work, the processes used, or a combination of all of the above.

Good training departments will have structured and organised processes for imparting training to all employees, giving particular regard to the needs of employees in key roles. There will be formal mechanisms for assessing performance, capturing training needs and recording training received.

Learning will be assessed for effectiveness, in the form of a simple review of basic competence, an attempt to measure impact on organisational performance, or a more thorough and systemic audit of the competence system in place.

When organisations are finding talent hard to find, the business case for development needs to highlight the competitive advantage to be gained from growing organisational knowledge, addressing skills gaps, building 'bench-strength', and the role of learning in the employee value proposition.

Competence

Organisations measure training in a variety of ways. Total training spend as a proportion of payroll costs is a common metric, not least because of the way that it provides a convenient link for budgetary purposes. Training hours per person is a similarly common metric. Both of these measures can encourage an investment in cheap, off-the-shelf, tick box type training that may not effectively deliver what the organisation needs.

A more appropriate focus is to start with the role and the training needs of the organisation and its employees:

How many job descriptions have been agreed and signed off by the organisation and the job holder? How many roles have clearly identified competence requirements? How many information, instruction and training interventions does that create for all employees to be competent? How many of those interventions have been fulfilled?	What proportion of employees are subject to an annual assessment or appraisal that includes an assessment of training needs? How many of training needs have been identified from this process? How are these training needs related back to the job role? How many of these needs have been fulfilled? How many employees are fully trained?

Collectively, these elements make up the training needs. Delivery against these needs provides a value for training penetration.

Factors like cost per learning hour, cost per employee, and cost as a proportion of payroll are important, but they should be weighed against these measures. Other metrics worth considering are the extent to which fully trained employees are offered developmental training, how frequently do employees need refresher training, and how well are those metrics achieved?

Training will only be effective if it influences employee behaviour and organisational performance. Employee attendance on courses, employee assessment (examination) scores, employee opinion (feedback forms), and Kirkpatrick measures can help to determine training effectiveness.

Factors like average lead time to competence, numbers of employees fully competent, or percentage completed, average attendance on training, percentage of employees briefed before training took place, the percentage of time spent by internal trainers in the classroom and percentage of training cancelled can provide indications of training effectiveness.

By classifying training into type: compliance, management, operational systems, behavioural training, etc., it is possible to identify the proportion of training required by the organisation. Reconciling this with training needs fulfilled, provides an indication of the effectiveness of training against targeted themes or priorities.

Analysing costs from this perspective may help organisations to discover alternative ways of training, or combining training events to improve training quality and reduce costs.

Capability

Sickness

Organisations can significantly influence performance across these metrics by being responsive and flexible in dealing with capability problems. High levels of absence can reflect a low level of control (short term absence) or management (long term absence).

Sick Pay

The CIPD[249] reported an absence level of 6.9 days per employee in 2015 (approximately 2.5% of working time), up 10% on the year before. They estimate an average cost of £554 per employee, but costs vary widely, ranging from £400 per employee in private sector services, to £789 per head in public sector services. Collectively, these amount to an annual cost of £17 billion to employers.

According to the CIPD, 87% of organisations now collect absence data. Almost a quarter of organisations do not record annual sickness rates[250] and there remains a variety of approaches which means that data is broadly indicative but should not be regarded as precise for benchmarking purposes.[251] Barely more than a third (37%) monitor the total cost of absence or set targets for reducing it[252].

The HSE estimate a cost of £1,227m in sick pay costs alone arising from workplace incidents, but this is likely to grossly under-estimate true costs as the scale of incidents is under-reported (HSE).

Recording factors like sickness absence as a percentage or as a number of working days, and as a sick pay cost provide an indication of the size of the problem, but analysing the data to understand the extent to which absence is caused by short term (acute) conditions, injuries, and more serious (chronic) illnesses can provide a basis on which to improve sickness levels by targeting investment on the most significant causes. Knowing how many employees suffer from chronic conditions can help to put costs of sickness into perspective and ensure that investments are most effectively targeted.

Medical referrals and health surveillance activities can help to identify areas of work that may cause more significant problems if early interventions do not happen. Knowing what percentage of employees suffer from chronic conditions that may be made worse by work will help to understand the scale of the problem and the scale of the intervention necessary to address it. The national statistic is around 4% of the working population, although a further 2% have left the labour market because they can no longer perform work.

Accidents at Work

The number and type of accidents at work provide meaningful data nationally to provide a consideration of risks within any organisation, but an understanding of the history of accidents within the organisation will provide a much more targeted approach to address the causes of injury, illness, and absence from work. Numbers of accidents, lost work day cases, and reportable accidents and illnesses provide an indication of the causes.

Costs of sickness, overtime costs, temporary labour, labour turnover, recruitment and training can all arise as a consequence of workplace injuries and illnesses and affect overall HR performance data. Other costs such as lost time, damages, material losses and repairs to equipment, production delays, loss of contracts and loss of business reputation may have a far greater impact on the HR department, and are likely to distract HR practitioners from other activities. The wider implications across the business can significantly impact productivity, competitiveness[253], and sustainability.

Musculoskeletal Disorders

The HSE are particularly keen to address musculoskeletal disorders in the workplace and have developed a seven point plan for employers to assess organisational performance:

- Understand the issues and commit to action
- Create the right organisational environment
- Assess the risks from manual handling in your workplace
- Avoid, or where this is not possible, reduce the risks
- Educate, inform and consult your workforce
- Manage any case of injury
- Carry out regular checks on programme effectiveness

The HSE identify a range of HR metrics as indicators of musculoskeletal conditions at work. More importantly, they identify that factors such as labour turnover, sickness absence and health surveillance data can identify concerns of organisational importance, long before they cause irreparable upper limb disorders.

Mental Health

The CIPD report highlighted the significant percentage of organisations reporting an increase in stress and mental health related absences. Leading the CIPD to print this call to action:

> *'The pressure people are experiencing as a result of the wider context we're operating in makes a focus on employee health and wellbeing important. Ignoring employee health and well-being can result in significant costs to an organisation in terms of sick pay and temporary staffing cover as well as having a negative impact on employee morale, colleague workloads and ultimately business productivity.'* CIPD Annual Report 2014

Despite this, the CIPD reports that less than a third of organisations have increased their focus on employee wellbeing. Where organisations have responded, it has often been on the 'cure' processes like Employee Assistance Programmes, (EAPs) rather than prevention through organisation design (to reduce the causes), and training (to build resilience). Understanding take up of EAP may provide a business case for earlier action.

Performance

Although performance assessment is going through a period of change at the moment, elements like employee assessment, awareness of training needs, and pay linked to performance still remain.

Ensuring that employees know what is expected of them, and how they are expected to achieve their goals are increasingly key elements of any system following events across several high profile industries.

Similarly, understanding the reasons for success (or failure) for employees is important if organisations are to continue to improve. Successes in one part of a busy may be transferable to others whilst lessons learned from failures are the best way to ensure that failures do not happen again.

Where failings occur because of employee performance, actions need to be taken. Sometimes, performance can be affected by capability or conduct, and where this is the case, organisations have to intervene. In the case of conduct, there can be a fine line between acceptable and unacceptable behaviours. In the case of capability, organisations may need to make different interventions, perhaps through training, role –redefinition, or other approaches.

If work circumstances have led to capability problems, for example because of poorly implemented change programmes, or health problems associated with current ways of working, organisations need to act quickly, and more widely than the individual visibly suffering.

Across health, safety and corporate risk, performance measures are key to establishing that oversight is effective and controls are in place. As such, records of employees with current disciplinary warnings demonstrate that control has been applied where necessary.

Similarly probationary periods not completed, or extended, provide an indication of the effectiveness of recruitment and induction processes, as does the number of new starters reaching 'satisfactory' performance in their first year.

The number of employees reaching or breaching trigger points relating to sickness and lateness processes may indicate whether an organisation is effectively controlling and managing absence, whilst and sickness related warnings may provide an indication of process robustness, other interventions such as medical referrals, flexible working arrangements, or job changes may be a better indication of sickness process effectiveness.

Calculating Bradford factors may be a useful way to establish and prioritise interventions relating to sickness performance because of the way that it provides an indication of short versus long term absence information. Similarly, understanding underlying trends and causes can help support the development of a robust strategy.

Where organisations use performance appraisals, measures like the average performance level of leavers, the percentage of high and low performing staff, the percentage whose performance has dropped, and an analysis of performance versus tenure can provide useful measures of system effectiveness.

Other factors like the percentage of return to work interviews completed, probation reports completed, appraisals completed on time and with agreement, or trigger point actions carried out will provide a measure of line manager buy-in to HR processes and an indication of potential exposure at tribunal if policies and procedures are not being followed consistently.

Reward

Reward processes and mechanisms need to carefully balance an array of competing forces, including macro-economic factors, organisational performance, legal duties, flexibility, financial control, and employees' perceptions of self-worth.

The array of different options available to employers creates communication and administration challenges, but this is part of modern reward. Benefits are seen as a mechanism that organisations can use to increase employee engagement.

Reward typically consists of basic pay, additional pay and bonuses, but commonly includes a variety of additional benefits ranging from employee share ownership and company cars, through to additional holidays and employee assistance programmes.

Against this backdrop, it is easy to see how benefits information can get confused, expensive to administer, and fail to achieve the increased retention and employee engagement sought at introduction.

Reward influences behaviour, retention and a variety of other factors that influence health, safety and corporate risk. Knowing whether pay is consistent within the business contributes to a sense of equity across employees.

Individual perceptions of self-worth always vary, so having a formal mechanism that can explain why people earn what they do demonstrates recognition. The first metrics therefore are the percentage of employees paid through a fair and effective system based on a suitable job evaluation process.

Often job evaluation systems are linked to grading structures. Within the grading structures, how many employees are paid below or above the midpoint, how many employees would be regarded as outliers of their grade range?

Total reward is often made up of a variety of factors which include bonus. How is the bonus calculated (is it loaded towards short term or long term goals, does it consider behaviours as well as results?)?

Higher levels of bonus can introduce a higher level of risk. What proportion of total cash is made up through bonus payments? What is the lag between performance and receipt of bonus? What percentage of bonus is generally paid? Too what extent can employees actually influence their bonus?

Holidays can provide an important measure of the extent to which employees are feeling stressed or pressured. Employees not taking holidays, or taking holidays but remaining 'always-on' may be reflective of an organisational culture that does not recognise the benefits that a well-earned rest can bring.

Where flexible benefits are offered, to what extent are they taken up? This is not purely a financial assessment of value, but if they have been introduced to boost motivation and engagement and there is little take up, the result may be the opposite of the benefit sought.

Employee Engagement

Evidence shows that employee engagement increases productivity and creativity and so improves organisational performance. Good practice from the HSE is that good leadership provides clear direction to, and receives feedback from, the rest of the organisation.

In some cases, there are statutory processes for informing and consulting with staff, particularly if the organisation employs more than 50 people, or if the organisation is planning to implement new processes, technology or equipment.

There are similar duties in relation to a propose transfer of undertakings, or where redundancies are proposed. When it comes to safety, there is clear guidance on what should be consulted on, with whom, and when.

Measurements of employee engagement or organisational climate (for example employee surveys, properly carried out) can contribute towards a greater understanding of underlying organisational issues that may be causing long term stress, anxiety or depression issues across the organisation.

Communication levels (the number of employees receiving downward communications on organisation performance, plans, etc., or participating in upward communications such as raising safety concerns, contributing to suggestion schemes, or participating in cross-functional or other business improvement teams.

Employee engagement also increases when employees seeing taking an interest in what they are doing – so measures like the number of times the senior team walk the shopfloor, and the quality of those visits.

Employers have a duty to encourage employees to raise concerns and to put effective systems in place to address them. Whilst many organisations would hope that they would not receive any, the more important measure is the extent to which these concerns are effectively and satisfactorily addressed.

Low levels of employee involvement may be indicative of poor levels of line management or supervisor engagement, or a wider concern relating to levels of trust between senior and operational personnel.

Sickness levels can be an indication of engagement, in part because discretionary absences increase when an employee does not feel motivated to go to work, but also because employees may require absence at short notice whilst job hunting and may not feel inclined to explain the real reasons.

Grievance levels can indicate whether employees are satisfied with organisational processes or by their supervisor. The ultimate measure is through the number and costs of employment tribunal applications and civil claims. Scoring zero in these two areas is a sign that things do not go wrong, and when they do, processes enable matters to be resolved in-house.

References

[244] Achieving Best Practice in your business, High performance work practices: linking strategy and skills to performance outcomes, DTI, CIPD, 2005

[245] Salaries as a Percentage of Operating Expense, SHRM Leading Indicators of National Employment Report, 2008

[246] Developing process safety indicators: A step-by-step guide for chemical and major hazard industries, HSE, 2006

[247] UK Insurance Key Facts 2014, Association of British Insurers, 2014

[248] Analysis of compensation claims related to health and safety issues, Laura Peebles, Tanya Heasman and Vivienne Robertson, HSE. 2003

[249] Absence Management, Annual Survey report, CIPD, 2015

[250] Absence Management, Annual Survey report, CIPD, 2014

[251] The feasibility of comparing sickness absence surveys and the Labour Force Survey, HSL for the HSE, 2008

[252] Absence Measurement and Management Factsheet, CIPD, March 2015

[253] Health and safety management and business economic performance, Sheikh, Gardiner & Brettell, HSE, 2006

PROTECTING EMPLOYEES

Personal Protective Equipment (PPE)

Although PPE is generally the last line of defence[qq], in some cases it is a statutory requirement in its own right, for example the use of head protection[rr] on construction sites. PPE comes in a variety of forms including:

- Head, eye and face protection
- Respiratory protective equipment[ss]
- Hi-visibility clothing
- Hand, arm, leg and foot protection
- Hearing protection
- Drowning protection
- Fall protection
- Protection from cold, hot, wet, chemical, sunshine, electricity, radiation, etc.

Where there is no choice but to use PPE as a control measure, the Personal Protective Equipment at Work Regulations 1992 and the associated Guidance[254] sets out specific requirements in relation to provision, compatibility, suitability, maintenance, replacement and storage.

The Regulations do not apply to uniforms, ordinary working clothes, or protective clothing supplied in the food industry primarily for food hygiene purposes. It is worth considering the relationship between workplace clothing, uniforms, and the risks associated with work.

Effective uniform clothing may address some of the workplace hazards in a manner that positively reflects the employer brand whilst the provision of, for example, embroidered 'fleeces' may provide a degree of warmth for some workers, but may not provide adequate protection because they may not be windproof, and may melt or ignite (depending on fabric selection) if workers are engaged in grinding, cutting or welding operations.

There are fleeces which are designed to work with risks of heat and fire.

[qq] The seventh of the eight Principles of Prevention is that priority should be given to collective over individual protective measures.

[rr] Construction (Head Protection) Regulations 1989

[ss] Some PPE is subject to specific regulation in its own right, such as head protection on construction sites or the requirement to ensure that respiratory protective equipment provides a secure face fit.

Provision

The PPE Regulations require employers to provide PPE to employees unless the risk *'has been adequately controlled in another way'*. The regulations also set out a very specific series of definitions relating to suitability:

(a)   It is appropriate for the risk or risks involved, the conditions at the place where exposure may occur, and the period for which it is worn;

(b)   It takes account of ergonomic requirements and the state of health of the person or persons who may wear it, and of the characteristics of the workstation of them;

(c)   It is capable of fitting the wearer correctly, if necessary, after adjustments within the range for which it is designed;

(d)   So far as is practicable, it is effective to prevent or adequately control the risk or risks involved without increasing overall risk;

(e)   It complies with any legal provision on design or manufacture with respect to health or safety in UK or any other relevant Community directive applicable to that item of personal protective equipment.

In practice, suitability is a function of the task being undertaken, the environment in which the employee is working, and the individual themselves. As such, a strict approach to PPE across a business or site is unlikely to be appropriate. For example strenuous work may 'steam up' some forms of eye protection, bulky equipment may be unsuitable for work performed at height or in confined spaces, and individual employees may have specific allergies. Effective employee consultation is more likely to result in the most appropriate PPE selection.

All PPE should carry the CE Mark and should comply with the requirements of the Personal Protective Equipment Regulations 2002 relating to design and manufacture.

An employee cannot be charged for the provision of PPE which is only used at work. If an employee does not return the PPE at the end of his employment, then, provided it has been stipulated in the employment contract, the employer may deduct a charge for the equipment from the employee's salary, but the employer cannot charge a 'returnable deposit'.

Suitability

In order to ensure suitability that meets the requirements of the regulations, organisations must first have identified that the risks requiring PPE could not have been avoided in another way. They must then consider the characteristics of the remaining hazards – for example: vapour, dust, spray, mist, liquid, and the specific hazard involved (e.g. is the substance carcinogenic?).

The characteristics of the PPE must then be compared with the characteristics of the hazard, for example because a dust mask may not provide suitable protection against liquids or vapours.

Consideration must be given to any additional risks that the PPE may create, for example impaired visibility or heat stress, and the impact the PPE may have on other identified necessary PPE (see below).

Compatibility

Where the presence of more than one risk to health or safety makes it necessary for employees to wear or use more than one item of personal protective equipment simultaneously, such equipment must be compatible to the extent that one does not undermine the effectiveness of another.

A good example of this is provided in the form of eye and respiratory protection. Wearing a pair of goggles and a breathing mask over the nose at the same time may hamper the tightness of the goggles or the mask to the extent that substances may cause harm to the eyes or lungs.

Maintenance and Replacement

As with all equipment provided by the employer, it must be maintained and cleaned to ensure that it remains in an efficient state, in efficient working order and in good repair.

The maintenance system should include regular examination, testing, cleaning, repair and replacement. In the event that PPE is shared, it should be suitably cleaned and disinfected to reduce the risk of health of subsequent users.

Some PPE such as fall arrest systems requires regular planned inspection by a competent person which should be recorded. There is no requirement to record testing for all PPE, although organisations may regard the recording of an examination as a useful way to ensure that it happens. In any event, manufacturers' instructions should be considered against the context of the nature of the work being undertaken and the environment in which it is being used.

PPE which is not single-use or disposable must be subject to regular cleaning. It is not unreasonable to expect employees to clean their own equipment, although this duty should be explained to the employee, be subject to routine checks, and where any cleaning fluids are used, they should be supplied to the employee so that (1) the selected chemical is identified and suitable and (2) the employee does not have to pay for them. Rules relating to the repair and disposal of safety equipment should also be made clear to employees.

Suitable storage facilities should also be provided to ensure that PPE is not damaged by the environment, is contaminated, or lost. In some cases, for example where PPE may get wet or dirty in normal use, drying and cleaning facilities must also be provided.

Information, Instruction and Training

As with many safety regulations, information, instruction and training must be provided to reduce the risk of harm.

Employees should be informed in a comprehensible manner of the risks the PPE will avoid, the purpose and manner in which the PPE should be used, and any action necessary from the employee to ensure that the equipment remains in an efficient state, working order and good repair. The 2002 Regulation required that the employer ensures that this information remains available to employees and that where appropriate, employers should organise demonstrations in the wearing of PPE at suitable intervals.

The HSE have provided guidance in relation to the information, instruction and training requirements of the regulations. They identify that training should be provided systematically to everyone involved in the use or maintenance of PPE. To this end:

- Users must be trained in the proper use of PPE, including how to correctly fit and wear it, and what its limitations are.
- Managers and supervisors must be aware of why PPE is being used and how to use it properly.
- People involved in maintaining, repairing and testing the equipment and in its selection for use will also need training.

As a part of the systematic approach to training, initial and refresher training should be provided and records should be kept to assist with the efficient administration of the training programme. Comprehension is a requirement of the Regulations and so an important part of the training process must be a mechanism for checking understanding. This is all the more relevant where PPE is complex, employees may have learning difficulties, or where English is not an employee's first language.

Training should include elements of theory as well as practice in using the equipment, and should be carried out in accordance with any recommendations and instructions supplied by the PPE manufacturer. The extent of the instruction and training should be proportionate to the complexity of the equipment,

Theoretical training should cover an explanation of the risks present and why PPE is needed; the operation, performance and limitations of the equipment; instructions on PPE selection, use and storage; factors which can affect the protection provided by the PPE such as other protective equipment, personal factors, working conditions, inadequate fitting, and defects, damage and wear; and how to recognise defects in PPE and arrangements for reporting loss or defects.

Written operating procedures such as permits to work involving PPE should be explained.

Practical training should include the:

- Putting on, wearing and removing the equipment;
- Inspection and, where appropriate, testing of the PPE before use;
- How to maintain PPE, which can be done by the user, such as cleaning and the replacement of certain components;
- Safe storage.

Guidance from the HSE is that PPE should be used only after adequate training and instructions have been given to the user so they understand why, how, where and when it is to be used.

Supervision

The HSE also provide guidance on the importance of Supervision including their specific training requirements:

- *Supervision is vital to ensure PPE is properly used.*
- *It is important that those with a supervisory role are also provided with adequate training and instructions so that they have the necessary skills to carry out the job.*
- *Spot checks are a useful way of monitoring how well PPE is used and corrective action can then be taken if spot checks reveal misuse.*

Equality Factors

Gender, ethnicity, build and many other factors mean that one size will not fit everyone. There is no exemption from the regulations for disabled persons. There is, however, a requirement to ensure that the equipment is adequate and suitable, and this requires the ergonomic requirements of the individual to be considered. Where this results in the construction of a bespoke piece of equipment which is not CE marked, specific requirements must be met by the designer/manufacturer.

Mobile/Agency Workers

A site may be better placed to define a single standard for PPE for workers at the site. In these circumstances, the site may provide the worker with the appropriate PPE which means that the employer does not have to. In these circumstances, it remains the duty of the employer to ensure that supplied PPE meets the requirements necessary to protect their employee, particularly taking into account the nature of the work that the employee may be performing.

Safety Signs and Signals

There are specific rules defined for the use of safety signs and signals at work. These are defined in the Health and Safety (Safety Signs and Signals) Regulations 1996 and its Guidance[255]. Safety signs are an important means of communicating risks to employees. However, in order for them to be effective, it is important that they are located in prominent places, maintained in good condition, and that employees are trained to understand what the sign means, and why it is significant. In this context, maintenance programmes should reflect the nature of the signage (including whether it is illuminated) and the environment in which the signs are located (in general, the more hostile the environment, the more frequently the signs should be checked).

It is important to remember that employers and others have duties to take precautions to control the risks that workers may be exposed to. The principles of prevention define the hierarchy of controls that should be followed in order to safely reduce risk. Signage is a method of providing instructions to employees, and as such, is at the bottom of the hierarchy. It will normally be used in conjunction with other control measures.

There are four main types of sign:

- Mandatory signs (round shape, white pictogram on blue background) instructing workers what they MUST do. For example, wear eye protection, hearing protection, respiratory protective equipment, etc. The blue colour should take up at least 50% of the sign.
- Prohibition signs (round shape, black pictogram on white background with red edging and diagonal line) instructing workers what they MUST NOT do. For example, preventing employees with pacemakers from entering locations with high electro-magnetic fields. The red colour should take up at least 35% of the sign.
- Warning signs (triangular shape, black pictogram on yellow background with black edging) warn workers of hazards. For example identifying the location of confined spaces, overhead lines or other hazards. These are often located by mandatory or prohibition signs indicating what action should be taken to reduce the risk. The yellow part should make up at least 50% of the area of the sign.
- Direction signs (rectangular or square shape, with a whit pictogram on a green background) direct employees towards emergency exit routes, first aid or other facilities (not fire equipment). The green content should make up at least 50% of the sign.

- Fire signs (rectangular or square in shape, with a white pictogram on a red background) indicate the location of fire equipment. The red part should take up at least 50% of the sign.

- Chemical warning signs (which do not form a part of these regulations) are diamond shaped and have a black pictogram on a white background and a red border.

Organisations often establish their own signs and signals which do not conform to national standards – for example flashing blue or yellow lights indicating that a particular vehicle movement or chemical process is taking place.

Employers and those responsible for sites in which other workers, for example contractors, are working, use signs to fulfil their duty to give information to workers on the risks associated with working at their site. It is important that contractors are provided with sufficient information to be able to recognise the signs and signals in use.

In the same way, graphical symbols can be helpful to ethnic minorities and workers with learning difficulties that may struggle with complex descriptions, and has the added benefit of being always there, provided it is located appropriately and regularly maintained.

The Safety Signs and Signals Regulations cover a wide variety of signs and other methods of signalling. They define the terminology to be used such as safety sign, health sign, and fire safety sign; and their safety colours and symbols; signboard (used to describe a board with a series of signs), illuminated signs, acoustic signals, verbal communications and hand signals.

There is some discretion to modify the pictograms. This may be appropriate to reflect a specific site requirement. For example the standard symbol for eye protection in the guidance is a head wearing a pair of glasses. If the risk relates to significant volumes of liquid, goggles may be more appropriate and under those circumstances, the symbol should wear goggles to avoid confusion.

The Regulations do not relate to chemical markings (see chemicals), work equipment markings (see work equipment) or road markings on the public highway, although they do apply to internal routes used by vehicles and pedestrians.

When considering what signage/signalling is necessary, consideration should be given to the environmental conditions – for example in an area of high noise, requiring PPE, not only should consideration be given to noise warning and mandatory hearing protection signs, but additional consideration should be given to the effectiveness of an acoustic fire alarm.

Additional consideration should be given to the needs of the workers in the area, for example, employees who are partially sighted, or have significant hearing loss may struggle to see or hear signage or signalling provided and reasonable adjustments may be necessary.

Health & Safety Information

There is a statutory duty on employers under the Health and Safety Information for Employees Regulations 1989 to display the statutory health and safety poster in a location where it is reasonable accessible, visible and readable. In cases where an employee is not based in a location where he may have reasonable access to the poster, he can be given the leaflet.

Both the poster and the leaflet are revised from time to time and it is the duty of the employer to make sure that employees have access to the most up to date version within nine months of its approval.

First Aid

Requirements for First Aid are defined by The Health and Safety (First-Aid) Regulations 1981 and supporting Guidance[256]. These regulations require an organisation to manage first aid provision, including kits, facilities, and information and training.

The Regulations are not prescriptive. The regulations require that first aid provision is adequate and appropriate in the circumstances. The assessment should consider:

- The nature of the work and workplace hazards and risks;
- The nature of the workforce;
- The organisation's history of accidents;
- The size of the organisation;
- The needs of travelling, remote and lone workers;
- Work patterns;
- The distribution of the workforce;
- The remoteness of the site from emergency medical services;
- Employees working on shared or multi-occupied sites;
- Annual leave and other absences of first-aiders and appointed persons; and
- First-aid provision for non-employees.

Following a logical process, such as that defined in the guidance, will help employers to establish suitable and appropriate provision for first aid at work. This will consist of facilities and equipment (based on the information above).

Alongside the provision of equipment, the organisation should identify and train suitable personnel, taking into account the hazards at the workplace, the proximity to emergency services, and the organisation of the workforce, it is a relatively straightforward process to define the number of trained personnel and the level of their training.

There is a four layer training framework in place for First Aid Training:

- Appointed Persons
- Emergency First Aid at Work
- First Aid at Work
- Additional (Specific) Training

When the equipment is in place and the personnel are trained, it is important to share this information with all employees. First Aid systems only work well when all employees know what should happen when an employee is injured. This is commonly provided by means of a notice board, although advice on induction, and routinely makes sure that employees are aware of what to do in the event of an accident at work.

The HSE indicate that organisations with the lowest level of risk will require:

- An appointed person to take charge of the first-aid arrangements, including looking after the equipment and facilities, and call the emergency services when required. Arrangements should be made for an appointed person to be available to undertake these duties at all times when people are at work.
- A suitably stocked first aid kit.
- Information for all employees about what to do in an emergency.

The important point to consider is the careful consideration of first aid requirements based on the risks inherent in the organisation, and the need to consider the impact of employee organisation (shifts, locations, etc.) and holidays on first aid requirements.

Fire and Explosion

Employers Duties

Employers have specific duties under the Regulatory Reform (Fire Safety) Order[257] (RRO) to conduct a risk assessment to identify the potential causes of fire and to put in place control measures to ensure that risks are eliminated or controlled, so far as is reasonably practical.

Fires are caused by the combination of flammable materials, oxygen, and a source of ignition. The existence of these three is likely to cause a fire, whilst the removal of any of these three is like to prevent or cause a fire to stop burning.

There are two key roles in the RRO. The 'responsible person' – the person that has responsibility for ensuring that the organisation does what is necessary to comply with the legislation', and the 'competent person' – the person with the technical knowledge, skills and experience to advise the responsible person on the steps that he or she must take.

Other legislation (for example in the Workplace (Health, Safety and Welfare) Regulations) places requirements on employers that if followed will reduce the risk of fire (for example by preventing the build-up of waste materials). Whilst other legislation for high risk industries (such as DSEAR, COMAH, etc.) set down specific regulations to prevent or reduce the risk of fire across high risk industries.

The RRO requires risks to be addressed in a particular order:

- Avoid the risks altogether, for example by not storing flammable materials, not having sources of ignition, etc.
- Evaluating the risks that cannot be avoided (through the risk assessment described above).
- Combating risks at source – reducing volumes, isolating equipment, etc.
- Adapting to technical progress.
- Replacing the dangerous with the non-dangerous or less dangerous, for example by storing flammable materials in suspensions of non-flammable chemicals such as water.
- Developing a coherent overall prevention policy which covers technology, organisation of work and other factors relating to the work environment.
- Giving priority to collective over individual measures.
- Giving appropriate instructions to employees.

Organisations should also establish fire safety arrangements which are appropriate to the size of the undertaking and the nature of its activities, for the effective planning, organisation, control, monitoring and review of the preventative and protective measures. In most cases, these will need to be recorded.

Specific arrangements must be written by a 'competent person' who should be informed of any factors that may affect, or may be suspected of affecting the safety of any person who may be affected by the conduct of his undertaking.

The arrangements should include:

- The provision of fire detection, alarms, and appropriate fire-fighting equipment taking into account the nature of the facility, its size, its use, and the nature of any chemicals or materials stored there.
  This should include the nomination, training and supply of equipment to competent[tt] persons, and the establishment of contacts with external emergency services, particularly as regards fire-fighting, rescue work, first-aid and emergency medical care.
- The provision of emergency routes and exits[uu] to a place of safety to facilitate evacuation as quickly and safely as possible which are suitable for the facility and which open in the direction of escape.
- Procedures for ensuring that employees who may be exposed to serious and imminent danger are informed of the hazard and are aware of the steps to taken to protect them from it, including evacuation procedures that enable workers to stop work, to immediately proceed to a place of safety in the event of serious, imminent and unavoidable danger, and to remain away until the serious and imminent danger has passed.
- Emergency and evacuation procedures including safety drills with sufficient competent persons to facilitate them, and particular arrangements for workers who need to access restricted areas such that they receive specific instructions on how to respond.
- Procedures for the routine maintenance of fire equipment so that they remain in *'an efficient state, efficient working order and good repair'*.

Information and Training

The responsible person must provide his employees[vv] with comprehensible and relevant information[ww] on the following:

[tt] Competence in this context is described as sufficient training and experience or knowledge and other qualities.

[uu] Emergency doors must not be: sliding and revolving doors, locked or blocked. Emergency routes and exits must be indicated by signs and where necessary must be illuminated sufficiently to be clear in the event of a failure of normal lighting.

[vv] Similar information should be supplied to the parents of any children that may be employed at the location, and to contractors who may be undertaking work at the premises.

[ww] Additional information should be supplied to those working in locations where dangerous substances are stored.

- Identified risks and the preventative and protective measures to address them;
- Emergency procedures;
- Those in nominated emergency roles – either as fire-fighters or evacuation personnel;
- In the case of a shared building, the same information relating to the incidents of others.

Employers should provide suitable and sufficient instruction and training on the precautions and actions to be taken by the employee in order to safeguard himself and other persons on the premises. It should be provided in a manner which reflects the results of the risk assessment.

The training should be provided to employees on appointment, and where changes are taking place or have taken place to either the role, the work equipment, the technology, or the systems of work used. The training should be repeated periodically and adapted to reflect any new or changed risks. Training should take place during normal working hours.

Employees Duties

Under the RRO, employees have a duties to take care of themselves and relevant others and should co-operate with their employer to enable the employer to perform or comply with their own duties. They should also inform the employer and fellow employees of a work situation that represented a serious and imminent danger to safety, and any matter that might amount to a shortcoming in the protection arrangements.

References

[254] Personal protective equipment at work (Second edition) Personal Protective Equipment at Work Regulations 1992 (as amended) Guidance on Regulations, HSE, 2005

[255] Safety signs and signals - The Health and Safety (Safety Signs and Signals) - Regulations 1996, Guidance on regulations, HSE, 2013

[256] First aid at work The Health and Safety (First-Aid) Regulations 1981, Third Edition, HSE, 2013

[257] Regulatory Reform (Fire Safety) Order, HMSO, 2005

WHEN THINGS GO WRONG

The Health & Safety Executive

The Health & Safety Executive (HSE) was created under the Health & Safety at Work etc. Act to:

> *Do such things and make such arrangements as it considers appropriate.*

Under the law, the HSE is empowered to assist and encourage, research and train, inform and advise. Following an accident, occurrence, situation, the HSE is empowered to investigate and report, or authorise another party to do so, and conduct an inquiry.

The law provides the authority for the HSE to appoint Inspectors and sets out the powers at their disposal which are wide reaching. Local Authorities are assigned similar responsibilities and authority under the Act.

Powers of Inspectors

Inspection and Examination

An Inspector has the power to enter premises at any reasonable time, or, in a situation which he believes to be dangerous, at any time). He can take a constable with him if he believes that he may find obstruction in the execution of his duty, or any other person, and any equipment or materials required for which the power of entry is being exercised.

Once on site, Inspectors can:

- Make such examination or investigation for the purpose of investigating the concern held (above) and in accordance with that investigation or examination:
    - Direct that premises investigated in accordance with the above shall be left undisturbed;
    - Take measurements, photographs, and such recordings as he deems necessary;
- Take samples of articles or substances in the premises or from the atmosphere in the vicinity of the premises;
- Cause articles or substances to be dismantled, subjected to processes or tests (but not so as to damage or destroy them), or take possession of them for so long as is necessary for the purposes of examination, to ensure that it is not tampered with, and/or to ensure that it is available for evidence in any

proceedings relating to a Notice. Specific rules relating to the taking of samples provide for:

- o Samples to be taken in the presence of a responsible person;
- o Consultation on the dangers that may arise;
- o A leaving of a notice at the location where the sample was taken, and where possible, provide a sample to a responsible person.

- To require any person whom he has reasonable belief to be able to supply any information relevant to the examination or investigation above to answer such questions as the inspector things fit to ask (and to sign a declaration of the truth of his answers). No answer given in pursuance of this requirement shall be admissible in evidence against that person (or the spouse or civil partner of that person) in any proceedings.

- To require the production of, to inspect and to take copies of documentary records required to be kept under the relevant statutory provisions, along with any other documentary evidence relating to the examination or investigation.

- To require any person to afford him such facilities and assistance with respect to any matters or things within that person's control or in relation to which that person has responsibilities as are necessary to enable the inspector to exercise his powers of inspection.

- Nothing in the above compels the production by any person of a document of which he would on grounds of legal professional privilege be entitled to withhold.

What might an inspection look like?

The HSE provide information about what their workplace inspections are likely to entail. Details can be found on the HSE web site[258]. This information can provide a useful tool in reviewing organisational arrangements where particular hazards or risks exist. The toolkits can be used to measure whether the organisation would meet the expectations of the HSE.

It is important to remember that when an Inspection takes place, particularly following a serious incident, HR Practitioners are likely to be caught between a number of new roles identified following the incident:

- Ensuring employees are receiving any necessary communications, information and support that may be necessary in the immediate aftermath;
- Identifying, establishing and implementing any appropriate transition arrangements; and
- Supporting the organisation in preparation for a return to normal operations.

HR Practitioners may be asked to lead or participate in internal and external investigations, which may be led by the Police, the HSE, by legally appointed external advisors, or by an internal investigator, quite possible a combination of the above.

As a part of this process, HR Practitioners may be asked to provide evidence or witness statements as a part of that investigation, or to participate in a PACE – 'Police and Criminal Evidence' interview, either personally or on behalf of the organisation. The HSE provides information for their inspectors on their web site[259] but employees that find themselves in these positions are encouraged to take independent legal advice. Some organisations offer this service for free to employees and it is sometimes included as a part of a Directors and Officers Insurance Policy.

Fees for Intervention

Within the 1974 Act was provision for the HSE to charge fees for intervention. Following the Health and Safety (Fees) Regulations which came into force on the 1st October 2012, organisations who breach health and safety laws can now be required to pay 'fees for Intervention' to the HSE for costs associated with inspection, investigation and taking enforcement action.

There is a high variation in fees but the average is between £500 and £600 and increasing. There are approximately 65 Intervention fees levied every working day.

Notices

Inspectors can issue Improvement Notices if they believe that a person is contravening a statutory provision, or has contravened a statutory provision in circumstances that make it likely that the contravention will continue or be repeated. Prohibition Notices are issued when an Inspector is of the view that the activity involve, or as the case may be, will involve a risk of serious personal injury.

Notices are required to contain particular information including a statement that the inspector is of the particular opinion, what matters the notice relate to the statutory provision in question, why he is of that opinion, and a date by which the contravention will be remedied. In the case of a prohibition notice, a direction that the activities shall not be carried out unless the matters specified in the notice have been remedied. The law also sets out additional information relating to the appeals procedure to be followed.

If an inspector has reasonable cause to believe that an article or substance is a cause of imminent danger or serious personal injury, he may seize it and render it harmless. If it is practicable to do so, the Inspector will take a sample. As soon as may be after the article or substance has been seized or rendered harmless, the Inspector shall prepare and sign a report setting out the particulars of the circumstances.

Organisations may appeal an Improvement or Prohibition Notice if they believe that the justification or process has not been carried out in accordance with the law.

Offences

The HSE can also prepare a case against an organisation for the Crown Prosecution Service. These hearings will be heard at the Magistrates or Crown Court. If found guilty, employers, and in some cases, individuals, can face imprisonment, a fine or both.

Imprisonment for up to 2 years, or a fine or both

- General duties of employers, persons concerned with premises, and manufacturers
- General duties of employees to others at work, and the duty not to interfere with or misuse things provided pursuant to certain provisions
- Contravention of any health and safety regulation or prohibition arising from regulation or licence to which he is subject
- Contravention of a requirement imposed by an inspector; or to prevent any other person from appearing in front of an inspector
- Contravention of any requirement or prohibition imposed by virtue of an improvement or prohibition notice
- Make a statement which he knows to be false or recklessly to be false; to make a false entry in a register, book, notice or other document; or to attempt to deceive
- Failure to remedy a breach in accordance with a court order

Imprisonment for a term not exceeding 51 weeks and/or a fine.

- Intentionally obstruct an inspector in the exercise or performance of his powers or duties.

A Fine

- Breach of duty not to charge employees for the provision of safety services or safety equipment
- Attempt to block investigations or enquiries or otherwise obstruct any person in the exercise of his powers
- Failure to supply information to the HSE or other enforcement agency in response to a notice requiring information
- To falsely pretend to be an inspector

The Legal Aid, Sentencing and Punishment of Offenders Act 2012 (Fines on Summary Conviction) Regulations 2015 passed on the 11th March 2015 enables Magistrates to determine a level of fine without being subject to a limit.

Factors Influencing Fines

Specific contributing factors are taken into account that can influence the level or scale of the fine.

These are:

Factors that increase fines	Factors that decrease fines
• Whether the incident and the scale of harm was foreseeable • The extent to which the defendant fell below the standard • Genuine efforts to remedy the defect • Failures to heed warnings or advice or accidents and near misses of a similar nature • A prompt acceptance of responsibility	• The attitude of the organisation to health and safety in relation to profit • High level of co-operation with the investigation • The extent to which non-compliance was present • A previously good health and safety record • A responsible attitude to health and safety

References

[258] http://www.hse.gov.uk/foi/internalops/fod/inspect/index.htm

[259] http://www.hse.gov.uk/enforce/enforcementguide/investigation/witness-questioning.htm

INDEX

About the Author

John Huckstepp is a distinguished and award winning HR practitioner across government, health, chemical, call-centre, retail, rail, gas and manufacturing.

His approach has enabled organisations to significantly improve employee productivity and engagement, and simultaneously reduce incidents and insurance costs.

He has worked on major incidents, including a multiple fatality, and specialises in the link between human resources, culture, health and safety and corporate risk.

John is a Chartered Fellow of the CIPD and a Specialist Member of the International Institute of Risk and Safety Management (IIRSM). He holds a Master's Degree in Human Resource Management from University of Salford Business School (The Times Higher Education Business School of the Year).

Currently John educates practitioners on high impact – low pain human resource management; supports central and devolved government; and helps small to medium enterprises to create foundations for growth.

His work on the impact of national culture on health and safety in global organisations was published by the Institution of Chemical Engineers in 2015 and presented at their Hazards 25 Conference in Edinburgh.

Acknowledgements

If it had not been for those that shared their knowledge and put their trust in me, this book would not have been possible. I am incredibly grateful to those that have given me those experiences over 25 years in Human Resources and Health & Safety.

The book writing process has been greatly helped by a virtual team including a cover designer in Bath, a publisher in London, a Coach in Cheshire and various others across the UK. Their support has been challenging and inspiring in equal measure.

Lastly, the book has been a family story across four generations (a real four G experience) with parents providing challenging editorial and data support, my wife helping with content, guidance and other support, children reminding me there is a reason for this, and grandchildren providing sequencing and artistic support throughout.

Note to the Reader

This book provides guidance on how HR activities can significantly impact risk (positively and negatively). It is not intended to constitute legal advice, and whilst every effort has been made to ensure that the information in this book is accurate at the time of print, the publishers and the author cannot take responsibility for any errors or omissions, howsoever caused.

No responsibility can be accepted by the author or publisher for loss or damage arising from the actions or inactions of any individual or organisation arising from the content of this book.

As with all books of this nature, information changes over time. A range of references have been provided throughout the book. Readers are encouraged to seek additional information where necessary, through their own research or via the author at www.ablankcanvas.eu. If the book has inspired you, why not come along to one of the conferences (www.hs4hrconference.co.uk) or consider an in-house course.